MW00564429

NAVAL SHIPHANDLING

NAVAL
SHIPHANDLING

FOURTH EDITION
R. S. CRENSHAW, JR., CAPTAIN, U.S. NAVY (RETIRED)

NAVAL INSTITUTE PRESS   ANNAPOLIS, MARYLAND

Copyright © 1975, 1965, 1960, 1955 by the
United States Naval Institute, Annapolis, Maryland

All rights reserved. No part of this book may be
reproduced without written permission from the publisher.

Library of Congress Catalog Card Number: 74–26360
ISBN: 0–87021–474–8

Printed in the United States of America on acid-free paper ⊗

16   15   14   13   12   11

foreword

From the earliest days of our Navy it has been recognized that, among other desirable qualifications for a great ship commander, the following requisites are paramount: he must first of all be a fighting leader of men, and then, to a very high degree, an exceptional tactician, an able gunnery officer, and last but not least, an expert shiphandler.

In the days of sail and John Paul Jones it was the most skillful shiphandler who placed his ship in the most advantageous fighting position in relation to his opponent. The weather gage and the raking position, combined with superior gunnery and the will to fight, usually determined the victor in single-ship duels—as they did also in fleet actions, as was so convincingly demonstrated by Nelson at the Nile and Trafalgar. Our own Paul Jones gave an excellent illustration of how a determined and skillful captain could win victory although his *Bonhomme Richard* was inferior in most respects to the *Serapis*, and Dewey was equally successful at Manila.

Knowledge of the sea in all its moods is a prime requirement of the successful commander. Such knowledge and experience can be acquired only by going to sea in all kinds of ships. Many of our great naval captains began their seagoing in merchant ships. Paul Jones, Hull, and David Porter were experienced mariners before they served in naval vessels. They learned at an early age that the sea is an unrelenting taskmaster who speedily eliminates the weak and inefficient but richly rewards the skilled and daring mariners. The transition from sail to steam made little change in the courage and skills required. On the contrary, the great advances in speeds and tonnages of varied types of vessels imposed even higher qualifications on successful commanders. The skillful commander will bring his ship unscathed through all kinds of weather and sea conditions fit to fight without the necessity for "voyage repairs." Good shiphandling includes the exercise of good judgment in preventing damage due to adverse sea conditions or inept handling in harbors and around docks.

Notwithstanding the fact that skill in shiphandling cannot be acquired from books alone, it is none the less important that there be assembled for the beginner all available and pertinent information relating to this subject. This the Naval Institute has endeavored to do in *Naval Shiphandling*, which represents the efforts and experience of many officers over a long period of years. It will be of value and interest not only to the naval profession, but to the Coast Guard and Merchant Marine as well, particularly as these great organizations work so closely with the Navy in time of war, and have contributed so much in experience to the preparation of this book. Credit is also due to our master pilots and to the smallboat sailors of the U.S. Power Squadrons of America, and to numerous amateur yachtsmen who are all specialists in handling small craft under every condition.

Naval Shiphandling cannot fail to benefit all seamen everywhere, just as the knowledge and experience of seamen everywhere have contributed to the preparation of this book.

Fleet Admiral, U.S. Navy

publisher's preface

In the vast complexity of the Navy today, the practice of shiphandling has suffered because so much of the effort of the individual officer has been called to other duties. To the traditional fields of navigation, seamanship, gunnery, and engineering have been added the expanding fields of operations, communications, missiles, electronics, amphibious, air, and submarine operations, and a host of others, until it is all one can do to keep a minimum acquaintance with all the fields of naval science. Although the field of seamanship has expanded as steadily, if not as spectacularly, as the other fields to meet the increased scope of activity of the Fleet today, the seamanship experience of the individual officer is less than in former years.

In the "good old days" an officer learned his shiphandling by serving under and observing the "masters of the art." All officers at sea were engaged in deck duties, and the measure of an officer's ability was largely a measure of his ability at shiphandling. There were relatively few officers even on large ships, so all officers had a good opportunity to become expert in the fascinating art.

This book has been prepared to present the fundamentals of shiphandling as required in today's complex operations. In it the author has attempted to review the principles of shiphandling and to offer sound techniques for the solutions of the problems normally encountered. He has tried to offer a "why" along with each explanation of "how." The author's intention is to arm the reader with the principles involved and to prepare him for employing them intelligently, rather than to offer specific solutions to certain problems and then leave it to the reader to deduce the principles.

It is obviously impossible to assemble in one book all that is known on the subject of shiphandling. It was intended that the book cover the field adequately, yet care had to be taken to insure that it would not be bogged down by the sheer mass of information presented. Consequently, for each evolution there is usually presented only one method of solving the problem. One of the first things an officer learns at sea is that there are usually several adequate solutions to each problem. In each case in this book the author has selected for presentation that solution which he prefers. In some cases the superiority of the method presented is believed to be absolute and clear-cut, but in many cases the author freely admits that there are other methods equally as good. In all cases the method presented in this book has been tried and found to be sound.

Since the captain and the officer of the deck have to meet the same problems when they have the conn, this book has been written as though the author and the reader were standing together on the bridge of the ship under discussion and are exploring the problem of the conning officer. It is hoped thereby that the book will meet the needs of officers of all grades and extent of experience.

Finally, this work is dedicated to the thesis that shiphandling is the mastering of physical objects by the use of physical forces; that it is a science that can be mastered by the application of an alert mind to the principles involved and is not an occult art requiring an inborn talent for its mastery.

Inasmuch as physical principles embodying physical forces are technical in nature, it is impossible to treat them without certain technical terms and approaches. Therefore an understanding of the material in Chapter 2, "Forces Affecting the Ship," is absolutely necessary for anyone who aspires to be a competent shiphandler. However, every effort has been made to use such simple terms and explanations, with liberal diagrams, that any layman can read with ready comprehension.

There is no good reason why any officer who will apply himself to the examination of the objects and forces involved, and who will take the time to study and master the principles, can not become a competent shiphandler. Experience is a necessary ingredient in producing a competent shiphandler, but no amount of experience can substitute for a thorough understanding of the problem.

UNITED STATES NAVAL INSTITUTE

preface to the fourth edition

After more than fifteen years with the Fleet—a Fleet that was changing dramatically both in mission and composition—it was time to bring *Naval Shiphandling* in for a thorough overhaul. In November 1971, letters were addressed to all of the officers commanding ships in commission, inviting their comments on the third edition and their recommendations for change. The response was most gratifying, not only because of the numerous excellent suggestions and additions, but also for the confirmation that the basic scope and content of the book was standing the test of time.

In this fourth edition, extensive changes have been made in nearly every chapter in order to enhance the discussion, to introduce the new ships and practices entering the Fleet, and to improve the presentation. A chapter on the single screw ocean escort and a chapter on new hull types and propulsion systems represent major additions, while Chapter 16, "Landing Ships," takes on new importance with a discussion of the versatile LST 1179.

The improvements in this edition stem mostly from the extensive interest shown by the officers commanding the ships in the Fleet and their contributions. We would particularly like to acknowledge the contributions made by Commander G. S. Allen and his staff at the Surface Warfare Officers School, Newport; Captain Warren C. Hamm, Jr., and his staff at the Destroyer School; and Commander D. T. Lamb for the use of his treatise on the LST 1179.

Captain Felix S. Vecchione, who permitted extracts from his excellent pamphlet on the handling of ocean escorts to be incorporated in Chapter 7 on single screw ships, was lost in the crash of an airliner before the publication of this edition; his contribution was very important and is gratefully acknowledged.

Interesting examples of mariners at work were contributed by Captains J. E. Davis and L. A. Romatowski, Jr.; Commanders R. K. Leopold, John M. Langford, and S. S. Kingsley. Shiphandling tips were incorporated from the suggestions of Captains W. S. Guthrie, R. W. Watkins, and J. O. Lyon; Lieutenant Commander J. L. Post, and Lieutenant W. R. Heinecke.

Captain David S. Boyd and the officers of the Attack Submarine Division of

OpNav thoroughly reviewed and updated the chapter on submarines. Commander R. H. Overton, III, and Lieutenant Commander A. B. Shepard, of the Office of Operations at the U. S. Coast Guard Headquarters, carefully reviewed Chapter 14, "Polar Shiphandling."

One of the more significant changes in this edition is the incorporation of the new International Rules of the Road, 1972. We are indebted to Lieutenant Commander Frederick K. Smallwood, U. S. Navy, for alerting us to the change and for his recommendations for updating the chapter. As matters progressed towards the adoption of these new rules for Inland Waters as well, the advice and assistance of Commander Kenneth E. Wadman, U. S. Coast Guard, of the Office of Vessel Traffic Safety, Coast Guard Headquarters, was invaluable.

Space does not permit acknowledging all of the contributors, but the following officers also made important contributions to the book: Captains C. C. Carter, O. K. Hallam, and W. L. Harris; Commanders J. D. Chamberlain, C. G. Foster, Jr., E. C. Hagedorn, L. R. Magner, R. B. Rogers, J. R. Seesholtz, and E. B. Veek; Lieutenant Commanders J. B. Bonds, E. J. Dennis, J. O. Desrochers, and H. G. Henderson; Lieutenant J. L. Burke; G. S. Prentice and R. P. Smith.

R. S. Crenshaw, Jr.
Captain, U. S. Navy (Retired)

contents

SYMBOLS USED IN FIGURES

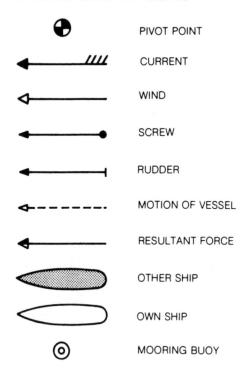

PIVOT POINT

CURRENT

WIND

SCREW

RUDDER

MOTION OF VESSEL

RESULTANT FORCE

OTHER SHIP

OWN SHIP

MOORING BUOY

PHOTOGRAPHIC CREDITS

B. J. Nixon, 40; Robert D. Moeser, 154, 276; General Dynamics, Quincy Division: 192; Ingalls Shipbuilding, 196; Newport News Shipbuilding and Dry Dock Company, 258; D. J. Sullivan, Jr., 271; Bell Aerospace, 329, 331: The Boeing Company, 330; Marinette Marine, 341; U.S. Coast Guard, 357, 362, 364, 458.

All photographs not otherwise credited are official U.S. Navy photos.

Note: While this text was in production, the standard system of classification of naval vessels, in effect since World War II, was changed to avoid confusion between similar types. The change principally affected missile frigates, patrol frigates, and escort ships, which are now classed as guided missile cruisers, frigates, or guided missile frigates. The old designations still appear in this edition.

NAVAL SHIPHANDLING

1
seaman's eye

The destroyer rounds the buoy and stands smartly up the harbor. She is lean and graceful as her powerful engines drive her along, and her clean lines seem to speak of her capacity to meet any task assigned her and to do it well. The men on deck are quick and alert as they complete their preparations for mooring, and the captain on the bridge has the easy confidence of a man who has been tried and proven.

She slows as she arrives at the congested part of the harbor, and then in one broad sweep she approaches the nest which is to be her berth for the night. Gently she is brought to a stop exactly abreast her nestmate, the lines go over smartly, she moves in broadside until she is moored securely, and in minutes the captain's absentee pennant is fluttering from the yardarm, signifying his day's work is done.

The entire evolution was carried out smoothly without a faltering step. The wind and current were judged exactly; every engine and rudder order was timed perfectly to bring the ship in to the desired position. The 180° swing was so graceful that the casual observer hardly noticed the obstacles which lined the path; the shoal water to port, the two mooring buoys in mid-channel, or the nest of destroyers which nearly blocked the approach. The timing and sense of position was so deft that one hardly noticed how extensively her nestmate had been yawing just before she came alongside. The destroyer skipper's excellent ship-handling had made an easy job of a difficult maneuver.

How did he do it? What inner sense told him when to shift his rudder, when to stop his engines? How did he judge his distances, how could he tell his speed?

Seafaring men have long had a name for it. They call it "Seaman's eye."

Before we dismiss this term as connoting some extrasensory ability on the part of real deepwater seamen, let's take a look at it. What is Seaman's eye and how does one go about acquiring it?

The expression has a much broader meaning than that of attributing a certain visual ability to a person. Actually, the human eye is at its worst at sea. In the vast expanse of water the distance to objects cannot be determined by the relation to known objects because of the general lack of the latter. At sea the range can be judged by the dip below the horizon, but even experienced mariners make large errors in estimating ranges at sea. Unaided, the eye of even the most experienced seaman is often erratic.

Seaman's eye is rather an expression of competence at sea. It is an expression connoting judgment and understanding. The captain with a reputation for Seaman's eye is one who can marshal all the information on the situation available to him, combine it with his intimate knowledge of his ship and her characteristics, and take his course of action with the judgment of the Master Mariner. This judgment is made up of intelligence, knowledge of ships and the sea, and an understanding of the physics of shiphandling.

Regardless of the special qualifications of a Line officer, the real source of his reputation is his ability to command at sea. One can be the most able engineer in the Fleet or the most successful gunner, but when the tales of great officers are swapped in the wardroom the most telling mark of the admired officer is his reputation as a shiphandler. A skipper might have many shortcomings, but if he is really the master of his ship, he is a success in the hearts of his officers and his men. Shiphandling ability is the common denominator of all real naval officers. It is the ultimate measure of expertness in seamanship, and it is the universal figure of merit in establishing an officer's ability as a mariner.

The ship itself derives her reputation largely from the skill with which she is handled. The ship may excel in spirit, she may break all the records in gunnery, she may be the best in the Fleet in CIC, or she may be a marvel of engineering efficiency, but these achievements might be known only to those few on the staff who keep the records or by the limited few who are aware of the relative standings of the ships of the Fleet. Just how *USS Tuscarora* made her landing at the fuel dock yesterday is common knowledge in the harbor. A ship famed for excellent maneuvers will draw a crowd of admiring critics each time she makes a landing or snatches a buoy, and her skipper is the unofficial hero of the port. A ship noted for careless seamanship or indifferent handling will deserve the scorn of the crews of her nestmates. She will be greeted by cries of "Clear the side!" or "Watch out, George, she's coming around again!" Her sailors will have to defend the dubious reputation of an inept captain. Her captain must endure the indifference accorded one of little ability. Good seamanship is the hallmark of naval ability, and good shiphandling is the means available to the officer to demonstrate his ability in this field.

Acquiring Seaman's eye

If ability at shiphandling is so important to a naval officer, how then does one acquire it? How can the junior officer prepare himself for his opportunity at command? Can he learn shiphandling from books, or is it an undefined art that can only be acquired through long years of association?

In the first place, a ship is a physical body that responds in a normal way to the forces brought to bear upon it. If we study the manner in which the ship responds to a certain type of force, and we study the source and characteristics of the force, we will be able to predict when the force will be present and what effect it will have on the ship. When we have acquired a complete understanding of the forces that come to bear on our ship and have explored the reaction of our ship to all of the different forces, we will be prepared to anticipate her movement under any set of conditions. A firm understanding of physical principles is the foundation upon which excellence in shiphandling must be based.

Consideration and study of the physical forces is not enough; the shiphandler must be familiar with the environment of the sea and he must have experience in handling ships if he is to acquire the judgment to correctly evaluate the conditions. How can the novice estimate the effect of the wind in approaching a buoy? How can he be expected to comprehend the world of relative motion into which he is suddenly thrust as his ship joins a complex formation? It takes years of experience on the bridge of an operating ship before an officer becomes accustomed to all of the situations in which his ship might be placed.

If such long experience is necessary to form the basis for the judgment needed by the shiphandler, perhaps one can only learn from experience. Perhaps this is a field in which only a long apprenticeship can properly prepare the aspirant. Perhaps the only solution is to observe the masters at their work and learn to follow their example.

Shiphandling, however, is one skill that cannot be mastered by imitation. One could watch a Master Mariner make a hundred perfect landings at a pier, but unless he understood the principles being employed, he could not go out and repeat the performance. No two evolutions are the same. There is always a difference of wind, current, or in the execution of a command; and the shiphandler must be able to evaluate when these changes occur and must be ready to make the necessary correction.

Shiphandling cannot be taught by example alone. Though it is highly interesting to learn how some other shiphandler solved his problem under a certain set of conditions, we might search forever to find an identical situation. The simple explanation of "what" was done is not useful in preparing us for our problems unless we have a clear understanding of "why" the action was taken.

The best preparation for handling the ship, then, is a combination of a study of the principles involved and sufficient experience at sea to be able to evaluate the situation. Neither extensive experience nor theoretical understanding can stand alone. The competent shiphandler must have both.

Preparing for command

There is a difference between having spent time on a ship at sea and having acquired experience at shiphandling. Officers should seize every opportunity presented to actually maneuver the ship. Commanding officers should insure that all officers are given a chance to acquire the necessary basic experience. No matter what the evolution, having had the conn and maneuvered the ship for a few minutes is a valuable piece of experience.

Not only should all opportunities for shiphandling by junior officers be seized, they should be created. The wise skipper is the one who schedules ample time for "box drill" so that all officers have the opportunity of making practice landings. Occasionally when operations permit, a period should be set aside for maneuvering close alongside another ship or making approaches on a buoy. A morning spent allowing officers to make practice landings at a pier will pay big dividends, not only in shiphandling ability but also in enthusiasm for the task. No matter how much an officer has considered "how he would do the job" and observed others actually doing it, there is nothing so instructive as actually doing it himself.

Another aspect of the necessity of preparing young officers to become competent shiphandlers is that, as an officer becomes more senior, it is automatically assumed that he has this ability until proved otherwise. He is assigned duties in accordance with his seniority and not necessarily in accordance with his qualifications. It is assumed that at a given seniority he is a competent shiphandler, and if this is not so, serious consequences can ensue. An officer who was denied the opportunity for experience in shiphandling during his junior years may suddenly find himself placed in command of a ship on a difficult mission. His inadequacy may have serious consequences. It is of the utmost importance that every opportunity be seized to train all officers in this most important phase of their duties.

A system of shiphandling

Having recognized the importance of shiphandling and considered the means through which this skill is acquired, we should explore the methods by which one arrives at a satisfactory solution to a shiphandling problem. If we understand the steps necessary in the solution of our problem, we can solve it in an orderly and efficient manner.

The first input to our solution is a study of the forces which affect our ship. We must understand their characteristics and magnitudes, and be able to predict which ones will come into play in a given set of circumstances. The second input to our solution is a thorough study of our ship and her particular handling characteristics. We should be familiar with her hull form, her propellers, and her rudders to be able to predict their interaction. We should know her equipment and its uses, and we should be familiar with her major dimensions. The last basic input in preparing to solve shiphandling problems is to calibrate our ship. We must experimentally determine what we can expect from a given engine or rudder order. We must know how far and how fast our ship will move in a given situation.

Having studied the forces, studied the ship, and calibrated her reaction to given controls, we are ready to meet specific shiphandling problems. To solve any particular problem we must carry out the following three basic steps:

1. *Measure the Situation*. Measure the ranges and bearings important to the maneuver. Measure the ship's speed, the depth of water, the velocity of the wind.

2. *Calculate the Maneuver.* Calculate the ranges at which to turn, the bearings at which the speed should be changed, the time to maintain a course.
3. *Check and Correct.* As the maneuver progresses, continual revaluation of the situation is required. At each opportunity the accuracy of the maneuver should be checked and corrections made as required. There are too many variables to expect the initial solution to hold good throughout an extended maneuver.

If the shiphandler follows these basic steps in facing his problem, he can perform an accurate maneuver with confidence in its success. Measurement by use of the instruments with which our ship is equipped, calculation by means of easily employed approximations and thumb rules, and checks by the same means will allow any officer to perform excellent maneuvers.

An air of mystery has often cloaked the good shiphandler. Many have avoided trying to explain why certain results are obtained because they felt the causes must be too complex to understand. Many very excellent shiphandlers seem to have no system of maneuver; they handle the ship by intuitive feel, and are at a loss to explain how they decide when to give a certain command. Most discussion on the subject merely outlines the results without exploring the causes.

If we are to maneuver with precision, it is necessary that we measure the situation exactly and frequently to know where we stand and to judge what to do next. If we have calibrated our ship so that we know what she will do when a certain order is given, and if we have accurately measured the range and bearing to our destination, we can maneuver with confidence to our destination, providing of course that we have gauged the wind and current accurately. The secret to understanding the situation is to have all the available information at our fingertips and to use it all.

Calibration

The first step in accurate shiphandling is to calibrate the ship so that we know what she will do. Test the ship with the engines opposed equally to insure that we actually do not get any way on ahead or astern while twisting. Note the turning rate when twisting at ONE THIRD and when twisting at TWO THIRDS. It will probably be found that it is necessary to twist at TWO THIRDS to achieve a good turning rate.

The distance required to come to a stop when going ahead at various speeds while using various backing powers is vital information for the conning officer. For instance the distance the ship moves ahead before stopping when BACK ONE THIRD is ordered while going ahead at five knots should be kept in mind because it is very useful when going alongside or making a buoy. And the distance the ship moves ahead before coming to rest when BACK TWO THIRDS is ordered at 15 knots is vitally important knowledge when recovering torpedoes or picking up a downed aviator. When taking over a ship, the new captain should take his ship out and measure these values for himself. A conning officer should familiarize himself with these values to be sure he is ready for emergencies. It will pay dividends later in accurate shiphandling.

The amount the ship "surges" during a speed increase or decrease should be remembered. Perhaps the best way to explain the meaning of "surge" is to give a typical example. Suppose our ship is making 20 knots and is coming up from behind to join a column which is proceeding at only 10 knots. We accordingly drop our own speed to 10 knots. But by the time our ship slows down from 20 knots to 10 knots, we will have closed up on the ship ahead of us in column by perhaps 350 yards. In other words, in slowing from 20 knots to 10 knots we have closed by 350 yards, or 35 yards per knot of speed change. We call this ratio the surge, and the example given is about typical of the average destroyer.

The turning data also should be known and certain key values committed to memory. The minimum turning diameters at 10, 20, and 30 knots should be remembered and the turning diameters for 10, 20, and 30 degrees rudder should be memorized for a speed of 15 knots. The *rate* of turn in degrees per second using 30 degrees rudder at 20 knots is useful for solving maneuvering board problems when the turning circle has to be taken into account.

Measuring distance

Distance is a primary factor in shiphandling, and it is certainly the most difficult factor to estimate. There are many methods of measuring distance, and all of them are useful at times. Radar, though excellent for tactical maneuvers, is less useful for shiphandling, where the ranges of interest are 1000 yards or less. The stadimeter is still the most useful all-around range measuring device for close shiphandling, and the 7×50 binocular is good for darkened ship steaming if our radar is not effective at short ranges.

The stadimeter can be used in the conventional way and will give excellent ranges from 250 to 3,000 yards if used properly. However, it is often necessary to make an approach on an object floating in the water or on a ship the masthead height of which is not known. Using the stadimeter in the Horizon Method is very useful in such cases. To do this, the bridge height of eye for our own bridge is set on the stadimeter as "masthead height," and the horizon is brought down to the waterline of the object. The geometry of the situation is indicated in Figure 1–1. In actual practice, since the minimum height on the scale of a standard Navy stadimeter is 50 feet, and since the bridge height of eye on our destroyers is about 35 feet, double the height of eye can be set and the true range then found by dividing the scale reading by two. This has the advantage of allowing us to obtain ranges on objects as close as 125 yards, even though the lowest figure on the stadimeter is 250 yards.

The standard 7×50 binocular is very useful for judging the distance to a known ship (see Figure 1–2.) The full field of a 7×50 is 7° 10', or 125 mils. At 300 yards a destroyer, from the waterline at the stern to the top of the highest antenna, will just fill the field of view vertically. Therefore, if the destroyer fills one-half of the

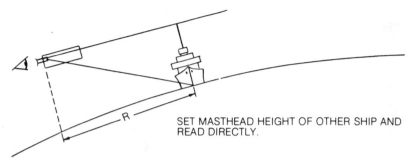

SET MASTHEAD HEIGHT OF OTHER SHIP AND READ DIRECTLY.

(a.) NORMAL METHOD OF USING STADIMETER.

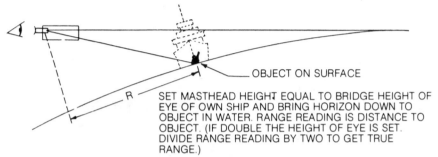

OBJECT ON SURFACE

SET MASTHEAD HEIGHT EQUAL TO BRIDGE HEIGHT OF EYE OF OWN SHIP AND BRING HORIZON DOWN TO OBJECT IN WATER. RANGE READING IS DISTANCE TO OBJECT. (IF DOUBLE THE HEIGHT OF EYE IS SET, DIVIDE RANGE READING BY TWO TO GET TRUE RANGE.)

(b.) HORIZON METHOD OF USING STADIMETER. THIS METHOD ASSUMES THAT OBJECT IS SO CLOSE TO OWN SHIP THAT THE LINE OF SIGHT FROM OWN SHIP TO HORIZON WOULD CUT A PSEUDO TWIN-SHIP LOCATED AT THE OBJECT IN THE WATER JUST AT THE BRIDGE.

FIGURE 1–1. Using the stadimeter to measure distances.

field, she is about 600 yards away; one-third, about 900 yards, etc. An aircraft carrier fills the field at approximately 430 yards, and a cruiser at about 375 yards. This is a rough method of measuring distance, but it will be found very useful when no other method is available.

The jackstaff and bullnose are convenient range marks when we are approaching something dead ahead. Some officers mark 500, 200, and 100 yard marks on their jackstaffs so that when they are standing on their normal conning station their line of sight past these marks hits the surface of the water 500, 200, and 100 yards ahead of the bow respectively. The accuracy of this system depends upon ship's speed and trim, but if the horizon mark is also indicated on the jackstaff as a reference, accurate ranges can be obtained.

Radian rule

Knowing the range to an object, the Radian rule or the "One in Sixty" rule comes into play. This is one of the most useful rules available to the shiphandler. It is based on the fact that since the radian subtends 57.3°, it is approximately correct

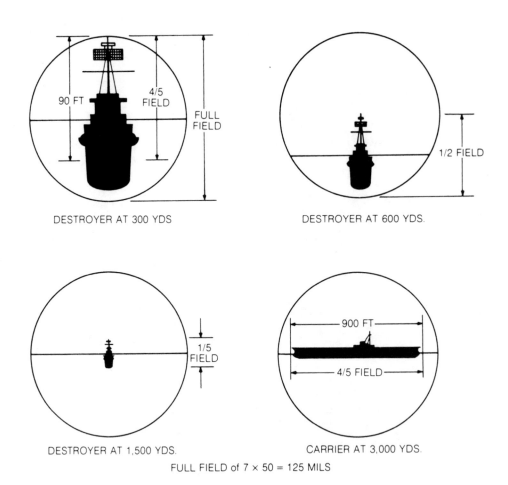

FIGURE 1–2. Using 7 x 50 binoculars to measure distances.

that the perpendicular distance subtended by 1° is one-sixtieth of the range. Thus if a 300-foot vessel "beam-on" subtends an arc of 1° at the observer, it is 6,000 yards away. At 6,000 yards a boat at the same range as a buoy but separated from it by 4½° is 450 yards from the buoy. If you wish to pass a ship 500 yards abeam when coming up from astern and the range is 3,000 yards, you divided 3,000 by 60, which gives 50 yards; since 50 goes into 500 ten times, then the spot 500 yards abeam of the ship ahead is 10° to one side of her. When using this rule, check points are selected at ranges easily divisible by 60.

Speed, time, and distance

Another important piece of shiphandling information is the exact relation between speed, time, and distance. The Three Minute Rule—the distance in hundreds of yards traveled in three minutes equals the speed in knots—is a fundamental. The following equivalents should be memorized:

 1 knot = 100 yards in 3 minutes
15 knots = 500 yards per minute
 1 knot = 33 yards per minute
 1 knot = ½ yard per second
 1 knot = 10 turns on the Revolution Indicator

These values are very useful tools in shiphandling. For instance, if we are fueling at sea and we drop back ten yards on the oiler in two minutes, this is five yards per minute or about ⅙ of a knot; hence, adding two turns should check our motion, and adding four turns should put us back on station in two minutes. If we are 125 yards behind station in column, we can be back on station in two minutes by adding two knots.

Approximate mathematics

The Radian rule and the speed equivalents are constantly useful in maneuvering at sea. Suppose that with speed at 15 knots, we are on the beam of the guide at 3,000 yards and we wish to move in to 2,000 yards. Using the rules we see that a 4° course change will move us *in* at 1 knot, or 33 yards per minute. If we desire to complete the maneuver in 10 minutes we must have a closing rate of 100 yards per minute, or three knots. This would require us to change our course toward the guide by 12° and add a few turns to keep our bearing constant.

It may seem that this is too much mental mathematics for an officer who is busy conning a ship. Actually, after a little practice the calculations become second nature, and they assist in achieving real excellence in shiphandling. The really efficient conning officer is constantly measuring, checking, and calculating as he handles his ship. Don't "guesstimate" the situation; *measure* it. Having measured it, compute your course of action by use of the thumb rules and "approximate mathematics" as illustrated above. The habit of precision is invaluable at sea.

2
forces affecting the ship

In order to predict the movement of our ship accurately, we must thoroughly understand the nature and magnitude of the forces which affect her. There are six general sources of force which can be brought to bear on our ship independent of any other vessel. They are the propellers, the rudders, the mooring lines, the ground tackle, the wind, and finally the current. The first four are controllable from the ship itself. The wind and the current (and this includes tidal currents), though not controllable, can be utilized to serve our aims if properly handled. Each of these forces can produce important effects, as indicated in Figure 2–1, so it is worth while to take the time to study and understand each of them. Let's remember from the beginning, however, that these are *forces* only, and that *motion* results only after *inertia* has played its part.

A modern ship may have a distributed mass of many thousand tons and may be several hundred feet long. Such a body not only has tremendous inertia to resist linear acceleration, but it also has a tremendous *moment of inertia* to resist rotational accelerations. The ship is resting in a fluid (water) covered by another fluid (air), both of which will offer a resistance to relative motion. Thus, when we apply a single force to the ship, we can expect an acceleration until the fluid resistance produced by the motion balances out the original force. This will apply to angular motion produced by an off-center force as well as by force applied through the center of gravity. Thus, when we apply any force to the ship, we can expect motion to gradually build up until a state of equilibrium is reached, at which time the velocity of the motion will become constant.

Basic principles

Forces in water manifest themselves as pressure differences. Water is incompressible but by applying force to it we can build up a higher pressure in one area as compared to surrounding areas, and this difference in pressure will cause the water to flow from the area of higher pressure to the surrounding area of lower

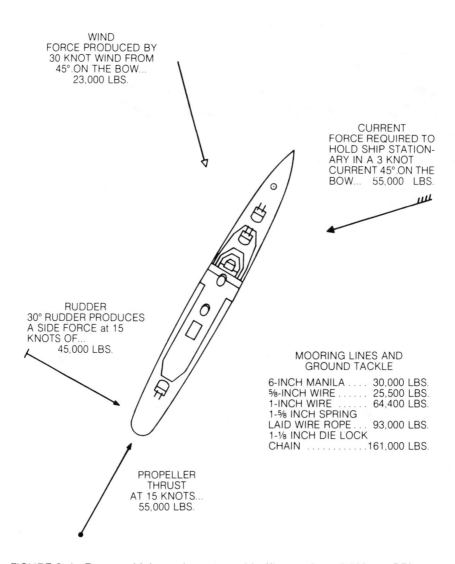

WIND
FORCE PRODUCED BY
30 KNOT WIND FROM
45°.ON THE BOW...
23,000 LBS.

CURRENT
FORCE REQUIRED TO
HOLD SHIP STATION-
ARY IN A 3 KNOT
CURRENT 45° ON THE
BOW... 55,000 LBS.

RUDDER
30° RUDDER PRODUCES
A SIDE FORCE at 15
KNOTS OF...
45,000 LBS.

MOORING LINES AND
GROUND TACKLE

6-INCH MANILA . . . . 30,000 LBS.
⅝-INCH WIRE . . . . . . 25,500 LBS.
1-INCH WIRE . . . . . . 64,400 LBS.
1-⅝ INCH SPRING
LAID WIRE ROPE . . . 93,000 LBS.
1-⅛ INCH DIE LOCK
CHAIN . . . . .161,000 LBS.

PROPELLER
THRUST
AT 15 KNOTS...
55,000 LBS.

FIGURE 2–1. Forces which can bear on a ship (figures for a 2,200-ton DD).

pressure. When we pull an oar through the water, for instance, we build up high pressure on the face of the blade toward which the blade is moving, and we create a low pressure on the face which is moving away from the water. During the motion, water flows from the high pressure region to the low pressure region. The greater the immersed area of the blade, the greater the area upon which the pressure can act. The greater the force applied to the oar, the greater the pressure difference. The average difference of pressure between the two sides, multiplied by the immersed area of the blade, is a measure of the force we are exerting on the water. Since the inertia of the water resists the force being applied by the blade end of the oar, this resistance, working through the oar, applies a force to the boat in the opposite direction. Resistance to the oar exists only when the particles of water are being set in motion by the movement of the oar. Without the force we apply to the oar, there would be no motion, no pressure difference, and no resistance. Thus we see that force, resistance, and motion are irrevocably interlocked when dealing in a fluid medium.

The above discussion illustrates the fact that all forces in water manifest themselves as pressure differences. If we are going to apply force on a waterborne object, such as our ship, we can do it only by creating a pressure difference across a part of the ship's structure. And if at any time our ship moves in any way, we know that some force is acting somewhere on our ship's structure—and we can locate that force by looking for the pressure difference that causes it.

In any large body of water, there are always two components of pressure present at any point: one is the static pressure due to depth, or sheer weight of the water above the point; the other is the dynamic pressure caused by motion in the surrounding water. In the sea the static pressure does not cause motion, because it is the same everywhere at any given depth level, and hence balances out as far as we are concerned.

Bernoulli's Theorem tells us that at any given depth in an open body of water like the sea, the sum of the static pressure and the dynamic pressure is always constant. Normally there is little motion of the water, so the static pressure is all that needs to be considered. When a ship passes through the water or a propeller blade slices into it, however, the water is set into motion and the static pressure is reduced by the amount of the dynamic pressure. Though it is usually the decrease in effective static pressure brought about by setting the water particles in motion that produces our hydrodynamic effects, knowing the magnitude of the dynamic pressure will tell us the pressure difference to be expected from the motion.

The magnitude of the dynamic pressure is given by the expression:

$$P = \frac{pV^2}{2g}$$

where:

P = Dynamic pressure in lbs/ft²

p = Density of the moving fluid in lbs/ft³

V = Velocity of flow in ft/sec

g = Acceleration due to gravity, 32.2 ft/sec²

The resulting pressure difference caused by the motion of water is therefore proportional to the *density* of the fluid and the *square* of the velocity of motion.

Bernoulli's Theorem and the above expression apply to air movement also, but since salt water at 64.4 lbs/ft³ is 855 times more dense than standard moist air at .0752 lbs/ft³ the dynamic forces on a ship resulting from the flow of water past its hull and appendages is vastly greater than those caused by the flow of air. On the other hand, the velocity of air relative to the ship may be much higher than normal water velocities, and since the dynamic pressure component increases as the *square* of the velocity, the dynamic effects of strong winds on a ship's structure can be quite large. It may be useful to remember that the velocity of air must be approximately 30 times the velocity of water for the resulting dynamic pressure to be the same. Stated another way, 30 knots of wind is the equivalent of 1 knot of current.

A last general characteristic of water that is important in our study is its continuity; it tends to exist as a continuous body, without gaps or holes except as caused by extraordinary forces. If a volume of water is moved away so quickly, by a propeller blade, for instance, that the pressure differences there are insufficient to accelerate water *in* as fast as it is being moved *away*, then a gap would occur on the back side of the propeller blade. This gap is known as *separation*.

A companion phenomenon occurs when, in a high velocity stream, the velocity gets so high and the pressure so low that the pressure in the stream drops to the vaporization point of water. In this case drops of water become vaporized in the area described, in a manner similar to boiling. This phenomenon is known as *cavitation*.

Separation and cavitation are of interest to the shiphandler, because, when they occur, they upset the pattern of streamlines and change the resulting forces. These phenomena are likely to occur around abrupt changes in the underwater body of a ship moving at high speed, or about the blade of a propeller that is being rotated rapidly.

Hydrofoils

Before going into the various hydrodynamic effects associated with a ship and its motion through the water, some definitions are in order:

Hydrofoil. Any relatively thin, plate-like member, such as a propeller blade or rudder, designed to obtain a lift force when inclined to the flow of the water.

Angle of Attack. The angle at which a hydrofoil is inclined to the relative free stream flow.

Lift. That component of the reaction force on a hydrofoil which lies in a direction perpendicular to the relative free stream flow of the water.

Drag. That component of the reaction force on a hydrofoil which lies in a direction parallel to the relative free stream flow of the water.

A flat plate placed at an angle in a stream of water, as indicated in Figure 2–2(a), acts as a hydrofoil and causes the water to move out of the way on the leading side and to accelerate to move in behind the trailing side. This creates a high pressure on the leading side and a low pressure on the trailing side. This difference of pressure exerts a lift force on the plate as indicated in the figure. With smooth flow, this force is proportional to the angle of inclination, the dynamic pressure, and the area of the plate. Since an abrupt change of flow is required at Point A, separation could exist at such a point, and could alter the pressure distribution over the surface of the plate. If the plate is shaped as indicated in Figure 2–2(b), however, the acceleration of the water will be more gradual and separation will be avoided.

The rudder is obviously a hydrofoil, designed to produce the lateral forces used in the control of the ship's heading. The rudder force acts through the rudder

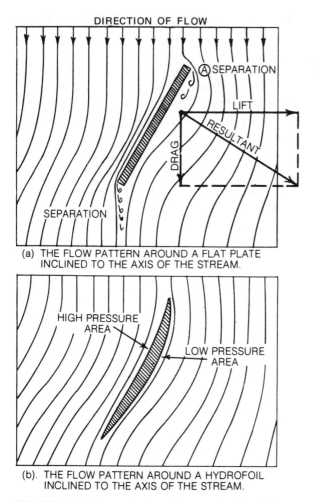

DIRECTION OF FLOW

(a) THE FLOW PATTERN AROUND A FLAT PLATE INCLINED TO THE AXIS OF THE STREAM.

(b). THE FLOW PATTERN AROUND A HYDROFOIL INCLINED TO THE AXIS OF THE STREAM.

FIGURE 2–2. Flow patterns about an inclined plane.

stock, pushing the stern to starboard or to port as the rudder is inclined to the flow of water past it. The amount of the resulting force is proportional to its area, the dynamic pressure, and the angle of attack.

The hull itself is a hydrofoil which, when inclined to the flow of water past it, feels both a side force and a turning moment tending to force it back into alignment with the water flow. In a turn at a fixed rudder angle, a constant turning rate is reached when the moment resulting from the inclination of the hull to the water flowing past it equals the turning moment produced by the rudder. The actual angle of attack of the rudder is equal to the rudder angle with respect to the ship minus the angle of inclination of the ship with respect to its true direction of motion.

Keels and skegs are also hydrofoils, installed to resist certain motions. Normal keels and skegs are aligned with the centerline of the ship and produce a turning moment whenever the ship becomes inclined to the flow of the water. Bilge keels or "rolling chocks" are specially designed fins, curved to conform to the flowlines of the water as it moves aft past the hull of the ship, but which become inclined to the flow pattern and produce a correcting moment when the ship rolls to either side.

A most important thing to remember about any hydrofoil is that the resulting force is proportional to the square of the velocity of the water actually flowing past it, and this may be much different from the speed of the ship through the water. For example, if a rudder is mounted directly astern of a propeller, a large rudder force can be obtained from the screw current as the propeller turns ahead, even though the ship has not yet begun to move appreciably. Conversely, a back bell might cause only a very slight current to flow past the rudder, so no appreciable rudder force will be felt until the ship is moving through the water smartly.

The propeller

One of the most important sources of force on a ship is her own propeller. One would expect, since the propeller is designed to propel the ship, that turning the propeller AHEAD would cause the ship to move *straight ahead*, and that turning the propeller ASTERN would cause the ship to move *straight astern*. This is not necessarily the case, however, and the shiphandler must study the action of a propeller in order to be able to predict its action on his ship.

The objective in designing a propeller is to produce the maximum thrust along the line of the shaft from a given rotational force or torque applied to the shaft itself. A fixed blade propeller is designed for optimum performance at one particular speed of the ship, usually the maximum speed, but it can be depended upon to operate efficiently at all normal speeds. The actual speed of the ship through the water is less than the ideal speed (pitch × rpm) because the blade of the propeller must be inclined to the direction of the water flow relative to the blade in order for the water to exert force on the blade and drive the ship. The cross-section of the blade is shaped to provide the greatest *lift* and the required strength, but at the same time to reduce separation and cavitation to a minimum.

To operate at other than design speed, the rotational speed of the propeller is changed to the rpm corresponding to the new speed. With a well-designed propeller the speed varies nearly linearly with shaft rpm. This relation holds true until a speed is reached where separation and cavitation become pronounced.

The water exerts force on the propeller by the differential pressure on the opposing faces of the blade. Therefore this force must be perpendicular to the mean face of the blade. Since the blades are inclined, this force is inclined to the propeller shaft rather than along its axis. However, since there is normally more than one blade on any propeller, and since the blades are disposed symmetrically around the axis, all of the radial components cancel out and the remaining thrust is along the axis of the shaft. It is because of the necessity for exact balancing of the radial components of force that the blade alignment of a propeller is so important. Though the propeller and shaft are well supported to withstand large forces along the axis of the shaft, the length of external shafting and the small number of relatively weak supports (the struts) form a structure poorly designed to withstand large radial forces at the propeller. A seemingly unimportant nick or dent in a single blade can alter the balance of the radial forces significantly, even though the useful thrust obtainable from the propeller is not significantly affected. It is because of the upsetting of the radial forces that a damaged propeller causes so much vibration or pounding.

A propeller is designed for a given ahead speed, but it works quite well turning astern also. The pitch of the propeller is the same going astern as it is going ahead, the major difference being that the blade cross-section is now reversed from that best suited for preventing cavitation and turbulence. When operating astern, a given propeller is less efficient than when going ahead. This means that more power will be required for a given shaft rpm astern than for the same rpm ahead, but approximately the same thrust will result from a given rpm whether turning ahead or astern.

Though the propeller is designed to force water through itself parallel to the shaft, the actual flow is somewhat different, as indicated in Figure 2–3. The character of the flow is due to the acceleration of the stream as it passes through the propeller, and to the rotation imparted by the propeller. The amount of distur-

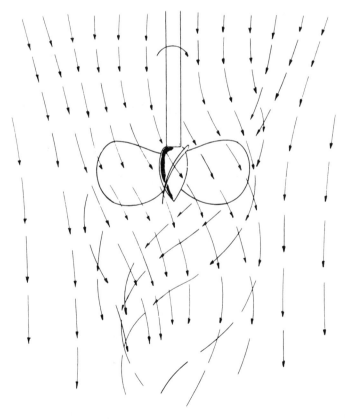

FIGURE 2–3. Flow pattern about a driving propeller.

bance of the parallel flow varies with the difference in velocity between the mean flow through the propeller and the mean current of the surrounding water. Thus a minimum disturbance of the parallel flow through the propeller occurs when the propeller is doing the least work. A great deal of disturbance occurs, however, when the ship is at a standstill and the propellers are being turned rapidly. And the maximum disturbance is created when the ship is moving in one direction and the propellers are being turned with maximum power in the other direction.

There is also a tangential component of motion imparted to the water by the propeller. Since the force from the propeller blades is nearly perpendicular to the blade surfaces, the initial acceleration of the water must be in line with this force. Thus the propeller, as it rotates, imparts a rotational motion as well as a backward motion to the water. This effect is evident in the spiral discharge from a propeller, as indicated in Figure 2–3.

The flow pattern about the propeller is of great interest in determining the forces on the ship. Although the direct effect of rotating the propeller is obtained as thrust along the propeller shaft, the secondary effects of the current flow are often just as important in handling the ship. It is often the adroit use of the secondary effects of the propeller's rotation that allows us to accomplish intricate maneuvers.

SIDE FORCE FROM A SINGLE SCREW*

As a propeller rotates to drive a ship through the water, in addition to producing *thrust* along the axis of the propeller shaft, it produces a *side force* at the stern of the ship which is quite appreciable. This side force must always be considered in the calculations of the shiphandler, and it often is the determining factor in whether or not a particular maneuver can be accomplished. It is of interest, then, to explore the origin of this unexpected force.

An isolated propeller deeply submerged in a large body of water will experience no appreciable side force as it turns. All radial components of the lift on the propeller blades will cancel, and the only force experienced will be along the axis of the propeller. The case of a propeller being used in an actual ship, however, is considerably different from this ideal case. The propeller is not deeply submerged, it is in the immediate vicinity of the ship's underwater body, and it is surrounded by ship's structure such as the shafts, struts, and rudders. The flow of water across the propeller disc is neither parallel to the axis of the propeller nor uniform in intensity. In an actual ship, side force is always experienced as the propeller turns.

As a vessel moves through the water, she tends to drag some of the water along with her because of skin friction. If we measure the velocity of the following wake at different distances out from the surface of the hull, we get a picture similar to Figure 2–4. Close to the hull, the velocity of the water relative to the ship is very

---

*This section is based on a paper prepared by the David Taylor Model Basin entitled, "Propeller Action in a Single-Screw Ship."

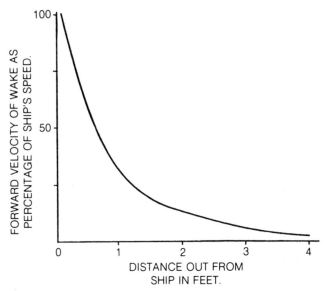

FIGURE 2–4. Thickness of frictional wake.

small; that is, the water is being carried along with the ship. At some distance out from the hull, the relative velocity approaches the velocity of the ship. We can take some arbitrary point (such as where the velocity of the following wake is 2 percent of the ship's speed) as the limit of the boundary layer and can thus examine the thickness of the frictional wake. The frictional wake, starting from zero thickness at the bow, increases towards the stern until it reaches a thickness of several feet in some cases. The net effect is that an envelope of water immediately adjacent to the ship is given a forward motion by the passage of the ship.

The propeller, being behind the ship, has to work in this wake. It is as though the propeller were advancing through the water at a lower speed than the ship. Thus if a ship moving at 15 knots had a following wake of 3 knots in the vicinity of the propeller, the propeller would be advancing at only 12 knots *relative* to the water.

Actually, due to the shape of the hull and appendages, the velocities in the wake may vary greatly from place to place. Behind blunt endings of the structure, the wake may be moving forward bodily with the ship. A variation in the wake pattern may cause unsymmetrical propeller forces.

The wake pattern has been measured on many models. A typical wake distribution for a single-screw merchant ship is shown in Figure 2–5. This indicates by contours the distribution of fore-and-aft velocity over the propeller disc. It will be seen that this fore-and-aft velocity relative to the propeller drops in places to 20 percent of the ship's speed.

In addition to the fore-and-aft motion, the water also has an *upward* and *inward* motion in the vicinity of the propeller. This motion is imparted to the water as it closes in behind the stern. This upward component of velocity of the wake also has an important effect on propeller behavior.

21   FORCES AFFECTING THE SHIP

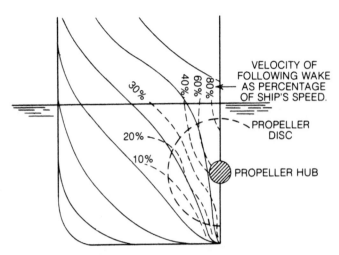

FIGURE 2-5. Wake behind a single-screw ship.

Having obtained a general picture of the wake pattern, we can now turn to the propeller. It is usual to simplify the study of propeller action by considering a typical section of the blade. Figure 2–6 indicates that the velocity of the blade section relative to the water is the resultant of two components:

1. A forward component, velocity V_A, equal to the ship's speed minus the wake velocity.
2. A tangential component due to the rotation of the propeller equal to $2\pi rN$ (r being the radius under consideration and N the rpm).

The velocity relative to the blade section, V_0, is found by combining the forward and rotational components as shown in the figure. The inclination of V_0 to the face of the blade is the angle-of-attack (α). The effect of the current striking the blade at this angle is to develop lift and drag, and these forces can be readily resolved to give thrust, T, and torque, Q, as shown in the figure.

As a typical section rotates around the disc, it meets many different wake areas. The variation of V_A as the wake velocity varies will cause changes in α, T, and Q. Hence the propeller will not deliver a steady thrust nor absorb a uniform torque.

As a result of variations as it rotates, a propeller produces side forces in addition to thrust along the propeller shaft. The side forces produced by the propeller of a single-screw ship can be broken down into the following four parts:

Following wake effect

In the vertical position behind the hull (blade A, Figure 2–7), the blade passes through a region of high following wake. This results in an increased angle of attack and greater thrust and torque when the blade is in this region. The reaction to this, with a right-hand screw, is a force tending to move the stern to port when going ahead. At the same time, a blade passing through the bottom part of the disc would

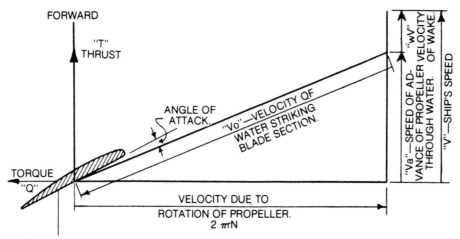

FIGURE 2–6. Velocity diagram for propeller blade.

experience an opposing reaction; but since the following wake in this lower region is much weaker and extends over a much smaller area, the action of the upper blade would predominate. *The following wake effect, then, is to produce a net force tending to move the stern to port and cause the ship to veer to the right.*

Inclination effect

The axis of the propeller shaft is inclined to the axis of water flow past the propeller because of the inward and upward movement of the water under the stern. The inward movement is symmetrical on both sides of the stern and can be neglected, but the upward movement produces a marked effect. As a blade moves downward to its horizontal position (blade B, Figure 2–7), it meets water which is moving upward as well as aft. This is equivalent to increasing the relative velocity *and* the angle of attack at the same time, and thus an increase in thrust is experienced. On the opposite side, the port side for a righthand screw, a decrease in thrust is experienced. *The net effect of the reaction to the inclined flow, then, is a torque tending to twist the ship to the left.*

Helical discharge effect

The helical discharge from the propeller of a single-screw ship impinges directly on the rudder. That part of the discharge above the propeller hub creates a force on the rudder tending to move the stern to starboard, while the lower half creates a force tending to move the stern to port. Because of the increased blade angles of attack in the upper arc due to the following wake effect, the discharge current from the upper half of the arc is stronger. *The net effect of the helical discharge, then, is to tend to turn the ship to the left.* (This effect can be altered or increased by an unsymmetrical rudder, especially if the rudder does not extend across the entire disc.)

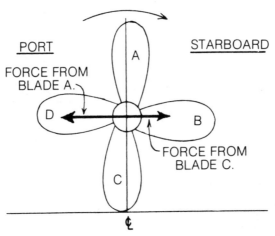

FIGURE 2–7. Side force resulting from following wake on a single-screw ship.

Shallow submergence effect

If a vessel is at light displacement, the propeller may break surface and cause a decrease in transverse force in the upper arc. When the ship has little way on, the propeller frequently draws air from the surface when appreciable power is applied, and experiments have shown that the effect is the same as if the blade broke the surface. In either case it is as though the blade were working in a less dense medium. *The shallow submergence effect, then, is to tend to move the stern to starboard and cause the ship to veer to the left.*

A single-screw ship, when going ahead, is therefore subject to several different actions—some opposing—and the actual behavior of a given ship will depend on the relative magnitude of the forces. One must experiment with a given ship to determine the magnitude and character of the side force that will be encountered. Experience shows, however, that most single-screw ships have a tendency to turn to the left when going ahead.

Getting under way

With the ship at rest and just starting to move, the stern usually moves to starboard. Since the forward motion of the hull is negligible, the wake is also negligible, and one must examine other conditions to find the source of the side force. Only the shallow submergence effect of those outlined above is independent of the wake.

If one observes the water in the vicinity of the propeller when the screw is started rapidly, he will notice a "churning" action as air is drawn down into the propeller disc even though the propeller is well below the surface. Experiments have shown that this air affects the upper half of the disc predominantly, and *the effect is a resultant force to move the stern to starboard.*

Backing

When turning the propeller astern with the ship dead in the water, the side force on the propeller arises from the same cause as when starting ahead, but the direction of the force is reversed. *From the propeller alone, then, the force on the stern is to port.*

When backing the propeller with the ship dead in the water or moving astern, the propeller is biting into undisturbed water, so the following wake effects that come into play when moving ahead are not present. The discharge of a backing propeller is directed against the stern of the ship, and the upper half of the spiral discharge tends to bank up against the starboard side of the counter while the lower half of the spiral hits the lower part of the skeg and spills under the keel. *The result is a force tending to move the stern to port.*

Since both effects tend to carry the stern to port, a *single-screw ship with a righthand screw has a strong tendency to back to port.*

Since the suction current is much less concentrated than the discharge current, it has little effect on the rudder of a single-screw ship when backing. Consequently, such a ship must rely nearly entirely on sternward velocity for rudder effectiveness. For this reason it is necessary for a single-screw ship to build up appreciable sternway before the tendency to back to port can be overcome by use of this rudder.

In summary then, in a normal single-screw ship, the side force acts in a direction as though the blades were bearing against the bottom, and the direction of the side force depends only upon the direction of rotation of the propeller. When operating with little way on or backing, this is clearly the case; but when proceeding ahead, the conflicting forces may reduce the side force markedly or even reverse it. There may be cases where a single-screw ship has a tendency to veer to the right when moving ahead.

SIDE FORCE WITH TWIN SCREWS

In the normal twin-screw installation, the propellers turn in opposite directions when driving ahead or astern, and the side forces then cancel. To increase the maneuverability of these ships, it has become the convention to allow the side force to augment the moment resulting from the shafts being offset from the centerline. Thus we find the propellers turning so that the blade tips are moving outboard during the upper half of their travel when driving ahead. This calls for a righthand screw on the starboard shaft and a lefthand screw on the port shaft. To determine the magnitude of the side force to be expected in a twin-screw ship, we should consider the character of the flow in the vicinity of the propellers. Figure 2–8(a) shows the actual character of the wake in the vicinity of a propeller of a destroyer moving at high speed. The arrows indicate the transverse components of flow and clearly show the upward movement of the wake under the stern and the helical motion imparted to the discharge stream by the propeller. The numbers indicate

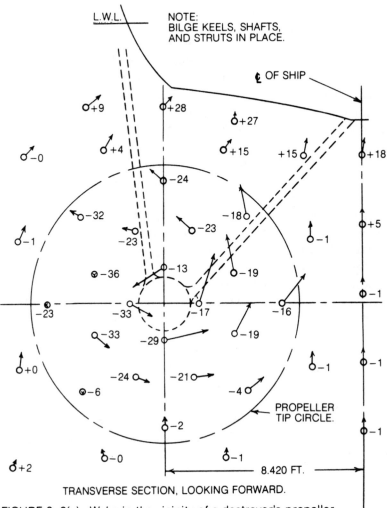

TRANSVERSE SECTION, LOOKING FORWARD.

FIGURE 2–8(a). Wake in the vicinity of a destroyer's propeller.

the velocity of the following wake as a percentage of the ship's speed—positive numbers indicating following wake, negative numbers indicating rearward motion with respect to still water.

Analyzing this wake pattern for the effects discussed above for the single-screw case, the following facts become apparent:

Following wake effect

The blade tips as they pass closest to the hull are working in a following wake of only 15 percent of ship's speed, and throughout the majority of the propeller disc there is no appreciable following wake. Consequently, the following wake effect is considerably reduced with normal twin-screw design.

Inclination effect

The inclination of the shaft axis to the direction of flow is just as marked with twin screws as with single. Not only is the upward motion of the wake still present, but, as shown in the side view of Figure 2–8(b), the inclination of the shaft is downward. Since the engine is inside the hull and hence the shaft must pass through the bottom to reach the propeller in any type of ship, the inclination effect is present in all types of ships.

Helical discharge effect

If the ship has a single rudder, it will probably not be within the region of helical discharge current, so this effect will be absent in such ships. In a twin-rudder ship, on the other hand, this effect is not only present but is greatly augmented by the shape of the rudder. Normal twin-rudder design for warships uses a spade rudder (narrower at the bottom than at the top, as seen from the side), and frequently the rudder extends only slightly below the axis of the propeller. Consequently such a rudder feels the upper half of the discharge current much more than the lower half, and the helical discharge effect is very large.

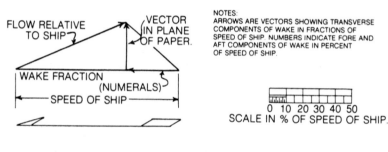

NOTES:
ARROWS ARE VECTORS SHOWING TRANSVERSE COMPONENTS OF WAKE IN FRACTIONS OF SPEED OF SHIP. NUMBERS INDICATE FORE AND AFT COMPONENTS OF WAKE IN PERCENT OF SPEED OF SHIP.

0 10 20 30 40 50
SCALE IN % OF SPEED OF SHIP.

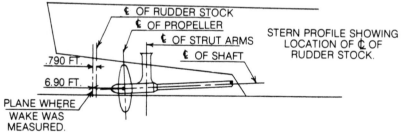

STERN PROFILE SHOWING LOCATION OF ₵ OF RUDDER STOCK.

WAKE IN TRANSVERSE PLANE
IN WAY OF RUDDER STOCK
DESTROYER D D 423
PROPELLERS TURNING AT 281 R.P.M.

LENGTH	341.3 FT.
DISPLACEMENT	2,246 TONS
TRIM	EVEN KEEL
SPEED	28.6 KNOTS
PROPELLER TIP DIAMETER	11.374 FT.
PROPELLER HUB DIAMETER	2.171 FT.
DATE OF TEST	MARCH 27, 1942

FIGURE 2–8(b). Wake in the vicinity of a destroyer's propeller.

Shallow submergence effect

This effect is less common with twin-screw design, especially with warships, since it is most unusual that a propeller tip will break surface. The churning and air drawing is present, however, so this effect is still to be considered.

Since the only opposing effect—the following wake effect—has been diminished in twin-screw design, the side force on a righthand screw turning ahead is definitely to starboard, and the side force for a lefthand screw turning ahead is definitely to port. The directions of the forces are reversed, of course, when the direction of rotation is reversed.

With twin screws, then, the side forces are large and are uniformly in the direction indicated by the direction of rotation of the propeller. When moving steadily ahead, the force to starboard on a righthand screw is not appreciably diminished by a following wake effect, so we can expect strong side force to be present even though normally cancelled by the side force from the opposite screw. When the ship is dead in the water, the side forces experienced from the propellers alone are of the same magnitude as those encountered in a single-screw ship. When backing, the side forces from a twin-screw installation are usually somewhat smaller than with a conventional single-screw ship because the structure into which the helical discharge is directed is less extensive.

Use of Side Force

In all types of conventional ships, a side force is experienced whenever the propellers are rotated. Though the magnitude of the force may vary with the type of ship, the direction is nearly always that indicated by the direction of rotation of the propellers (as though the blades were bearing against a more solid layer during the lower part of their travel). If the shiphandler has considered the origin of these forces, he will know what reaction to expect under any given set of conditions. For a certain ship, a little experimentation will indicate the magnitude and character of the side forces that can be expected, and the conning officer can turn these forces to good use in handling his ship.

RESISTANCE AND POWER*

While discussing the forces acting on our ship, we should also examine the power required to drive our ship through the water. On one hand it seems that relatively feeble power plants are sufficient to drive large ships at moderate speeds, yet vast amounts of power are needed to drive even small ships at 30 knots or more. There

---

*This section is based on *Speed and Power of Ships*, Book II ("Resistance"), by Rear Admiral David W. Taylor (CC), USN (Ret.).

seems to be a "wall" of resistance which suddenly appears as the ship approaches high speed.

A destroyer with 60,000 shaft horsepower can make only about 35 knots, yet a cruiser having six times the displacement of the destroyer can make the same speed with only twice the power. The battleship, the cruiser, and the destroyer have 3.7, 6.5, and 19 horsepower per ton, respectively, yet all have about the same maximum speed at sea. Though the greater horsepower per ton insures the ability to *accelerate* more rapidly at low speeds, it does not seem to provide a significantly higher maximum speed. The hulls of all fast warships are very similar in shape; is there a factor which depends simply on size? Why do we obtain better results with the larger ship?

To begin with, all fluid resistance results from motion and increases as a power of the velocity of motion. There is no static friction in the sea. If we apply a force, no matter how minute, on the ship, the ship will move and will continue to accelerate until a balancing resistance is created by the motion of the ship.

The resistance encountered by the ship also depends on the shape of the hull. In fluid resistance, it is the character of the immersed body which determines the magnitude of the retarding force. For this reason it is very advantageous that the underwater body have a smooth "streamlined" form.

Actually, as a perfectly streamlined body moves through the water, no power is required simply to displace the water to allow the ship to pass. In an ideal case, the pressures on the forward half of the body are exactly compensated by the pressures on the after half of the body, and there is no pressure difference to hold the ship back. We must look elsewhere than the simple displacement of water to find the sources of resistance which require the expenditure of our ship's power. Obviously, many of these sources of resistance to the motion of our ship are not readily apparent.

Frictional resistance

As a ship moves through the water, the particles of water immediately against the skin of the ship move along with the ship, the particles next adjacent to these are dragged along to a certain extent by molecular friction, and the next layer of particles is dragged along to a lesser extent, etc. These particles form an envelope of water about the ship which is being more or less carried along with the ship. The thickness of the "boundary layer" which is being dragged forward by the movement of the ship varies from a few molecules in thickness at the bow to several feet near the stern. Energy must be expended to impart this motion to the boundary layer, and the resulting resistance has become known as the frictional resistance.

Extensive experiments, beginning with those of Mr. William Froude in England in 1874, have shown that the frictional resistance of a ship can be expressed by the formula:

$$R_f = fSV^n$$

where:

R_f = frictional resistance
f = coefficient of friction (dynamic)
S = total wetted surface of the ship
V = velocity of the ship through the water
n = index or power according to which water friction varies

Froude found that for rough surfaces, the index (n) was 2.00, but that for hard surfaces it might be as low as 1.83. After very elaborate experiments, supported by later investigations with only slight variation, Froude established in 1888 Froude's Frictional Constants which give the index (n) as 1.825 for all sizes of ships. Since later experimenters found the value to be slightly larger, it is customary to use the following formula for frictional resistance:

$$R_f = fSV^{1.83}$$

It is sufficient for the shiphandler, however, to remember that the frictional resistance is proportional to the total wetted surface and approximately to the *square* of the speed.

Wave resistance

When a ship moves on the surface of the water, it creates waves. It is evident that these waves have energy (as one can observe when waves strike an obstruction), so the ship must have imparted this energy. The amount of energy being imparted to the waves by the ship could be determined if the energy of the waves could be measured. If we could evaluate the energy flowing away from the ship in the form of waves, we could evaluate the propulsive power expended in creating them.

The energy in a single wave has been found to be proportional to the breadth of the wave (its longest dimension) and the square of the height of the wave. The power (energy expended per unit of time) required to create a train of waves is equal to the energy per wave multiplied by the rate at which the waves are being created.

The principal waves which make up the wake of a ship are created at the bow and at the stern of the ship. It is as though two wave generators were travelling, one after the other, separated by one shiplength. These two wave systems interact with one another, and this interaction may increase or decrease the magnitude of the resulting waves.

As indicated in Figure 2–9, the waves created at the stern may tend to reinforce or cancel the waves created by the bow. If one of the crests of the bow wave system coincides with the first crest of the stern wave system, a reinforcement occurs, the resulting wake waves are higher, and the wave resistance (R_w) is increased. Should a crest of the bow wave system fall on the first trough of the stern wave system, a cancellation would occur, the resulting wake waves would be

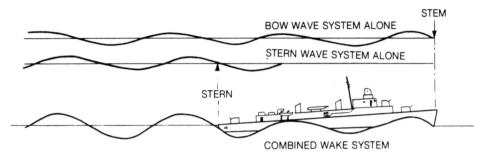

(a.) INTERACTION OF BOW AND STERN SYSTEMS, SHOWING REINFORCEMENT.

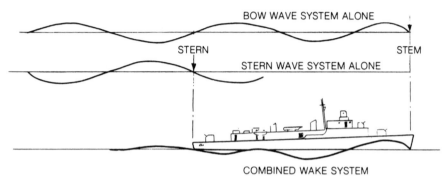

(b.) INTERACTION OF BOW AND STERN SYSTEMS, SHOWING CANCELLATION..

FIGURE 2–9. Interaction of bow and stern wave systems.

smaller, and R_w would decrease. The waves which are affected by this reinforcement and cancellation process are the transverse waves, the crests of which are perpendicular to the track of the ship and which travel initially at the speed of the ship.

The formula for the length (distance between crests) of a wave at sea in deep water has been determined to be:

$$l = .557 \, V^2$$

where:

 l = length of the wave in feet

 V = velocity of the wave in knots.

Thus as the speed of the wave (which is equal to the speed of the ship for transverse wake waves) doubles, the length between crests will quadruple!

In observing the waves which make up the ship's wake, we will note that the bow system commences with a crest which is just abaft the ship's stem. The stern system commences, on the other hand, with a trough in the vicinity of the propellers followed by a crest a little abaft the stern. Considering the locations of the first crests, we can consider that the two initiating points are separated by approximately one shiplength (L). Whether we get a reinforcement or a cancellation from the interaction of the two systems will depend on the ratio of the length between crests (l) and the length of the ship (L), or l/L. If the length of the wake waves created at the bow is equal to the length of the ship, or is an even fraction of this length, we will experience a reinforcement and a consequent increase in resistance.

To compare the length of the wake waves to the length of the ship, we can state the ratio as:

$$\frac{l}{L} = \frac{.557 \ V^2}{L}$$

which varies as the ratio:

$$\frac{V^2}{L}$$

Because it is usually convenient to plot resistance against speed, the square root of this ratio:

$$\frac{V}{\sqrt{L}}$$

where:

V = ship's speed in knots

L = ship's length in feet

is used in considering wave resistance. This ratio $\frac{V}{\sqrt{L}}$ is known as the *speed-length ratio* and is very important in consideration of resistance and power in a ship.

Actually, the wave-making length (distance between the first crest of the bow system and the first crest of the stern system) is not exactly equal to the length of the ship, so the regions of maximum R_w do not fall exactly where $\frac{V^2}{L}$ equals 1.0 or multiples thereof. The wave making length is usually slightly greater than the length of the ship (L) and will vary with the shape of the hull. However, the difference is not large and the speed-length ratio is a very useful key in studying the resistance encountered by a ship.

The amount of power consumed in creating waves is not easily expressed. If one were to attempt to find a simple formula in the form of $R_w = aV^n$, he would find that (n) varied from 1.5 to 11 for different parts of the speed range. Because of the reinforcements and cancellations mentioned above, any formula which expresses a smooth increase in resistance as speed increases is far from a correct representation of the situation.

By representing a ship by two disturbances, Professor T. H. Havelock of Armstrong College, Newcastle-on-Tyne, made an analysis which indicated that the wave resistance would be in the form indicated in Figure 2–10. Distinct humps and hollows in the resistance curve occur as the reinforcements and cancellations occur. The general decrease in resistance at very high speeds (speed-length ratio greater than 2), is experienced because, "when the travelling disturbance travels fast enough, the water does not have time to respond and is not disturbed as much as at lower speeds."* Actually, other experiments have shown that at very high speeds the ship rides up on its bow wave and a decrease in wave resistance is experienced.

Eddy resistance

As the water flows past the underwater body of the ship, if there are abrupt changes in the surface of the hull, separation and turbulence may occur. When the flow of water breaks away from the skin of the ship, such as at the after edge of a square sternpost, an area of confused eddying results. This area is aft of the ship's structure and is characterized by a lower pressure than is found in the surrounding water; therefore, a drag force is exerted on the ship as a result of eddies. Though a well-designed ship will have few such areas, the eddy resistance caused by blunt edges and projections must be considered.

*Speed and Power of Ships, by Rear Admiral David W. Taylor, CC, USN (Ret.), page 46.

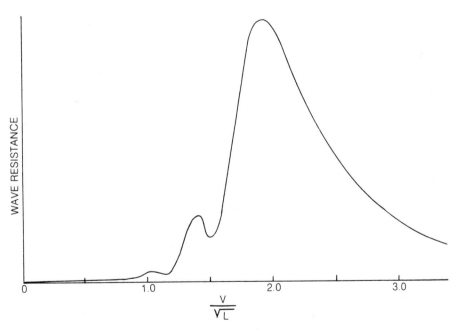

FIGURE 2–10. Wave resistance as a function of the speed-length ratio for two disturbances traveling through the water separated by one shiplength (L). (Based on Figure 56 of Speed and Power of Ships, by Rear Admiral David W. Taylor (CC), USN (Ret.).)

Eddy resistance (into this category is lumped all resistance caused by separation and turbulence around hull endings and hull openings) varies as the frontal area of the surface causing the disturbance and the square of the velocity of the water flow. Thus, even small causes of eddying may become important at high speeds.

Appendage resistance

The previous discussion has considered the simple hull of the ship without its appendages such as the propeller shafts, struts, rudders, bilge keels, etc. Each of these projections contributes to the resistance of the ship as it moves through the water, and, depending upon the nature and design of the appendage, any of the previous sources of resistance may apply.

In general, the underwater appendages of a well-designed ship are deep below the surface of the water, so they contribute little to the wave-making resistance of the ship. They are usually quite streamlined to minimize the eddy resistance, so our main source of resistance is the frictional resistance. Thus we can consider that the appendage resistance is generally proportional to the wetted surface of the appendages and the square of the velocity of flow past them.

Air resistance and wind resistance

Determining the air or wind resistance of a ship with a complex superstructure is very difficult except by experiment. Though certain data are available on the resistance of flat plates at various inclinations, it would be nearly impossible to evaluate the effect of the multitude of interacting surfaces in the superstructure of even a small ship. Consequently there are no formulae which apply to this source of resistance.

Experiments on a number of ships show, however, that air resistance varies in the range of from 1½ to 3 percent of the total water resistance of the ship at maximum speed. This leads to the conclusion that the air resistance is only a minor factor as compared to the water resistance of a ship, and can be neglected in most considerations.

Though simple air resistance (the resistance to the ship's motion through still air) may be neglected, wind resistance cannot be overlooked. A ship steaming at 10 knots into a 20-knot wind (thus feeling a 30-knot relative wind) may be expending as much as 20 percent of her power to overcome wind resistance. Another factor to be considered is that the maximum resistance to motion ahead may occur when the relative wind is on one bow instead of dead ahead. Thus the direction of the wind may have an effect in determining the resistance. A last factor in considering the wind is that a wind with a beam component usually necessitates the use of rudder to hold the ship on her course, and even a small rudder angle increases the drag of the ship appreciably.

Squat

As the ship increases speed she sinks bodily in the water, and then, at the critical speed (speed-length ratio about 1.2), the bow begins to rise and the stern begins to sink as the ship "squats." As the first crest of the bow wave system moves aft from the bow with increase of speed, the bow begins to be buoyed up by its own wave, and so the bow rises. If we remember the interaction of the bow and stern wave systems, we can see that the stern will sink into the hollow created as the first trough of the bow wave system coincides with and augments the stern system hollow near the screws. As the ship squats, her resistance increases abruptly.

Shallow water effect

As the ship enters shallow water, the character of the wave changes. A wave created at a given speed in shallow water has a longer wave length than a wave created at the same speed in deep water. Consequently, the reinforcements and severe squatting occur at lower speeds in shallow water than in deep water. Thus, in shallow water, the resistance of the ship rises more rapidly as the speed increases.

Because the severe reinforcements occur at a lower speed in shallow water, it is possible for certain very high speed ships to reach a higher maximum speed in shallow water than in deep water. This is possible because they are operating beyond the peak of the wave resistance curve (Figure 2–10), and as the whole curve shifts to the left as a result of the longer wave length in shallow water, the wave resistance at the speed they are steaming actually decreases.

Total resistance

The combination of all of the above-mentioned sources of resistance is shown in Figure 2–11. Though the particular curves shown do not illustrate the hump and hollow character of wave resistance in deep water, this characteristic is quite marked in the shallow water curves. The general sinkage of the ship at the lower speeds, and the squatting and abrupt increase in resistance as the speed is increased, can be clearly seen. It will be noted that if a ship, scaled up from the model, had the power to overcome the equivalent of 60 lbs. resistance for the model, she could make a higher speed (that is, operate at a higher speed-length ratio) at this power in shallow water than in deep water.

Rough water effects

In addition to the general sources of resistance which the ship encounters in smooth water, there is additional resistance if the surface of the water is not smooth. As the ship encounters seas from ahead, her trim is constantly changing and she

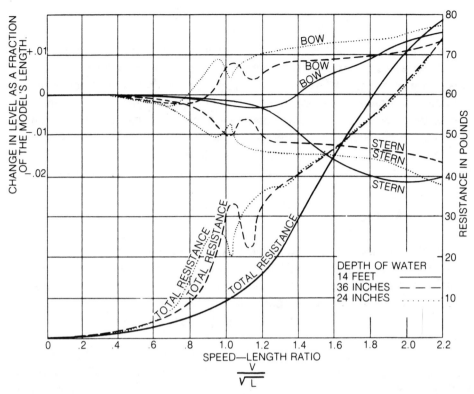

FIGURE 2–11. Resistance and changes in level of a 20-foot model of a high-speed warship.

crashes into the approaching seas. As she rolls in response to the waves, the shape of the submerged portion of her hull is constantly changing. These effects cause an increase in the resistance to her forward motion.

The pitching of the ship is the most severe deterrent to speed that is caused by rough water. It increases all the normal sources of resistance and, additionally, may cause losses in propulsive efficiency as the screws race when they come near the surface.

Rolling, though causing increased resistance, is much less detrimental than one might think. It is difficult to determine experimentally the increase in resistance caused by pure rolling, but certain experiments indicate that inclinations up to 20° cause an increase in resistance of only a few percent. Rough seas, however, do have a marked effect on the ship's resistance and the power required to drive her.

The cube rule

It is seen, therefore, that the causes of the resistance encountered by a ship are very complex. Though the thumb rule long used by marines that "the power required and the fuel consumed for a given speed go up as the cube of the speed" is applicable in certain speed ranges, the rule does not hold true for all ranges, especially when wave resistance becomes an important factor. The power required at any speed is equal to the total resistance multiplied by the speed (force × velocity = power), and for the "Cube Rule" to be correct, the resistance would have to vary as the square of the speed. We have seen that this is far from true for all cases.

The resistance of the ship is the sum of all of the factors mentioned above, and it is not susceptible to simple analysis. The shiphandler should be impressed, however, with the fact that the resistance encountered, the power required, and the fuel consumed increases drastically as the speed increases. When the speed is increased until squatting is encountered, the resistance increases even more rapidly, and the steaming efficiency of the ship is severely reduce.

The length of a ship is a very important factor in determining the resistance, and the speed-length ratio is an excellent index in considering the resistance. Two similar ships operating at the same speed-length ratio will require power in the ratio of the squares of their lengths. The higher the speed-length ratio, especially beyond critical speed ($\frac{V}{\sqrt{L}}$ greater than 1.2), the greater the proportion of total power which is expended uselessly in creating waves.

The wastage of power in creating surface waves leads one to the interesting realization that a streamlined submarine, cruising at a sufficient depth to be free from surface effects, can attain a higher speed for a given power than an equivalent ship on the surface at the same power. A deeply submerged submarine encounters resistance which is proportional to the square of her speed, but the surface ship encounters a much higher resistance for the same speed. It is because of this wastage of power in creating wake waves that inventors are constantly searching for ways of causing a ship to "plane" at high speeds and thus be able to escape this major source of drag on a conventional hull.

Wind

Another important source of force on the ship is the wind. This force warrants thorough study because it is not only outside the control of the shiphandler but is quite changeable. Though the wind is often a hazard to the shiphandler, it can also be a very useful aid. By carefully playing the effect of the wind on the ship we can do things that would have been impossible through the use of the engines and rudders alone.

The wind normally acts to force the ship bodily *downwind*. The force it exerts is proportional to the square of the velocity of the wind, the cross-sectional area presented normal to the flow of air, and the form of the superstructure in the air flow. If we double the velocity of the relative wind, we quadruple the force on the ship from this source. If we turn the ship so that a larger cross-section is presented normal to the wind, the resultant force is increased. If the superstructure of the ship is irregular and presents many flat surfaces to the wind, the force of the wind will be larger than if the superstructure presents a smooth, streamlined form.

It is relatively easy to predict the reaction of the wind on a given ship. If the ship has high freeboard and is of shallow draft, the force from the wind will be great, the resistance to motion from the water will be small, and the ship will respond quite readily to the wind. If the ship is of deep draft and presents a small streamlined body to the wind, the wind effect will be minimal. This also applies to the sections of the ship. With a given ship, if the bow is high, the stern low, and the ship trimmed down by the stern, the wind will tend to carry the bow *downwind*. Generally speaking, a ship lightly loaded is more sensitive to the wind than one heavy laden.

If we remember that the propellers and rudders give us means to apply force to the stern only, it is apparent that to force the ship to turn into a beam wind, it is necessary to overcome the wind force tending to blow the bow downwind. We must move the *stern* downwind faster than the wind is moving the *bow* downwind. If the bow presents a much larger "sail" area than the stern, the side force needed at the stern might be quite large. Since the side forces available from the engines alone are relatively small, it is often necessary to gain considerable headway before the additional force from the rudder is sufficient to overcome the wind.

Current

The last general force to be considered is the force due to current. The resistance of the underwater body of the ship to the flow of water is very similar to the resistance of the superstructure to the wind; however, the force resulting is much larger for a given velocity because the density of the medium is much greater. The streamlining of the hull is most important, and the top speed of a given ship is that speed at which the total resistance of the hull exactly balances the maximum force that can be delivered by the propellers.

The resistance of the underwater body to the flow of current is proportional to the square of the velocity of the current and the cross-sectional area presented to the flow, and is inversely dependent upon the streamlining of the body with respect to the direction of the flow. Obviously the resistance of the hull to a given current from ahead would be much smaller than the resistance to the same current from abeam.

Since the current is by definition the movement of the water, the ship is normally carried along with this movement. If we handle our ship as though there were no current and the stationary objects were moving at the speed of the current but in the opposite direction, we would have little trouble predicting the behavior of the ship. This simple solution is satisfactory for a steady current, but unfortunately the current is not steady in the vicinity of stationary objects. However, the special problems of current in the vicinity of docks and buoys will be covered later.

Actually, it is impossible to have a current relative to the ship other than from ahead or astern except by the application of forces external to the ship. If the flow of current relative to the ship is to be other than parallel to the axis of the keel, there must be some restraining force provided by mooring lines or ground tackle.

The shiphandler must always consider the current in maneuvering his ship near stationary objects. He must add the current vector to the vector of his own ship's motion through the water to determine his true movement relative to the ground. As he changes his speed through the water he must remember that the current velocity remains generally constant, and he must compensate for it. Finally, as he handles his ship broadside to the current, he must expect to be swept along with the current unless he uses external means to restrain the ship, and in that case the forces required will be relatively large.

SUMMARY

We have now examined the forces that come to bear on a ship due to the environment in which it operates and the manner in which it is propelled and controlled. We have considered the reasons why these forces exist, and we have prepared ourselves to be ready to estimate these forces for a given ship in a given situation.

The shiphandler must always be alert for evidences of conditions which will affect the handling of his ship. He must watch his bunting and rigging to determine the relative wind, and he must watch the surface of the water for signs of the true wind and current. If he is completely aware of the forces playing on his ship, he can compensate for the undesired effects and make use of the helpful effects.

A thorough understanding of all of the forces which can act upon the ship is the cornerstone of ability at shiphandling. Unless the shiphandler thoroughly understands the forces that come to play on his ship, how they act, and how they can be controlled, he cannot hope to handle his ship efficiently.

3
propellers and rudders

Though many forces come to bear on our ship, we control her through her engine(s) and rudder(s). More exactly, we control her through her steering wheel and engine order telegraphs, or "annunciators," mounted in the pilothouse of the ship. It would be convenient if these control devices were connected directly to the propellers and the rudders and desired control settings could be instantly affected, but this is not so. Even in the most modern ship there is a considerable lag between the ordering of a rudder or engine setting on the bridge and the actual execution of the order. The ship may have more than one propeller and more than one rudder, and their relative position and interaction may have a strong effect on ship response. Finally, the ship is controlled through voice commands which must be clearly understood and carried out if we are to achieve the desired result.

We actually steer the ship by setting the rudder at various angles with respect to the centerline of the ship. Right rudder causes the bow to turn right when moving ahead by forcing the stern to the left. Left rudder causes the bow to move left when going ahead. The rate of turn will be approximately proportional to the rudder angle, which is limited by mechanical restraints to 35° in most Navy ships. When moving ahead at a moderate speed so that the velocity of flow past the rudder is adequate, most ships steer quite nicely and a good helmsman can keep them on course using only a few degrees of rudder to either side.

Moving at low speeds or attempting to turn when the ship is nearly dead in the water is a different story. Below a certain speed the rudder force available from even a fully deflected rudder is not sufficient to overcome other forces working on the ship and she is said to have lost "steerageway." When the ship has lost steerageway, her heading can no longer be controlled by her rudder alone and we must resort to the propeller and its possible action on her rudder. It is the clear understanding of the interaction of rudder and propeller which permits the shiphandler to accurately control his ship.

If a rudder is directly abaft a propeller so that the propeller wash impinges directly upon it, the rudder will provide a steering force in response to the screw current, regardless of the motion of the ship. If the propeller is reversed so that the rudder is now on the suction side of the propeller, the effect is usually greatly reduced. If the rudder is so installed that it is entirely outside of the screw current, its action will depend entirely upon the motion of the ship through the water.

In any case, in a conventional ship where the rudders and propellers are installed at the stern of the ship, control forces from rudder and propeller can only be applied at the stern. The ship must be maneuvered by moving the stern about; the normal installation gives no direct control of the bow. When dead in the water, a force at the stern will cause the ship to pivot at an angular rate proportional to the square root of the force.

The number and placement of both propellers and rudders is obviously of great interest to the shiphandler. With twin screws and correctly placed twin rudders a ship can be handled with great ease and accuracy in all but the most extreme conditions. With twin screws and a single rudder she can still be turned at speeds below steerageway, but not nearly so easily as a ship with twin rudders. With a single screw, even with an excellent rudder, life gets much more difficult, and there are actually some maneuvers which cannot be accomplished at all without some assistance besides the ship's own propeller and rudder. A single-screw ship dead in the water cannot get any action from her rudder unless the engine is going ahead, quickly resulting in ship motion ahead, which might be unacceptable. Going astern, the situation is even less controllable, because a single-screw ship tends to veer to port when she backs and her rudder, with no screw current impinging on it, is not effective until the ship is moving through the water at a considerable rate.

The reason for the strange behavior of the single-screw ship and for a part of the capability of the twin-screw ship is the propeller side force, the source of which was analyzed in the previous chapter. To master our ship, we must understand this side force to put it to good use when possible and to know when it might cause difficulty.

SINGLE-SCREW SHIPS

Side force from the propeller

In a single-screw ship the *magnitude* of the side force caused by the propeller will vary with the type of ship and the character of the underwater structure in the vicinity of the propeller, but the *direction* of this force depends on the *direction of rotation* of the propeller only, and will be as though the lower blades of the propeller were bearing on the bottom and pushing the stern to the side as the shaft rotates. A propeller turning to the *right*, or clockwise, as seen from astern, will tend to force the stern to the right as shown in Figure 3–1. A propeller turning to the *left*, or

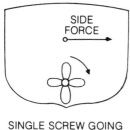

SINGLE SCREW GOING
AHEAD.

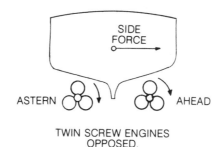

TWIN SCREW ENGINES
OPPOSED.

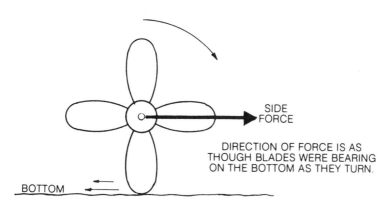

FIGURE 3–1. Side force on a propeller.

counter-clockwise as seen from astern, will tend to force the stern to the left. When the direction of rotation is reversed, the direction of the side force is reversed.

When moving ahead at a steady speed in a single-screw ship, the side force on the propeller is not large. In order to insure good propulsive efficiency, such a ship is carefully designed to minimize the side force (and the amount of rudder required to overcome it). When backing or maneuvering with little way, the side force may be much larger.

When a single-screw ship backs, the helical discharge from the screw is thrown directly into the ship's structure, and the side force experienced is usually the strongest encountered under any circumstances. For this reason, it is difficult to prevent the stern moving to port when backing a single-screw ship with a righthand screw.

When maneuvering with little way on, the propeller may be driving at a high speed while the ship is moving relatively slowly. With this high "slip" condition, separation and turbulence may cause an unusually powerful side force to be felt.

Thus, regardless of the motion of the ship, a side force is experienced as a result of the rotation of the propeller, and this force must enter into the calculations of the conning officer in estimating the motion of his ship.

The rudder in a single-screw ship

In a single-screw ship, since the rudder is placed directly astern of the propeller, the screw current is usually the dominant factor in determining the effectiveness of the rudder. When the screw is going ahead, the velocity of flow past the rudder is almost exactly the discharge current of the screw, regardless of the ship's motion. Under these circumstances very large side force can be supplied by the rudder independent of the ship's speed through the water. So long as the screw is going ahead, we can depend on good rudder effectiveness.

When the propeller is turning astern, however, the strong discharge current is not directed against the rudder, and the relatively unconcentrated suction current has little effect on the rudder. Consequently, such a ship must rely nearly entirely on sternward velocity to provide the flow necessary to produce strong rudder forces. For this reason a single-screw ship must build up considerable speed astern before she responds well to her rudder. If *strong* rudder forces are desired, the propeller must be turning *ahead*.

Resultant force on a single-screw ship

Though we have considered the thrust, the side force, and the rudder action separately, it is the resultant of all three that determines the motion of a ship. We must combine the separate components into a single resultant force if we are to be able to predict their combined reaction of the ship.

If we define as *screw thrust* the component of propeller action that acts in line with the propeller shaft, we can lump all other components of propeller action in the horizontal plane into a single athwartships component which we can call *side force*. Since the force on a rudder inclined to the flow is nearly perpendicular to the faces of the rudder, we can define the *rudder force* as a force perpendicular to the faces of the rudder. Since all of these forces act at nearly the same place near the stern of the ship, we can for all practical purposes consider their combined effect as a *single resultant force* acting at the propeller. We control the ship by controlling this resultant force.

In addition to the active forces mentioned above, there is the drag of the hull as it moves through the water. This drag force depends upon the speed of the ship through the water, and it can be considered to act at the center of gravity in a direction opposite to the movement of the ship through the water. If the force we apply at the stern is exactly equal to the drag force, and if the line of action of the applied force passes through the center of gravity, a steady state is achieved and the ship will proceed at a steady speed with no tendency to turn.

If, on the other hand, the line of action of the resultant force at the stern does *not* pass through the center of gravity of the ship, there will be a torque on the ship and the ship will turn. The amount of this torque will be equal to the force on the stern multiplied by its effective lever arm with respect to the center of gravity of the ship. For all practical purposes, the center of gravity of a ship can be considered to lie on the centerline.

Since we control the ship by controlling the force on the stern, it is useful to set up a system for determining this force. If we can consider all of the forces on the stern to be acting at one place, we can construct a vector diagram to determine the resultant force on the ship. The drag force can be viewed as a reaction force, as can the resistance torque which opposes the rotation of the ship in the water, and thus they can be omitted from the resolution of active control forces on the stern.

Figure 3–2 illustrates the range of variation of the force on the stern obtainable by the use of the rudder while the ship is being driven ahead at a constant speed. It will be noticed the side force allows more transverse force to be applied to starboard than to port. Thus the ship can turn more rapidly to port than to starboard. Figure 3–3 illustrates the effects of the screw and the rudder while the ship is dead in the water. The side force is shown greater than when the ship is moving ahead, which is the normal experience in single-screw ships. When the screw is turning astern, the side force completely overshadows the rudder force available while the ship is dead in the water, and the resultant force is always to port. Thus, though it is possible to twist the ship to the right with the screw turning ahead, she twists much

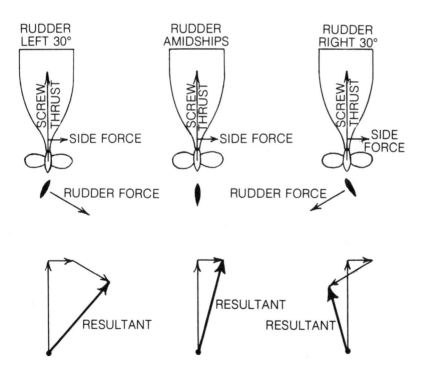

FIGURE 3–2. Resultant force on a single-screw ship when going ahead.

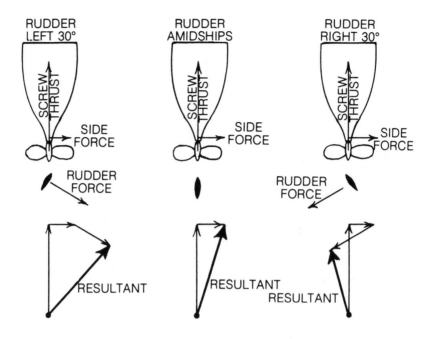

(a.) ENGINE RPM FOR 5 KNOTS AHEAD, SHIP DEAD IN WATER.

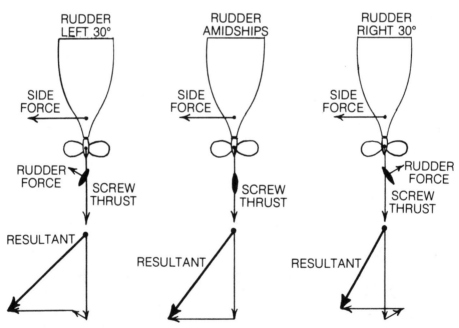

(b.) ENGINE RPM FOR 5 KNOTS ASTERN, SHIP DEAD IN WATER.

FIGURE 3–3. Resultant force on a single-screw ship with no way on.

better to the left. With the screw turning astern while dead in the water, the stern goes to port regardless of the rudder.

In Figure 3–4 we construct the vector diagrams for the engine driving astern while the ship also is moving astern. In this condition the rudder is once again effective, and a condition is selected where the rudder is able to overcome the side force and produce a resultant with a component to starboard. It is evident from the figure that much greater forces can be applied to port than to starboard.

TWIN-SCREW SHIPS

Most Navy ships have twin propellers, and some of the largest have four. Normally, when driving ahead, the propellers turn outboard, the starboard propeller turning clockwise and the port propeller turning counter-clockwise, as seen from astern. Providing a ship with an even number of opposed propellers eliminates many of the troubles found in single-screw ships. As long as the propellers are driving together, the side forces (which depend on the direction of rotation) are cancelled out, whether the screws are turning ahead or astern. On the other hand, if the propellers

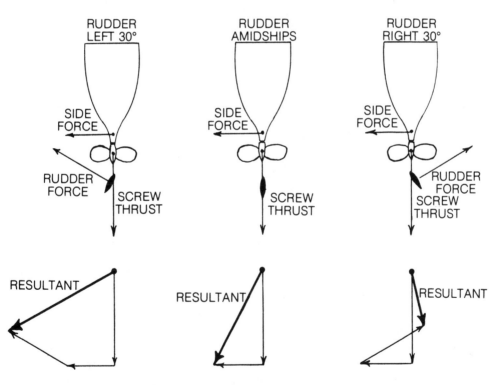

SHIP MOVING ASTERN AT 10 KNOTS WITH ENGINE
RPM FOR 10 KNOTS ASTERN.

FIGURE 3–4. Resultant force on a single-screw ship when going astern.

are *opposed*, one turning ahead and the other astern, the side forces then augment each other. Thus, with two or four screws, we have an ideal situation where the side forces cancel out if we are proceeding steadily ahead or astern, yet we can obtain an augmented side force by *opposing* the screws when we so desire.

In addition to the augmented side force with the screws opposed, we obtain a torque or twisting effect on the ship, because the shafts are displaced from the centerline. Since the thrust line from each screw passes to the side of the center of gravity, the torque applied by each propeller is equal to the thrust of the propeller multiplied by the perpendicular distance from this thrust line to the center of gravity. Since the screws are opposed, the torques augment each other and the resulting moment tends to turn the ship. The greater the distance between the propellers (with parallel shafts), the greater will be this effect.

When the screws on opposite sides of the ship are opposed, a circulating current in the horizontal plane is created by the suction and discharge streams of the propellers, as indicated in Figure 3–5. When this current impinges on a part of the ship's underwater structure, it produces a force. Forward of the screws there are many obstructions to this flow, and a strong athwartships force is experienced. Abaft the screws, only the rudder(s) are encountered, and if these are turned to conform to the flow, little force results. Consequently, the effect of the circulating current can be considered to be a side force on the structure forward of the propellers.

All of the effects mentioned in the above paragraphs resulting from opposing the engines of a twin-screw ship, with outward turning screws, act in the same direction. In combination they can produce a strong resultant side force which can play an important part in maneuvering the ship.

When the twin-screw ship is going ahead on one screw only, there is a tendency to veer to the side opposite from the screw in use. This tendency is, of course, caused by the side force and the offset position of the driving screw. At low speeds, the tendency is quite marked, but at higher speeds this tendency can be overcome by the use of a moderate amount of rudder.

When backing with only one screw, a stronger turning effect is noticed. In this case we have not only the normal side force and torque due to the offsetting of the propeller, but also a strong additional side force caused by the helical discharge current. When backing, the propeller throws a strong helical current into the struts, which are above the shaft, causing a strong athwartship force. This causes a much stronger side force than when the screw is turning ahead.

Following the above observations we can draw a diagram as indicated in Figure 3–6, showing the direction of the force that we can apply to the stern of a twin-screw ship by turning each screw individually. The average direction of the resultant force from using a screw in a given direction is indicated in the figure, and if the length of the vector is made proportional to the rpm of the shaft, we can combine the vectors to determine the resultant force on the stern of the ship from the two propellers. It is useful to keep Figure 3–6 in mind when maneuvering with the engines.

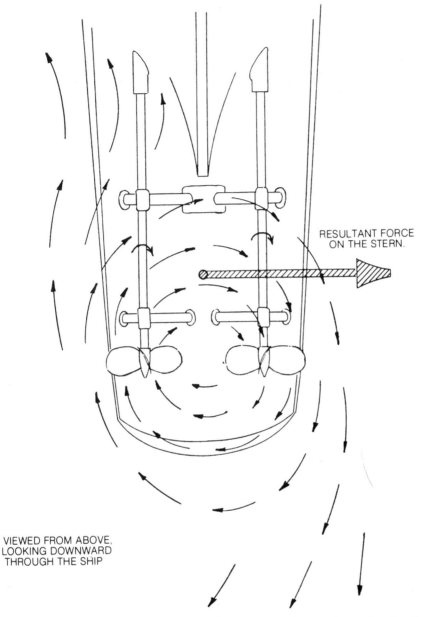

RESULTANT FORCE
ON THE STERN.

VIEWED FROM ABOVE,
LOOKING DOWNWARD
THROUGH THE SHIP

FIGURE 3–5. Circulating current caused by opposing the engines, showing the resultant force on a destroyer's typical underwater structure.

The rudder, with twin screws

The rudder of a twin-screw, single-rudder ship is mounted on the centerline just abaft the screws. As indicated in Figure 3–7, it does not feel the discharge current from the propellers when it is positioned "amidships." Consequently, when using

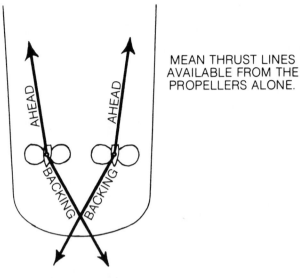

MEAN THRUST LINES
AVAILABLE FROM THE
PROPELLERS ALONE.

PROBLEM: TO FIND FORCE ON STERN WITH:

STARBOARD ENGINE AHEAD AT 100 RPM.
PORT ENGINE BACKING AT 50 RPM.

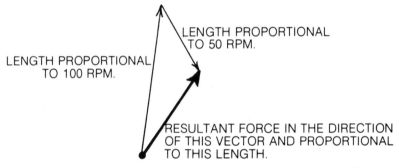

LENGTH PROPORTIONAL
TO 50 RPM.

LENGTH PROPORTIONAL
TO 100 RPM.

RESULTANT FORCE IN THE DIRECTION
OF THIS VECTOR AND PROPORTIONAL
TO THIS LENGTH.

FIGURE 3–6. Diagram for determining force on the stern from propellers alone.

small rudder angles, only the *forward motion of the ship* through the water has any appreciable effect on the velocity of flow past the rudder and hence on the force obtainable by use of the rudder. At larger rudder angles, however (usually about 15° or more, depending on the type of ship), the after edge of the rudder enters the discharge current from the propeller on the side to which it is turned. Thus, at large rudder angles an augmented effect is obtained if the screw on the side to which the rudder is deflected is turning ahead.

Many modern types of vessels are equipped with twin rudders. In this design the rudders are mounted directly astern of the propellers, as shown in Figure 3–7, and their effectiveness is increased by the screw current impinging directly on the rudders. Since the screw discharge can produce a high velocity current at the rudder regardless of the ship's motion, it is this screw discharge that is the

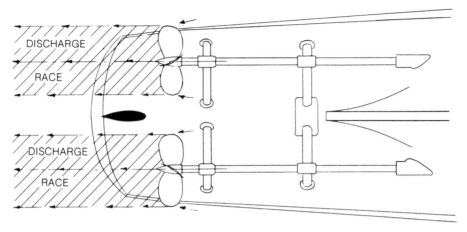

(a.) SINGLE RUDDER. RUDDER BETWEEN SCREW DISCHARGE RACES.
VIEWED FROM ABOVE, LOOKING DOWNWARD THROUGH THE SHIP.

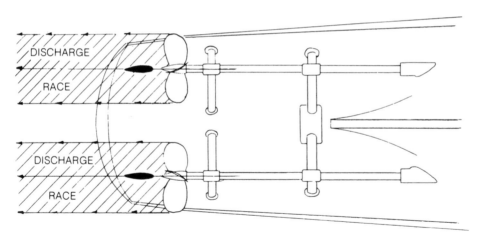

(b.) TWIN RUDDERS. RUDDERS IN CENTER OF DISCHARGE RACES.
VIEWED FROM ABOVE, LOOKING DOWNWARD THROUGH THE SHIP.

FIGURE 3–7. Comparative positions of single and twin rudders in twin-screw ships.

controlling factor in rudder effectiveness. If the screws are opposed, the one going
ahead will have the greatest effect on the rudder action for this reason. In fact, with a
twin-screw, twin-rudder ship, we can quite easily twist in our own water, with no way

on, by opposing the engines equally and using full rudder in the direction we desire to turn. The side force from the rudder astern of the propeller which is driving ahead more than overcomes the weak opposing force of the other rudder.

Resultant force on a twin-screw ship

To construct the complete vector diagram for the forces on the stern, we must first resolve the off-center effect of the screws by replacing the resultant couple by an equivalent side force acting at the screws. Having done this, we can consider that all the forces act at the centerline between the screws, and thus can resolve the single resulting force by a vector polygon. This, of course, overlooks the longitudinal distance from the screws to the rudders, but this discrepancy produces only a minor inaccuracy. Figure 3–8 is an example of the vector solution for the force on the stern of a twin-screw, twin-rudder ship.

By using the various combinations available with a twin-screw ship, we can create a force in any desired direction at the stern. Our speed through the water will vary the amount of side force that we can apply, and generally speaking, the amount of side force we can produce will be much less than the fore-and-aft force that is at our command. Nevertheless, by proper selection of the engine and rudder combination with a twin-screw ship, we can create a force at the stern in any direction we desire. Figure 3–9 indicates the engine and rudder combination required for producing force in each of the relative octants. A twin-rudder vessel is indicated because this type is the most versatile type. The figure assumes that the ship has no way on, and it will be noted that the rudders are positioned to achieve a maximum effect from that rudder which is astern of the screw that is going ahead.

In handling a ship it is very difficult at times to judge correctly what is the actual current in the vicinity of the screws and the rudder. Even the most experienced shiphandler will misjudge the direction of the flow during an intricate maneuver, and will put his rudder over the wrong way. When in doubt as to the combined effect of the engines and rudder, watch the surface of the water in the vicinity of the stern. Since the water is accelerated in the direction *opposite* to that of the force on the stern, the mean resultant flow from the stern will indicate the *direction* of the force we are obtaining. The *magnitude* of the force can be estimated by the *strength* of the flow.

Turning

We have discussed the rudder and the screw forces that act at the stern of the ship, but we have not explored *how the ship* reacts to the application of these forces. So long as the resultant force vector passes through the center of gravity, no rotation is produced. When a side force is applied by the rudder and screws, with the ship dead in the water, the ship pivots about a point about 30 percent of the distance from the bow to the stern. One might expect the ship to spin about its midpoint—

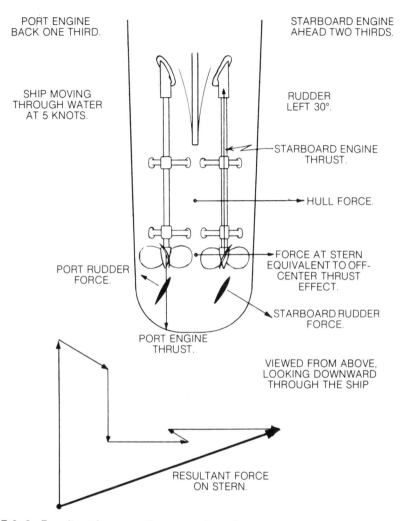

PORT ENGINE
BACK ONE THIRD.

STARBOARD ENGINE
AHEAD TWO THIRDS.

SHIP MOVING
THROUGH WATER
AT 5 KNOTS.

RUDDER
LEFT 30°.

STARBOARD ENGINE
THRUST.

HULL FORCE.

FORCE AT STERN
EQUIVALENT TO OFF-
CENTER THRUST
EFFECT.

PORT RUDDER
FORCE.

STARBOARD RUDDER
FORCE.

PORT ENGINE
THRUST.

VIEWED FROM ABOVE,
LOOKING DOWNWARD
THROUGH THE SHIP

RESULTANT FORCE
ON STERN.

FIGURE 3–8. Resultant force on the stern of a twin-rudder, twin-screw ship.

and thus it should, from the application of a pure torque—but in the case of an unbalanced side force applied at the propeller, the ship must move broadside in response to the unbalanced directional force, as well as rotate in response to the resulting torque. Thus the combination of the side motion and the rotation causes the ship to appear to rotate about a point considerably forward of the midpoint. Figure 3–10 illustrates how a ship turns about its *pivot point* when twisting with no way on.

When under way and proceeding ahead, the pivot point moves forward as the speed increases, until, at normal operating speeds, the pivot point is abaft the stem about 15 to 20 percent of the length of the ship. This shifting of the pivot point is caused by the hydrodynamic effects of the flow past the hull.

When under way, the only means we have of controlling the ship is through her engines and rudder, and both of these act near the stern of the ship. Thus we can

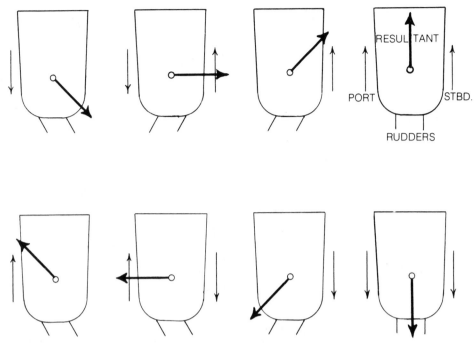

FIGURE 3–9. Resultant force with various screw and rudder combinations.

consider that we *steer* the ship by *forcing the stern* from side to side. To make a turn we force the stern to the side *opposite* to the direction in which we wish to turn, and this has two effects. First, the hull of the ship is inclined to the initial direction of motion, and this produces a large force pushing the ship in the direction of the turn; and second, the thrust from the screws is now inclined to the initial direction of motion, and this also forces the ship off its former course in the direction of the turn. This is a continuous process, and as the ship proceeds around in its turn, the centerline of the ship is inclined toward the center of the turn. The stern rides to the outside and the bow to the inside of the mean path of the ship. The ship as a whole proceeds as though the pivot point were making a smooth turn.

It is a useful concept to consider that we are maneuvering the pivot point through the water when we handle the ship. We can always *twist about* the pivot point to correct our alignment, but we can't *move* the pivot point *sideways* with the engines and rudder.

Control commands

Though we have discussed the use of the engines and propellers in general terms, it is apparent that we must have precise control of the propellers if we are going to handle the ship skillfully. To do this we must define our engine commands, and this is not as simple as it might appear.

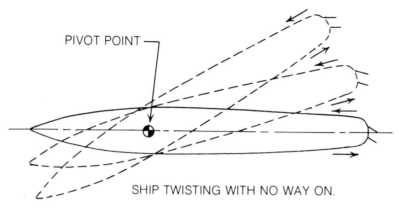

SHIP TWISTING WITH NO WAY ON.

FIGURE 3-10. Pivot point of a ship twisting with no way on.

It would be advantageous to be able to oppose the engines exactly in certain situations and thus be able to twist the ship in her own water, getting no way on in either direction. Since the pitch of the propellers is equal, we could do this by ordering equal rpm in opposite directions on the two shafts. However, if BACK ONE-THIRD were defined simply as a given number of rpm astern, it would call for a great deal more power if ordered while the ship was proceeding at full speed ahead than if ordered while dead in the water. In fact, in a destroyer an eager throttleman might drag off all the steam from a boiler in trying to produce 100 rpm astern quickly for a BACK TWO-THIRDS bell if the initial speed ahead were high. Because the amount of steam required to produce a certain rpm varies with the speed through the water, many ships define their backing speeds as steam pressures on the turbines. This system avoids the trouble described above, but it sacrifices the precision possible when using the shaft tachometers to produce exact rpm.

The order STOP is not as simple as it appears. Remembering that we are delivering force with the engine, we would like the engine to cease supplying force when we give the order STOP. If we meant to have the shaft stop rotating, we might have to apply a great deal of power to keep the shaft from rotating merely from the effect of the current flowing past it. Most ships have adopted the definition of STOP which calls for all throttles closed and the propeller idling. The command STOP SHAFTS is an emergency order meaning to stop the shafts from rotating while passing an obstruction.

The exact definitions used in a given ship will depend upon a number of factors, but under any circumstances it is essential that all hands have a clear and accurate understanding of all of the orders used. Whether on the bridge or in the engineering spaces, the engine orders must have the same meaning. The definitions in Table 3-1 were set up for a destroyer and have been found to be very useful. They are adequate to meet the most stringent demands. This system capitalizes on the advantages of both the *steam pressure* and the rpm *systems* of defining backing bells, since the steam pressure is used until the rpm is reached, and the rpm thereafter.

TABLE 3–1. Engine Orders (for a destroyer with a 600 psi propulsion plant).

ENGINE ORDERS

AHEAD ONE-THIRD	rpm for 5 knots ahead
AHEAD TWO-THIRDS	rpm for 10 knots ahead
AHEAD STANDARD	rpm for 15 knots ahead
AHEAD FULL	rpm for 20 knots ahead
AHEAD FLANK	rpm for 25 knots ahead
FLANK RUNG TWICE	rpm for 30 knots ahead
FLANK RUNG THREE TIMES	rpm for 35 knots ahead
STOP	all throttles closed
BACK ONE-THIRD	60 lbs. pressure on astern turbine until 50 rpm reached. Then rpm astern for 5 knots
BACK TWO-THIRDS	120 lbs. pressure on astern turbine until 100 rpm reached. Then rpm astern for 10 knots.
BACK FULL	200 lbs. pressure on astern turbine
BACK EMERGENCY	Backing throttle open completely, except steam pressure at throttle not allowed to fall below 500 lbs.
STOP SHAFT	Apply sufficient steam to stop all rotation of shaft

In Navy ships the orders are given to the engines by means of the engine order telegraphs, which order the direction and general magnitude of the speed desired, and by the revolution indicator, which specifies the rpm desired. The telegraphs can be read in all of the engineering spaces, but the revolution indicator is normally installed only in the engine rooms. The system of multiple rings indicated in Table 3–1 is provided to keep the firerooms informed of changes of speed beyond the range of the telegraphs.

On the standard engine order telegraph, in addition to the STOP position there are five positions for AHEAD speeds, but only three positions are used for BACK speeds. Because of the symmetry of construction of the actual Navy units, this leaves two unused positions in the BACK arc on all of the transmitters and indicators. By simply lettering in the proper labels, we can utilize these two spare segments for STOP SHAFT and BACK EMERGENCY. Thus by the expedient of more completely using the equipment provided, we obtain means of ordering these very useful commands.

The prior discussion has dealt with engine telegraph orders exclusively, but the revolution indicator is also a very important link in our engine command system. It is an essential aid in precise shiphandling when engine changes less than five knots are desired. Quite often when exact control is required at a speed intermediate between the increments of the telegraphs, the revolution order becomes the controlling means of command. Under these circumstances it is the normal practice to keep the engine telegraphs set on the increment nearest to the speed actually desired. We must remember, however, that moving the telegraphs will signal a speed change of at least five knots to those stations not equipped with both a telegraph receiver and a revolution indicator, and all stations will take action. If the telegraphs are being moved simply to match the revolutions, and if a large incremental change is not desired, the conning officer must be careful that the engineers are notified of his desires. If this is not done, an inefficient and smoky operation will result as the fire rooms prepare for the change that never comes to pass and then have to change their firing rate drastically to compensate for their undesired forehandedness.

Since two instruments are used to give commands to the engines, it is essential that a system be worked out which specifies *which* shall be followed in case they give conflicting orders. Most ships adopt the rule that the *latest command* holds, regardless of the instrument upon which received. Thus, if we are steaming at 18 knots with the telegraphs set at STANDARD, and we wish to correct the situation, we must set the telegraphs at FULL and then ring off and ring back the appropriate turns for 18 knots. If this were not done, the engine rooms would follow the command FULL calling for 20 knots, because it was the latest command.

The revolution indicator can be used with the engines opposed if this condition has been adequately defined. In this case, the engine rooms answer the telegraphs for *direction* and the indicators for *amount*. Obviously this system cannot be used when it is desired to oppose the engines at different powers. Under circumstances where it is desired to use unequal power, the increments of the telegraphs are normally quite adequate.

Since there is a problem of the interaction of the engine telegraphs and the revolution indicator, it is convenient to set up a system to eliminate the revolution indicator when it is not needed. This is the normal case in a harbor, and it is useful to define MANEUVERING BELLS as the system where the engine order telegraphs are used exclusively and the revolution indicator is ignored. Conversely, the normal system using both the telegraphs and the revolution indicators is defined as STEAMING BELLS. It is convenient to order MANEUVERING BELLS by setting the revolution indicator on a certain number *beyond* the range of the engines, such as 777 rpm. The return to STEAMING BELLS is ordered simply by ringing up the desired number of turns.

For the same reasons that engine orders need exact definitions, rudder orders must be precisely defined. The order STANDARD RUDDER can no longer be used, because ships are now required to turn to specific tactical diameters depending on the composition of the force and regardless of speed. The amount of rudder to produce even a single tactical diameter will vary with the speed. Since the helmsman reads his rudder angle indicator in degrees and the conning officer checks it on the open bridge on a repeater graduated in degrees, it is most desirable that all rudder angles be ordered in degrees. The command should be "RIGHT, EIGHTEEN DEGREES RUDDER," or "LEFT, THIRTY-FIVE DEGREES RUDDER," instead of

"RIGHT, STANDARD," or "LEFT, HARD RUDDER." The slight difference in number of words is more than compensated by the resulting certainty that the order can't be misinterpreted.

The conning officer should school himself in giving his orders clearly and properly. Orders to the engines should invariably be given in the sequence: *engine, direction, amount*. Thus the proper command would be "STARBOARD ENGINE, AHEAD, TWO-THIRDS," or "PORT ENGINE, BACK, FULL." In the same manner rudder orders should be given in the sequence: *direction, amount*. Since there is only one control for the rudders regardless of how many are installed, the word "rudder" is normally left until the end of the order.

All orders should be given in a clear, loud voice. Although the man to execute the order may be standing next to the conning officer, it is important that all hands in the conning station hear the order so as to keep them abreast of the situation and functioning at maximum efficiency.

Kinetics vs statics

One of the most important concepts to understand in the mastering of one's ship is that we are dealing with *kinetics*—motions produced by forces. We cannot *place* our ship and expect her to stay there. We can achieve accelerations proportional to the forces we bring to bear on our ship; these accelerations will, with the passage of time, produce velocities of motion in our ship; and we have learned that fluid resistance to motion is proportional to the square of the velocity. A force on our ship can thus be expected to produce a velocity, usually built up rather slowly, until the fluid resistance exactly counteracts the force, after which the motion will continue at a steady velocity. This concept applies to angular motions as well as linear motions. When we apply thrust with our propellers, the ship accelerates until the resistance counteracts the thrust, after which the ship continues to move at this equilibrium velocity. With the rudder we set up a turning moment that results in a given rate of turn at equilibrium. When we remove the control forces or moments, the ship continues its motion but at a steadily declining rate as the fluid resistance takes over and brings the ship to rest.

Any force on our ship, regardless of how small, will, in the absence of counteracting forces, set our ship in motion. Once in motion, linear or angular, our ship will continue this motion until countered by another force. We cannot depend entirely on fluid resistance to end the motion, because it is dependent on the motion and approaches zero as the velocity approaches zero. A motion of our ship, once started, will continue until some force is applied to stop it.

Shiphandling is the art of handling the velocities of a ship. We can increase or decrease her linear or angular speeds through the use of her engines and rudders. We must always observe and take into account the velocities of motion produced by the wind, current, and other forces from outside our ship. Once we have brought our ship to rest, we can hold her with lines and chains, but the novice will be astonished at the magnitude of force required to bring a ship to rest even from almost imperceptible motion. A large ship moving forward at only a knot or two will bite twenty feet into a heavy pier before coming to rest. Mooring lines snap dangerously if the conning officer tries to check a substantial motion with his lines. The shiphandler uses his engines and rudders, the wind and the tide, lines, tugs, and anchors to control the velocities of his ship, to set her on her course, or to bring her to rest at the place and in the orientation he desires.

4
destroyers

Though we can discuss the forces on a ship and the environment of the sea from a generalized point of view, as soon as we begin to examine specific problems which confront the shiphandler our solution will depend to a large extent upon the type of ship we are considering. Each type of ship has peculiarities which set it off from other types, and these must be taken into account when deciding upon a solution for a particular problem. If each evolution were discussed for all types at the outset, the discussion might become so involved that the reader would miss the principles. Consequently, it is best to cover the entire field of shiphandling from the point of view of a single type, and then later point out where other types require different treatment.

The destroyer is a particularly good type with which to first explore the problems which face the shiphandler. The destroyer was selected because she embodies the characteristics of even the most complex type while usually possessing the capacity to solve most of the problems which will face her. She was also selected because of the traditional excellence of destroyer handling in the fleet, and because of the fierce pride that destroyer officers have in this phase of their work.

Most officers feel that the peak of their careers is reached with the command of a destroyer. Although many have assignments of more prestige and achieve a rank much senior to that of a destroyer skipper, in their hearts the most satisfying tour of duty is that in command of a fine destroyer. Much of that satisfaction comes from the pleasure and sense of accomplishment that comes from having handled her well.

Within her sleek sides the destroyer possesses the greatest capacity for maneuvering of all ships. She is the fastest and most maneuverable major ship in the Navy. Though the carrier is immensely larger, has four propellers and much more power, she is treated like an invalid in port. A carrier is given only the safest berths, she never moves except on the most favorable tide, and she is usually attended by a bevy of tugs. Handling the destroyer is like driving a sports car; commanding a carrier is like being mayor of a city.

Actually, the destroyer is the largest ship in the fleet that is habitually handled without assistance. Displacing 4,000 tons or more, the modern destroyer is not a small ship. She is long and she is heavy, but her powerful engines give her the greatest horsepower-per-ton ratio of any major type of ship. In the hands of a competent shiphandler she can be made to do almost anything that any other ship can do, and she handles with a grace beautiful to behold.

Another reason why the destroyer has been selected as the ship with which to explore the field of shiphandling is that she is called upon for the greatest variety of duty. She is active in every phase of fleet operations from antisubmarine warfare to amphibious support. She is found in the screen of every major naval force, and she is an integral part of carrier air operations. In fact, except for the submerged operation of the submarine or the beaching of a landing ship, the destroyer participates in every phase of fleet activity. She is therefore the ideal example for discussion.

Destroyer types

Counted as destroyer types today we have ships with displacements of from 1,500 tons to 10,150 tons, lengths from 306 feet to 596 feet, and many combinations of screws and rudders. With such variation in size and characteristics it would seem impossible to consider destroyers as a single category, and indeed there are important differences among the various classes of destroyers. However, all of these ships are of similar hull form and possess very powerful engines in comparison to their displacement, and to the shiphandler the differences between the classes are generally in degree, not in principle.

The twin-screw, twin-rudder ships are the most numerous and they are also the easiest to handle. Among these we find many of the frigates, the DDGs, and the DD 931 and DD 692 class ships. Almost equally numerous have been the twin-screw, single-rudder ships which include two large classes of DLGs, the DD 445 class, and some of the new DEs. However, with the ever present pressure of economy, the reduced emphasis on high speed, and the increased emphasis on long range and endurance, we see increasing numbers of single-screw DEs replacing the more powerful and versatile general purpose destroyer.

Besides the differences in engines and rudders, the major factor of difference between the various types is the relative distribution of sail area. In a crosswind, one of the DDGs or a late *Forrest Sherman* (Figure 4–1) with its very high bow is much more difficult to handle than, for example, *Bainbridge* (Figure 4–2) with her lower and more evenly distributed sail area and deep draft. However, with the notable exception of the single-screw DEs, all of the types have sufficient engine and rudder power to be handled safely without assistance except under unusual circumstances.

For our discussion of the basic shiphandling evolutions, both in port and at sea, we shall be considering a twin-screw, twin-rudder ship of the size and capability of a *Forrest Sherman* or an *Adams* class ship. Where being equipped with only a single screw and single rudder would make a difference, and this will be true in almost all evolutions in port and where the speed of the ship drops below 5

FIGURE 4–1. USS *Forrest Sherman* (DD 931), a typical modern destroyer.

knots, we will reexamine the evolutions from the point of view of the conning officer of a large single-screw DE. For reference, the characteristics of the DDG 2 and DE 1052 classes are as follows:

Class Designation	*Charles F. Adams* DDG-2	*Frank Knox* DE-1052
Length	437 ft.	438 ft.
Beam	47½ ft.	47 ft.
Draft fwd.	21½ ft.	25 ft.
Draft aft	19 ft.	22 ft.
Displacement	4500 tons	4100 tons
Propellers	2	1
Rudders	2	1
Total horsepower	70,000	35,000
Maximum speed	33 knots	27 knots
Sonar dome	Keel mounted	Bulbous bow
Stabilizers	None	Fin
Crew (war complement)	24 officers	17 officers
	333 enlisted	228 enlisted
Anchors	2–6000 lb.	1–8000 lb. bottom of dome
		1–4500 lb. deck edge, port

Figure 4–3 shows the arrangement of the screws and rudders on a twin-screw, twin-rudder destroyer, *Gearing* in this case. The large propellers extend even beyond the sides of the hull, necessitating the installation of screw guards, and the rudders are installed directly in line with the screws. The relative flatness of the hull under the stern, a feature typical of high speed ships, also adds to the directional maneuverability of the ship.

Figure 4–4 shows the propeller and rudder arrangement on a DE 1052. In the large DEs, the rudder is mounted slightly to starboard of the centerline to make it possible to pull a shaft for repairs without removing the rudder, but it still receives the full force of the propeller wash. The rudder is mounted one-half a propeller

FIGURE 4–2. USS *Bainbridge* (DLGN 25), world's first nuclear-powered guided missile frigate.

diameter abaft the screw and is thus close enough to receive the fully concentrated screw current, assuring good side forces when the screw is turning ahead. Even mounted this close, however, when the propeller is turning astern, the inflowing screw current is not sufficiently concentrated to assure good steering unless the ship is moving astern through the water at a good rate. Note also the absence of hull structure immediately forward of the propeller—it is about 45 feet from the prop to the beginning of the skeg. The large skeg just ahead of the screw, common to most single-screw merchant ships and against which the backing screw current can play, is absent in this high-performance design. Nevertheless, these relatively powerful and versatile ships "back to port," as do their less powerful single-screw sisters.

With a single, relatively large propeller mounted centerline under the keel, the draft aft is greater than with twin screws. An offsetting advantage, however, is that the propeller is well protected by the hull, and the shiphandler need have little fear of damaging a propeller blade as his stern moves close to the pier. Propeller guards, of course, are unnecessary in a single-screw ship.

Sonar domes

The sonar dome in certain destroyer types has become a matter of major concern to the shiphandler. These large streamlined fairings, which house the ship's principal antisubmarine sensor, are mounted under the keel forward or actually built

FIGURE 4–3. Stern view of a 2,400-ton destroyer.

into the ship's forefoot, as shown in Figure 4–5. They are truly enormous and must be treated with great care since they are much more tender than the normal underwater structure of the ship, and any dent or abrasion can seriously reduce the effectiveness of the sonar. As shown, modern sonars increase the navigational draft forward by some 6 feet and become a major consideration in the arrangement and use of the anchors and chains. In a ship with one of these large domes, the shiphandler must never permit his ship to ride up on an anchor so that the chain tends aft under the ship. In the DE 1052, the hawsepipe for the largest anchor is

FIGURE 4–4. Model of USS *Knox* (DD 1052), an ocean escort with fin stabilizers.

actually mounted in the bottom of the sonar dome so the anchor and chain can be handled without endangering the dome.

Stabilizers

Increasing numbers of modern ships are being equipped with fin stabilizers. As shown in the photo of the model of *Knox* (Figure 4–4), the fins project out from the sides of the ship and thus present one more projection for the shiphandler to consider. The fins do not extend beyond the sides of the ship, but the conning officer must avoid bringing them into contact with any underwater obstacle.

Mooring lines

A sound knowledge of the mooring lines and associated deck equipment is vital to the shiphandler. In Chapter 2 we discussed the forces which come to play upon the ship in open water, but our study would not be complete unless we also discussed the means we use to adjust and secure the ship in her berth. Many a beautiful approach has been wasted by the inept use of the mooring lines.

Ships are moored to piers by a system of mooring lines which varies according to the size and character of the ship. In all of the systems the lines are classified in accordance with their employment as *breast lines* or as *spring lines*.

FIGURE 4–5. USS *Barry* (DD 933) in drydock. Note sonar dome.

A breast line leads nearly perpendicular to the keel of the ship and controls the distance of that part of the ship from the pier. A spring line leads obliquely but nearly parallel to the keel and controls the fore-and aft position of the ship with respect to her berth. "Springing" is a term applied to the use of spring lines to move the ship in toward the pier by surging forward or aft against a line which leads obliquely to the pier (Figure 4–6).

A destroyer is normally moored with six mooring lines, and the lines are identified by number, from forward aft, in the order in which they are run out from the ship as shown in Figure 4–7. Numbers one and six are breast lines and should be led out as nearly directly abeam as possible to hold the ship against the pier with the minimum strain. Numbers two through five are spring lines and should be led nearly fore and aft. Two and four lead aft and prevent the ship from riding forward, and three and five lead forward and prevent the ship from riding aft.

The separation of the functions of the lines greatly assists in handling the ship alongside. If care is taken that one and six are actually placed on the pier so

FIGURE 4–6. A destroyer moored to a pier, showing rat guards in use.

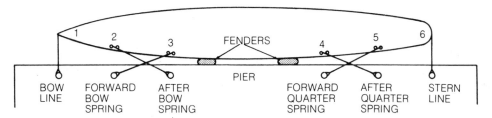

FIGURE 4–7. Proper positions for mooring lines of a destroyer.

that they act as breast lines and the other lines as spring lines, the conning officer can accurately predict the result he will obtain by working a certain line. When destroyers are nested with ships of the same class, there is no danger of leading out the bow and stern lines as anything but breasts, because there is no other place to lead them; but alongside a pier there is a tendency to lead them out too far forward and aft so that they actually serve as springs. At a crowded pier, insuring that the bow and stern lines are led out directly abeam will prevent interference with the mooring lines of other ships.

When the ship is secured, the mooring lines are normally "doubled up," which means that an extra bight of line is passed to the pier or other ship, giving three parts of line instead of only one part. Often skippers believe they are doubled when in fact only one part of the line is taking the strain. To insure that the three parts take equal strain, only a simple turn should be taken on the ship's bitts before the bight goes over to the pier.

Figure 4–8 shows a correctly secured mooring line, and Figure 4–9 shows a method of holding the strain with a "stopper" while the bight is being passed to the other ship.

Normally, as we come alongside, it is desirable to get numbers one and six over as soon as possible, because it is with these lines that we work ourselves in against the face of the pier. The spring lines come into play later as we are adjusting our final position. Consequently it is desirable that the bow and stern lines be as long as practical. Since mooring line comes in 100-fathom coils, 60-fathom lines for one and six, and 40-fathom lines for the spring lines work out very nicely.

It will be found useful to have one really strong mooring line on board. Wire is not desirable because it is awkward to handle and has so little spring. A nylon line is very strong, but has too much spring and manila is a thing of the past. Spring laid wire rope, a combination wire and hemp line, is a good compromise. A 1⅝-inch "spring lay" is more than three times as strong as best grade 6-inch manila line. It can be handled almost as easily as manila, it can be stowed in less space, .and it will outlast manila in normal usage by a good margin. It is a comforting thing to watch such a "strong line" take the strain when the safety of the ship depends upon that line holding.

In giving orders to the line-handling stations, it is mandatory that the order have the same meaning on the forecastle as was intended by the conning officer.

FIGURE 4–8. Correctly doubled mooring line.

The following examples and definitions are in common use in the fleet and can form the basis for all orders to lines:

SEND THE LINES OVER   Pass the lines to the pier, place the eye over the appropriate bollard, but *take no strain*.

TAKE A STRAIN ON ONE   Put line number one under tension.

SLACK ONE   Take all tension off of line number one and let it hang slack.

EASE ONE   Let number one line out until it is under less tension, but not slacked.

TAKE NUMBER TWO TO THE CAPSTAN   Lead the end of line number two to the capstan, take the slack out of the line, but *take no strain*.

HEAVE AROUND ON THREE   Apply tension on number three line with the capstan.

AVAST HEAVING   Stop the capstan.

HOLD WHAT YOU'VE GOT   Hold the line as it is.

HOLD FIVE   Do not allow any more line to go out on number five. (Caution— this risks parting the line.)

CHECK FIVE   Hold heavy tension on line number five but render it as necessary to prevent parting the line.

SURGE FIVE   Hold moderate tension on number five line, but render it enough to permit movement of the ship (used when moving along the pier to adjust position).

DOUBLE UP   Pass an additional bight on all mooring lines so that there are three parts of each line to the pier.

SINGLE UP   Take in all bights and extra lines so there remains only a single part of each of the normal mooring lines.

TAKE IN ALL LINES   Used when secured with your *own* lines, and it means to have the ends of all lines cast off from the pier and brought on board.

CAST OFF ALL LINES   Used when secured with *another* ship's lines in a nest, and it means to cast off the ends of the lines and allow the other ship to retrieve her lines.

Fenders

The fenders that are ready topside are a matter of concern to the conning officer. The most important items among fenders are the "big" fenders—normally a pneumatic fender about four feet long and three feet in diameter. A large destroyer normally uses three of these and they should be lowered to just clear the water at the extreme beam amidships. We normally ride against all three fenders when alongside another ship, but the perfect maneuver culminates in a gentle "one point" landing on the middle fender of the three.

In addition to the fenders amidships, we should have four more cylindrical fenders ready: two on the forecastle and two on the fantail. These can be smaller pneumatic fenders or "homemade" fenders of whatever material available, about

FIGURE 4–9. Method of holding strain while doubling lines.

four feet long and a foot in diameter. It is normally desirable to place one of these with its top about one foot above the deck edge just forward of the forecastle windbreak and another similarly placed abreast the after end of the deckhouse. The remaining two cylindrical fenders are kept "in hand" ready for use to protect the forecastle and the propeller guards respectively.

Finally, several ball fenders should be ready to be placed at the point of contact when the side of the ship comes into contact with the pier or the other ship. These are not as dependable as the cylindrical fenders because they are more easily squeezed out from between the ships, but they are easier to handle and can be put in place quickly as the situation develops.

Ground tackle

The capabilities of the ground tackle and the anchor windlass should be clearly understood by the conning officer. All destroyer officers should be able to handle the anchors and ground tackle without any help. If any officer has not actually worked the gear, he should take time out to get the experience. It will pay good dividends in appreciating the problems of the forecastle and developing the patience so desirable on the part of the bridge personnel.

The anchor windlass is driven by a hydraulic motor which has an electric motor as the prime mover. In case the windlass is overloaded, instead of stripping gears the safety valve lifts and no permanent harm is done. Through suitable gearing this hydraulic motor is connected permanently to the capstan, which always turns when the motor is turning. On the capstan shaft is the wildcat, a sprocket for taking the anchor chain which can be locked to the capstan shaft when desired. The wildcat is "connected up" when it is locked to the capstan shaft, and it is "disconnected" when unlocked. Also there is a brake which acts upon the wildcat and is rugged enough to hold the wildcat under almost any conditions.

A destroyer is normally equipped with two anchors and two chains. The longer chain is 120 fathoms, and the shorter 105 fathoms, and in addition there is a 5-fathom "bending shot" on each of the anchors. The conning officer should know which anchor on his ship has the longer chain. Should the need ever arise, one chain could be shackled to the end of the other and more than 225 fathoms provided, but we must make sure that the anchor windlass is powerful enough to recover the longer scope in deep water. (The windlass has to lift, in addition to the anchor, the weight of the chain necessary to reach the bottom.)

Although there are two anchors and chains, there is only one wildcat, so only one anchor can be worked at a time. However, there is a compressor on each chainpipe which can be used to restrain the chain. Whenever it is desired to shift from one anchor to the other, it is necessary to walk out sufficient chain from the chain locker, set the compressor to keep the chain from running back into the chain locker, disengage the chain from the wildcat, lift the chain over and clear of the anchor windlass, then rouse out sufficient chain on the other anchor, lift it over

FIGURE 4–10. The escort ship USS *Meyerkord* (DD 1058) maneuvers smartly off the Hawaiian coast.

the windlass, and finally engage it in the wildcat. All of this takes time, and the "bridge" must learn to allow for it.

The anchor windlass is conveniently designed so that the maximum peripheral force that can be applied by the capstan is 30,000 lbs, the breakage strength of a top grade 6-inch manila line. Thus, if using this size line, the windlass can apply all of the tension the line can stand. If one were to try to get more effect from the line by springing in, he would probably only succeed in parting the line.

Springing

The subject of springing is often misunderstood. There is a popular misconception that there are immense latent forces available from this technique which greatly exceed any other forces which we can apply to the ship. Springing is a very useful practice, but the adequate capstan forward and the precise control of the engines of today have resulted in springing seldom being employed.

In analyzing the action of springing, we can first define it as obtaining a sidewise force on the ship by moving forward or aft against a line led out obliquely to the pier, thus providing an arthwartships component of force as well as a restraining component parallel to the keel. Obviously the maximum force that can be applied by a single line can be no greater than the breaking strength of that line, and any component of a force can never be greater than the whole force. Thus the maximum springing force available from a single line can be no greater than can be obtained by the capstan.

It will be readily seen that to obtain maximum force from springing, the line should lead almost abeam. On the other hand, to allow maximum side motion with minimum fore-and-aft motion, the line should lead nearly fore and aft. Normally we spring with the line at an oblique angle different from the theoretical optimum because of line slippage and elasticity.

To obtain the absolute maximum side force on the ship, we must use *all* of the forces at our disposal. This is occasionally necessary when "crabbing" up to a berth against a very strong wind or current. We spring on as many lines as possible in addition to using the capstan on number one, employing the waist breast, and twisting the stern in with maximum practical engine power. Under these conditions it is usually best to lead all lines directly to the pier (i.e., not crossing the springs), and surging forward and aft by unbalancing the engines. With this arrangement all lines can be used for springing at the same time whether surging forward or astern. Have all linehandlers alert to "take in" the slack whenever they can get it, and to hold (but not part) the lines whenever they tend to take a strain. The ship can be worked in to the pier under very severe conditions when using all of the forces available.

FIGURE 4–11. USS *Charles F. Adams* (DDG 2) under way.

Heaving lines

Heaving lines and line-throwing guns play an important part when going alongside. The captain should encourage his line-throwers to practice to obtain maximum distance and accuracy, because the speed with which the lines can be sent to the pier is often decisive. It is best to have at least four line-throwers ready both fore and aft when making the approach. The men must not bend their heaving lines to the mooring lines until the "monkey fist" is on the pier. When a successful throw has been achieved, this heaving line can then be bent to the mooring line that is needed first—usually number one—regardless of which line-thrower makes the successful heave. Under difficult conditions it is best to bend the heaving lines for the additional mooring lines to the first line that goes over, instead of making further attempts to heave them over.

In addition to normal heaving lines it is very useful to have "bolo" lines ready both fore and aft. They usually consist of a lead weight or weighted "monkey fist" attached to the end of a nylon shot line with a throwing toggle about two feet from the weight. With a bolo, a skillful sailor can reach to fully twice the distance achievable with a normal heaving line, and because of the relative heaviness of the weight as compared to the line, a bolo is much more effective in the wind than is a normal heaving line.

The line-throwing gun should be used without hesitation whenever its use will assist the maneuver. We must guard against the crew becoming careless of safety when using the gun, and we must insist on having the men on the pier or on the other ship take cover when we are firing. The timely use of the line-throwing gun often speeds up the operation and occasionally allows the successful completion of a maneuver which otherwise would have required a second approach. Some shiphandlers pride themselves on never using a line-throwing gun, but they usually pay for their pride by sweating out precarious moments that the timely use of the gun would have avoided. It is more cause for pride to employ skillfully all the tools at our disposal than to demonstrate that we could get along with less.

Deck experience

It is invaluable training for a shiphandler to have had a tour of duty as first lieutenant. The handling of the lines and fenders is an art that is of vital importance to good shiphandling. An officer who has not had the benefit of experience in deck seamanship should spend as much time as possible with the deck force while they are handling the deck gear, so that he can understand the capabilities of the equipment and the problems of its employment. An officer must be a competent seaman before he can be a competent captain.

5
handling alongside

One of the most interesting and enjoyable phases of shiphandling is that of handling alongside. In discussing this phase we shall cover the problems of going alongside and getting clear of both piers and ships. The interesting situations and special problems are so numerous that they cannot be covered here, so we shall deal only with general principles. If the principles are understood, the solution to any particular problem will be readily apparent.

The guiding principle in handling alongside should be *safety*. It is simply poor seamanship and bad shiphandling if any damage is done to our ship or the ship or pier we are alongside. There are extremes of weather and cases of emergency when even the most able shiphandlers will bend a stanchion, but under normal circumstances it is positive evidence of bad judgment if any damage is done. In every case where damage has resulted, the conning officer concerned should analyze his actions to see where the mistake was made. Dash and smartness are traditional in destroyer officers, but it is neither smart nor dashing to damage your own or someone else's ship.

Going alongside

The most common error among inexperienced shiphandlers is to make the approach too *close* to the ship or pier they are approaching. They are afraid of not making the landing and have heard too many stories about legendary skippers making "one bell" landings and handing the lines over "doubled up." With a modern ship the shiphandler has no reason for lying closer than 10 yards from another ship or dock under normal conditions until he has all six lines over and he is ready to move in. A safety margin smaller than this is not sufficient to allow for a quirk of wind or a momentary unbalance between the engines.

The normal procedure for going alongside (Figure 5–1) should be executed as follows:

We approach on a converging course about 10° to 20° from the heading of our berth for a position so that our engaged side will be 20 yards out from the pier when we are opposite our berth; as we come opposite the berth, we swing parallel and stop the ship, get the lines over to the pier, and finally when all lies are set,

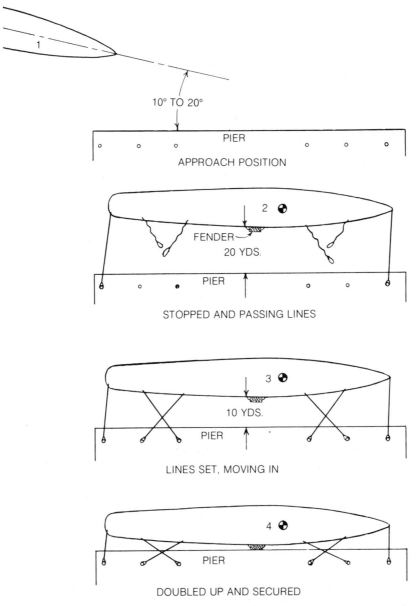

1

10° TO 20°

PIER

APPROACH POSITION

2

FENDER
20 YDS.

PIER

STOPPED AND PASSING LINES

3

10 YDS.

PIER

LINES SET, MOVING IN

4

PIER

DOUBLED UP AND SECURED

FIGURE 5–1. Sequence of maneuvers during a normal uncomplicated landing at a pier.

"walk" the ship in broadside, using the capstan on number one line and twisting the stern in with the engines. We take plenty of time moving in, and are careful to keep the ship exactly broadside. Our destroyers today are long and covered with gear at the deck edge, and the slightest inclination as the ship touches the pier face may cause damage.

The reason for the recommended initial inclination is to keep the stern free for swinging as long as possible and also to be ready to back clear should anything go wrong. It will be noted that the above procedure envisions moving in broadside instead of sliding in against the pier. Rubbing against the pier should be avoided if at all possible. Frequently projections on the pier or ship will catch and cause damage, and under any circumstances such action will rub the side paint off our beautiful ship.

When going alongside another ship in the stream (Figure 5–2), the same principles hold as for the pier except that the conning officer must be doubly careful. If the ship being approached is at a single buoy or is anchored, she may be yawing and hence the problem is further complicated. In this case the original approach inclination should be at least 20°, and the approach should be made a little wider to provide against a sudden swing of the other ship towards us. Because of these extra safety precautions it may be necessary to get the forward lines over first and then twist the stern *in* until the after lines can be gotten over. When twisting in this case, the forward lines, especially number one, should be

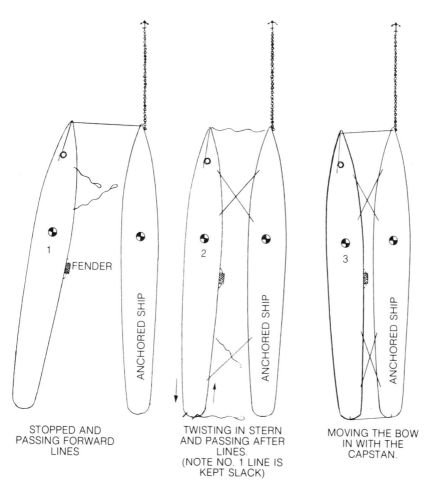

FIGURE 5–2. Going alongside a destroyer at anchor.

left slack to keep from spinning the other ship. Remember that she is essentially floating free, and if we pull her bow toward us, her stern will move away. It is not an uncommon sight to see a ship twist nearly 90° trying to move her stern *in* because the forward lines were not slacked. Because of the tendency of the other ship to spin and the lack of a capstan aft, it is often necessary to "see-saw" the ship in, slacking the forward lines when moving the stern in with the engines, then holding the after lines as we breast in the bow with the capstan. Actually the "see-saw" is imperceptible if the ship is properly handled, because the conning officer will adjust his forces so that the movement is continuous.

Wind, when going alongside a pier

Wind, of course, complicates the problem of going alongside. When the wind is blowing *off* the pier where we are to tie up, it is necessary to approach faster and closer in order to get the lines over before the wind has blown our ship away from the pier. But we must not let this lure us into approaching too fast and too close. If we conn from the engaged wing pelorus, and sight over a bearing circle set at the course we have ordered, we can see exactly where the engaged side of our ship is headed. Except for extreme circumstances, all courses ordered during the final approach should be such that if the engines did not respond exactly as ordered, our ship will still pass clear of everything.

The procedure when the wind is blowing *off* (Figure 5–3) is to get our "strong line" over forward as quickly as possible to hold the ship while we get the other lines over. As soon as the bow is secured to the pier, we can hold our stern up into the wind by the engines. If the bow is secure, the stern can be twisted up to the dock under almost any conditions.

If the wind is so strong that there is doubt that the bow can be managed quickly enough with the lines, then we approach rapidly, and when the bow is close to the pier and opposite its eventual position, we let go the engaged anchor. This anchor, snubbed up, will hold the bow up while we get the forward lines set, and it can be picked up later when we are in our berth.

When the wind is blowing *onto* the pier, in most cases the problem is simpler, because the wind is helping the maneuver, even though often it is boisterous with its help. The secret of this type of landing is to approach wide enough so that the ship is not blown down on the pier until we are ready. Don't be afraid to make it too wide, because the wind will eventually blow us down onto the pier if we are too far out in the beginning. Care must be taken to keep the ship parallel to the pier as we come into the berth. The wind will tend to blow the bow down on the pier and this will have to be counteracted by moving the stern in with the engines. The best solution is to touch the pier face exactly parallel, and not swinging. There is a temptation to touch with the bow *in* to keep the propeller guards from being damaged; but actually, if the bow hits first, it is far more likely to cause the ship to pivot and thus swing the propeller guards hard against the pier.

If the wind is blowing hard (over 20 knots) onto the pier, even though we

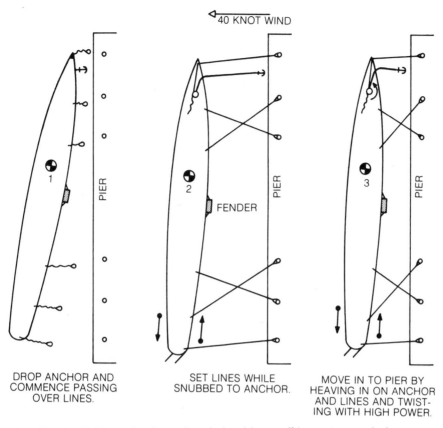

FIGURE 5–3. Making a landing when being blown off by a strong wind.

keep the ship parallel as we move in, the speed broadsides may be too great for safety. In this case we should approach to a position opposite the berth, but 50 yards out, and let go the windward anchor (Figure 5–4). This anchor will hold the bow up into the wind, and it will also give something to work against while keeping the stern off the pier with the engines. With these arrangements we can get our lines over in an orderly manner and move in to the berth as slowly as we desire. This procedure is especially necessary if we are going alongside another ship at the pier. After getting alongside, the anchor chain of the anchor we have dropped should be slacked to the bottom to keep it clear of passing ships. The anchor can be picked up upon leaving the berth, and it may actually be very useful for getting clear, especially if the wind is still blowing onto the pier.

Wind, when going alongside in the stream

Going alongside a ship at anchor or at a buoy, with the wind blowing, is a different problem because the other ship will head into the wind and usually will yaw considerably. This yaw can be reduced if the other ship shortens the scope of her

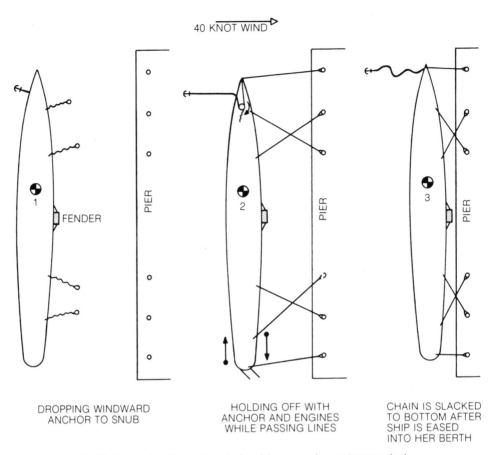

40 KNOT WIND

1 — DROPPING WINDWARD ANCHOR TO SNUB

2 — HOLDING OFF WITH ANCHOR AND ENGINES WHILE PASSING LINES

3 — CHAIN IS SLACKED TO BOTTOM AFTER SHIP IS EASED INTO HER BERTH

FIGURE 5–4. Making a landing when being blown on by a strong wind.

chain, but in a strong wind the swing becomes quite large. Many shiphandlers recommend studying the swing and seizing the opportunity to approach quickly from downwind while the moored ship has swung clear, but this will occasionally require backing clear because of an error in timing.

A ship anchored or moored to a buoy does not simply swing back and forth around her bow. Actually the ship becomes inclined to the wind and sails crosswind until restrained by her anchor chain. This spins the ship, presenting the other bow to the wind, and the ship then sails back on the other tack. This action is illustrated in Figure 5–5. The trouble with approaching from downwind is that the moored ship is actually *sailing toward us* when she presents a clear side.

A safer method (Figure 5–6) is to approach to a point abreast the ship but beyond her extreme swing, and then "sail" in broadside by inclining our ship about 10° to the wind and keeping her at this angle with the engines. The moment to get the lines over is as the other ship's bow reaches its extreme swing towards us. If our timing is off while using this method, we can bring our ship parallel to the wind and wait for the other ship to swing properly. We should get the forward lines

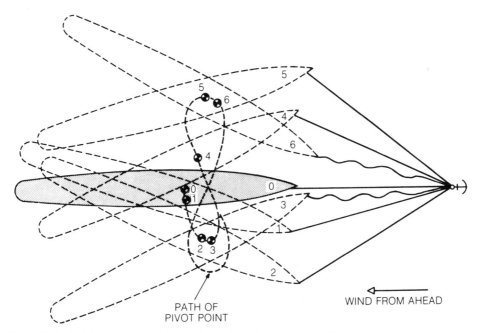

PATH OF
PIVOT POINT

WIND FROM AHEAD

FIGURE 5–5. Manner in which a ship swings in the wind when at anchor.

over as rapidly as possible because it may be necessary to take a strain on these lines to prevent the other ship's stern from swinging into our stern.

The problem of going alongside another ship at a buoy when the wind is blowing onto a nearby shoal (Figure 5–7), is a difficult one, but one frequently encountered. In this case a steering casualty or a momentary loss of power could spell disaster, so we must be careful to stay well clear of the shoal. Twisting in safe water, backing in to a point slightly ahead of the moored ship's beam but clear of her swing, and then sailing in as before, is a good solution to this problem. But we must have an anchor ready in case our swing is retarded.

Clearing from alongside

Getting clear from alongside is often more difficult than coming alongside, because, except for wind and current, there is no *direct* way to get our bow out from the other ship or the pier. The general procedure for backing out is to get the stern well clear and then back out rapidly, using *in* rudder initially to wing the bow out. There is a distinct tendency for the bow to suck in to the other ship as we back clear, and we must be careful that our engaged anchor does not rake the other ship.

The stern can normally be gotten out quite handily by taking in all after lines, taking all of the slack out of the forward lines, and twisting the stern out with the engines. This should be done quite slowly, with careful attention to the forward

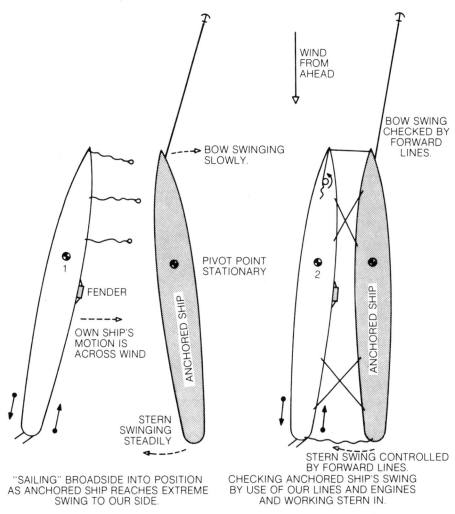

WIND
FROM
AHEAD

BOW SWINGING
SLOWLY.

BOW SWING
CHECKED BY
FORWARD
LINES.

1

FENDER

OWN SHIP'S
MOTION IS
ACROSS WIND

PIVOT POINT
STATIONARY

ANCHORED SHIP

2

ANCHORED SHIP

STERN
SWINGING
STEADILY

STERN SWING CONTROLLED
BY FORWARD LINES.

"SAILING" BROADSIDE INTO POSITION
AS ANCHORED SHIP REACHES EXTREME
SWING TO OUR SIDE.

CHECKING ANCHORED SHIP'S SWING
BY USE OF OUR LINES AND ENGINES
AND WORKING STERN IN.

FIGURE 5–6. Going alongside an anchored ship that is swinging to her anchor.

fenders, until the engaged bow is resting securely against the pier or ship alongside. The stern can then be twisted out handily as desired. When the stern is out sufficiently, stop all engines and slack the forward lines. The bow will normally bounce out a little as the pressure of twisting is released, and we can take in all lines and back straight out. If the bow does not come out, we can twist the bow *out* and the stern *in* momentarily before backing, since the above procedure has moved our pivot point away from the pier. Often it is useful to back with the outboard engine only, and use *in* rudder after having gotten the stern well out initially.

Another and gentler method of getting the stern out is to snub in the bow, using number one line and the capstan. This is slower, and there is less chance of an unexpected surge causing damage, but we cannot get the stern out as far with this method, and we cannot disengage as quickly as when using the engines.

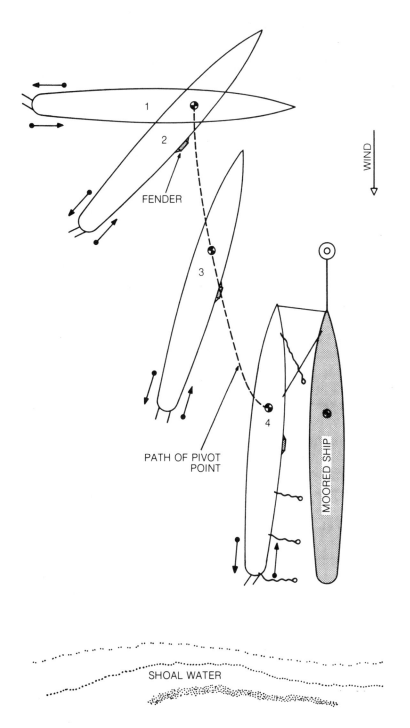

WIND

1

2

FENDER

3

PATH OF PIVOT
POINT

4

MOORED SHIP

SHOAL WATER

FIGURE 5-7. Going alongside a destroyer whose stern is being blown toward shoal water.

With a very strong wind blowing us onto the pier, it may be advisable to twist the stern out until the ship is nearly perpendicular to the face of the pier before backing out. Under such circumstances we will need extra fenders forward to keep the bow from damaging the pier, because the entire wind load on the ship will come to bear on the point of contact between the bow and the pier. If we can twist the stern out of the first 10°, with a wind blowing directly against the pier, we will have no difficulty twisting the remaining 80°, since the wind force becomes less effective in opposing the motion as our ship comes more into line with the wind.

Having moved the stern upwind, it is often advisable to capitalize further on the ship's tendency to back into the wind. As we clear, we can back directly into the wind to gain sea room before "squaring away" on our new course. Utilizing the ship's tendency to back into the wind can also be helpful when clawing away from a lee shore. Why go ahead and fight the tendency for the bow to go down wind, when the ship will readily back into the wind?

Whatever the method used when clearing from alongside a pier, the secret to success is to get the stern far enough out from the pier so that we can back clear with no danger of fouling obstructions. The stern is far enough out, under a given set of of conditions, if the ship will pull completely clear of contact with the pier as soon as she starts moving astern.

Occasionally circumstances demand that we back straight out. Such a situation exists when we are one of the inner ships in a nest, but must go out first. In this case we are forced to accept the rubbing of our sides, but normally this won't be serious. The first step is to insure that we have no projections which can catch on the other ships. When we are sure of this, BACK both engines TWO THIRDS or FULL until the ship begins to move astern, and then slow, if desired, to ONE THIRD. This will give a surge of screw current on both sides which will tend to force the ships apart and open a way for us to back clear. This surge of screw current is very useful when backing clear of solid piers or other ships. The more powerful the surge, the more effective it is in pushing us out from a pier or in separating the ships. But bear in mind that if the two engines don't answer together, the unbalance might cause the ship to twist rapidly.

Another method which is useful when clearing from the inside of a nest is to slack all the after lines or take them in, and BACK momentarily against number three lines, port and starboard. This will open out the sterns of the adjacent ships, and we can cast off and get on our way while the nest is open.

Flow effects

The effect of current between two ships or between a ship and a comparatively solid pier is interesting. If a steady current flows between two ships that are near each other and parallel, the *venturi effect* will exert a force tending to force the ships together. This force will be dependent on the proximity of the two bodies and the character of the restricted channel between them. The force experienced will be proportional to the difference between the square of the velocity of the flow *between* the bodies and the square of the velocity of the flow *on the outer sides* of the ships. On the other hand, if a surge of current suddenly is forced between the ships, it will tend to force them apart. It is as though water were quickly piled up between the ships, and as it flows out from the pile it forces the ships apart. Finally, the entire problem is often complicated by the fact that one ship is moving during the critical period.

As we back clear of another ship with which we were nested, there is always a force which sucks our bow in towards her stern and frequently moves her stern towards us. In spite of what we do, our bow does not pass the other ship's stern by as wide a margin as we would have expected from the original situation.

This effect is present because the water which our ship displaced while lying alongside must be replaced as we back clear. On our engaged side the water cannot be replaced easily because of the presence of our ship and the other ship, so the flow of water is from the outside, tending to force the ships together. This effect can be observed as we back clear from alongside. The distance between the ships at the closest point tends to remain constant as we back clear. Thus, the flat of our bow will be about the same distance out from the other ship's quarter as our bow passes her propeller guard, as it was from her side when it passed amidships. This effect is illustrated in Figure 5–8.

This displacement effect also works in reverse and is probably the reason why there are so many "close" situations with relatively few accidents. As two ships come close together sideways, the water between the two hulls acts as a cushion and prevents the ships from actually touching.

Going out ahead

The above discussion has dealt with *backing* out from a mooring only. Often it is more convenient to go out *ahead*, but there are several factors which must be considered when using this method to clear a mooring. Going out ahead violates the basic rule of "Keep your stern away from danger." When we back out from a mooring, our stern is the first part of the ship to reach open water and we are soon free to maneuver the stern of our ship at will. If we go out ahead we cannot swing our stern towards the ship or pier that we are leaving until we are completely clear. This means that during the clearing operation we can only turn *toward* the ship or pier. Because this is often completely unacceptable, we find ourselves restricted to not maneuvering at all as we go out ahead.

Though one must be careful when going out ahead, it is still a useful and safe maneuver if done properly. Since we have no other means of moving the bow of our ship away from the pier, we must have wind or current for this maneuver unless we go out parallel. Going out parallel is usually very unsatisfactory, because we will scrape along the whole length of the pier before we finally clear. In order to go out ahead safely, we must first have our bow well out from the ship or pier that we are clearing, and this requires a wind or current from ahead or from the engaged side.

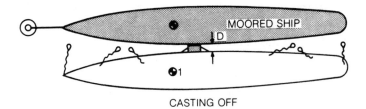

CASTING OFF

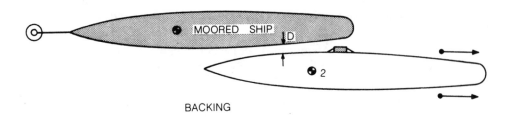

BACKING

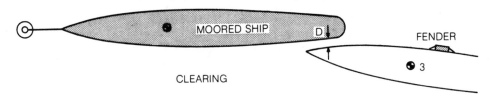

CLEARING

FIGURE 5–8. Displacement effect when clearing the side of another ship. The distance (D) tends to remain constant.

When going out ahead with such a wind or current, we slack the forward lines until the bow drifts out and the ship assumes the desired inclination. While doing this we must watch our stern to make sure that it does not bear in too hard against the pier we are leaving. As soon as we are ready, we cast off all lines and kick ahead on the outboard screw using inboard rudder. As soon as the stern comes clear, we can use both engines and move out expeditiously.

Going out ahead is seldom used from piers because we normally go into them ahead and we must usually back away to clear them. On the other hand, when moored to a ship that is swinging to its anchor or to a buoy, it is very often desirable and at times necessary to clear ahead. Normally the nest will swing so that the wind or current is ahead or slightly from the side of the ship that is anchored or moored to the buoy. It is therefore perfectly oriented for getting our bow out. Actually, if there is a good wind or current, it is safer to go out ahead than to back out. If we hold number five as we slack the forward lines, as shown in Figure 5–9, the bow will come out nicely. Then we can hold the forward lines, after the ship has reached the proper inclination, and the stern will move out from the ship. The secret to moving the bow out, but at the same time keeping the stern clear of the other ship, is to ease the lines slowly. This prevents the ship from

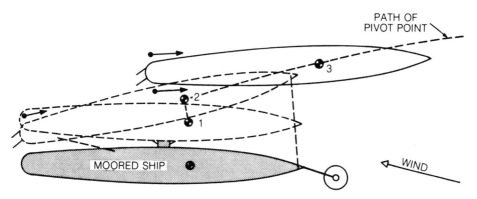

FIGURE 5–9. Going out ahead, using the wind to get the bow well out before starting.

pivoting and throwing the stern into the other ship. If we are using a current to get the bow out, we can use the rudder to help hold the stern away from the other ship.

If the nest that we are clearing is swinging, we must be careful that the wind does not catch our outboard bow after we have gotten the bow well out. Should this happen, the bow would be blown in rapidly, and we would have to commence the operation again, even if no damage were done. If we observe the swing carefully, we can get the bow out and be ready to clear as the nest reaches the extremity of its swing towards our ship. We must be ready to move away from the other ship rapidly, because it will be remembered that the stern of a ship yawing with the wind continues to swing *outboard* as the ship passes the limit of its excursion and starts on the opposite tack.

In a case where it is necessary to go out ahead, and there is no wind or current, we must go out "around the bow," as illustrated in Figure 5–10. In this case it is well to have the moored ship snub up to its anchor or to the buoy to insure that its anchor chain is held in as close to its stem as possible. We must work our lines so that the bow is inclined outward as much as possible and, when ready, cast off all lines and go ahead, using plenty of power. As soon as our pivot point is abreast the moored ship's bow, we can put the rudder over FULL towards the other ship. This will start moving our stern out from the other ship's side at the earliest safe opportunity. We must continue this turn around the moored ship's bow until our stern is well clear of the mooring. Since this maneuver is required only in the absence of wind and current, the conditions are ideal and little trouble will be experienced.

Steerageway

When handling a ship alongside, the controllability of the ship is of major concern to the shiphandler at all times. Because the ship is being brought to a stop, those controls which depend on the ship's motion become less effective as the ship

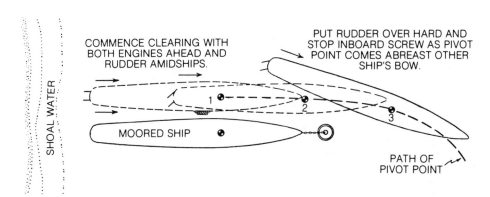

FIGURE 5–10. Going out around the bow when there is no wind or tide to help get the bow out.

slows. Obviously, when dead in the water, the rudder is ineffective unless the discharge current of a propeller is playing upon it.

A ship is said to have "steerageway" as long as she can be controlled by her rudder. The usual test is that the ship can still be held on a steady course by use of the rudder alone, and a ship is said to have "lost steerageway" when the bow wanders from the desired heading in spite of the rudder.

The rudder will exert *some* control force on the ship as long as there is *any* flow past it. The amount of force required to hold the ship on course will depend upon the magnitude of the forces tending to move her off course. These forces are caused by wind, current, or by unsymmetrical flow past the hull, and the magnitude of the resultant force will depend upon the conditions. The speed at which the rudder can no longer overcome them, then, changes as the conditions change. Consequently we must recognize that there is no definite speed at which a ship loses steerageway.

Loss of steerageway is not so serious with a twin-screw ship, because the necessary control force can be supplied by opposing the screws. As we go alongside, then, we should not be overly concerned about the loss of rudder effectiveness since we can take over with the screws. In the normal approach, the rudder and the screws are worked together, and the more the rudder loses its effect, the more the screws are used to maintain or change the ship's heading. With a twin-rudder ship, working ahead, the term "steerageway" loses its meaning, because ample rudder forces can be obtained regardless of the ship's speed.

Steering while moving astern

When moving astern, the steering of the ship is more difficult than when going ahead. There is no discharge current available for increasing the effect of the rudders when the engines are backing, and, despite the propeller side forces, the ship handles awkwardly. More has happened than just the reversal of the direction of motion.

The hull of a ship is designed for optimum stability when moving ahead. The sharp bow and general hull shape are selected for optimum performance when moving ahead. If the ship becomes inclined to the direction of flow, there is a restoring moment that ends to force the hull to line up with its direction of motion through the water. In the absence of a force such as a rudder force to hold her at an inclination, the well-designed hull, moving ahead, will straighten out and proceed on a steady course.

Moving astern is a different situation. The ideal hull form is now reversed, and the ship is proceeding with her blunt stern first, followed by the long tapered bow. Moving astern, the stability of the hull is much reduced, and on some ships the hull is actually unstable when moving astern; that is, when the ship becomes inclined to the flow, the resultant moment tends to increase the inclination. Such a ship, when backing, will tend to veer off to one side or the other, and it will take strong forces to bring her out of the turn.

If a ship is barely moving astern, the unstable hull forces mentioned above can easily be overcome by the side forces obtainable from the screws. At a bit higher speed, however, these forces may become larger than those obtainable by the screws, and in that case the ship will continue in a turn, once she starts, despite the action of the screws. At a still higher speed, the rudder effectiveness becomes high enough to force the stern around despite the divergent tendency, and the ship is once more controllable. Thus, if we wish to be able to control the ship's heading while moving astern, we should either move very slowly and control with the engines, or else move at a sufficient speed to insure the rudder effectiveness.

A destroyer drifting slowly astern can be handled quite effectively with the engines. When backing steadily at ONE THIRD on both engines, FULL RUDDER is required to swing the stern, and the ship is apt to veer unexpectedly. Backing steadily at TWO-THIRDS is required to obtain effective control with the rudder alone—and very large rudder angles are required even then to reverse her swing, once she starts turning.

Because of the difficulty of maintaining the ship's heading while going astern, it is wise not to attempt to back into tight places. Not only are we leading with the most vulnerable part, the stern, but we don't have the nice control that is available when moving ahead.

Dipping the engaged anchor

If there is any doubt about the engaged anchor clearing when handling alongside, we should insure that it won't catch on anything by moving it out of the way. It is very easy to "dip" the engaged anchor, and this will prevent damage by removing a major source. When miscalculations bring two ships together, it is usually the engaged anchor of the ship making the move that does the damage.

The troublesome anchor can quickly be swung clear by suspending it under the bullnose as indicated in Figure 5–11. A suitable wire is run out of the bullnose,

FIGURE 5–11. Sequence of actions in dipping the anchor.

back up the hawsepipe, and secured to the jew's harp of the anchor. When ready to dip the anchor, walk out the anchor until it clears the hawsepipe; next, take the slack out of the wire and secure the end on deck, and then walk out the anchor until it hangs suspended beneath the bullnose. In this position it is well inside the edge of the deck, and, should anything brush against it, it will simply swing around the stem to the unengaged side. This precaution with the anchor takes only a moment, but it will prevent damage by removing one of its most common sources.

Evaluating the situation

Handling alongside when there is both wind and current is a more complex problem. It is often not clear which of the two will have the predominant effect, and it is difficult to judge the combined effect of the two forces when they are not parallel. It is best to study the situation carefully, make an estimate of the effect on our ship at the various stages of the maneuver, and then be alert to modify our plan quickly if the actual effect is different from that expected.

It is very useful to *test* a confusing condition by slacking the lines for a moment to see what the *actual* movement of the ship is going to be. It is surprising how often the result of this test will demonstrate that the resultant force will carry the ship clear very nicely. One must remember, however, that this test indicates the effect which will be experienced only *at the start* of the maneuver. For instance, our ship might temporarily be shielded from the wind, but after a few yards of travel the wind might have an entirely different effect. In open water it is easier to predict the action of the wind and current on the ship, and as we move away from our moorings, we are normally moving towards open water. Thus the "slack lines" test will give us the initial condition, and our judgment can usually predict the open water condition. The remaining problem lies in predicting the transition from one situation to the other.

6
anchoring
and mooring

The art of anchoring and the use of the anchor tends to be neglected in the United States Navy. Foreign men-o'-war and merchant ships use their anchors a great deal more than our Navy ships, and often our shiphandlers deny themselves the use of this very important tool. In the absence of a bow thruster, the anchor represents the only means at our disposal to work directly upon the bow of our ship unless we are using mooring lines. If one doubts the utility of the anchor as a shiphandling aid, he should watch a capable Master maneuver his single-screw, lightly-loaded merchantman in a confined harbor without tugs. With the anchor "snubbing" the bow and resisting forward motion, high engine power can be used with resultant high side forces which facilitate the maneuver.

The anchor and its action

Though the anchor itself is usually formidable in size and weight, it is still amazing that a 3-ton anchor can hold a 4,000-ton vessel in her berth. If we depended upon the friction of the anchor against the bottom to hold us, the anchor would have to be many times heavier than the ones we use. Obviously we must have something more certain to hold us than the friction of the anchor against the bottom.

Navy ships carry either "stockless" or "light-weight type" (LWT) anchors or both. These anchors are designed to dig into the bottom and bury themselves so deeply that they can resist tremendous forces. If the bottom is too hard for the flukes to dig in, they are designed to catch on any suitable projection and to hold by this method.

When an anchor first strikes the bottom, it lies flat, as indicated in Figure 6–1. As soon as the ship begins to drag the anchor along the bottom, the flukes rotate and begin to dig into the bottom. The more the ship pulls on the anchor, the deeper

95

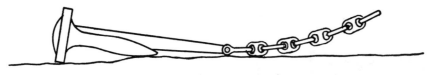

ANCHOR LYING ON BOTTOM BEFORE ANY STRAIN IS APPLIED.

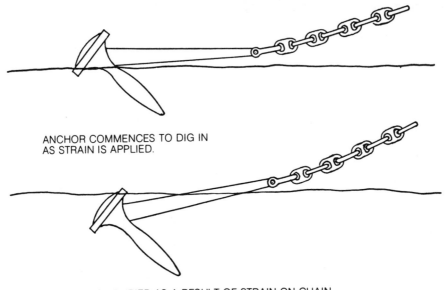

ANCHOR COMMENCES TO DIG IN
AS STRAIN IS APPLIED.

ANCHOR BURIED AS A RESULT OF STRAIN ON CHAIN.

FIGURE 6–1. The manner in which an anchor digs in.

the anchor digs in, and eventually the anchor buries itself. It can be seen that it is most desirable that the chain exerts its pull as nearly parallel to the bottom as possible. Otherwise the anchor will not have as favorable an opportunity to bite into the bottom.

If, while digging in, the pull of the chain on the anchor varies from side to side, it may cause the anchor to capsize and reverse its action. This may also be caused by striking a rock as indicated in Figure 6–2. If the anchor turns completely over, further strain on the chain will cause the anchor to dig itself out of the bottom. It is for this reason that it is most desirable that the pull on the chain be steady and in one direction while the anchor is digging in.

If the anchor does not hold, it may drag in a number of ways. First, if the bottom is too hard for the flukes to bite in, the anchor will drag with an intermittent, jerky motion as it catches on successive protrusions from the bottom. If, on the other hand, the bottom is soft enough but of uneven consistency, the anchor may begin to dig in, then capsize and come out, and then go on and repeat this process. In any event, dragging is evidenced by the chain alternately getting taut and going slack as the ship tries to take a strain.

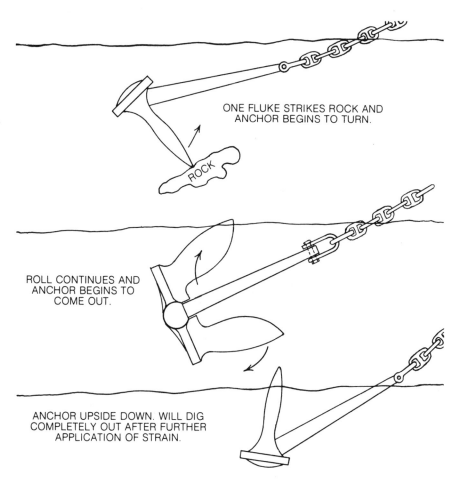

ONE FLUKE STRIKES ROCK AND
ANCHOR BEGINS TO TURN.

ROCK

ROLL CONTINUES AND
ANCHOR BEGINS TO
COME OUT.

ANCHOR UPSIDE DOWN. WILL DIG
COMPLETELY OUT AFTER FURTHER
APPLICATION OF STRAIN.

FIGURE 6–2. An anchor capsizing and digging out.

Since the anchor completely buries itself and is capable of holding against tremendous forces exerted by the ship, one might ask how we ever get it back up. When we weigh anchor, we heave in on the chain until the chain leads nearly straight up to the hawsepipe of the ship. This rotates the anchor, as indicated in Figure 6–3, and further pulling on the chain will allow the anchor to dig out. The trick of breaking the anchor out of the bottom is to exert the pull *vertically* instead of horizontally. Conversely, the secret to digging in the anchor is to insure that the pull of the chain on the anchor is *horizontal*.

If the anchor is held at short stay so that the chain tends near the vertical, as indicated in Figure 6–4, the anchor will not dig into the bottom because the flukes are above the horizontal. The shorter the scope of chain, the less the anchor digs in. When it is desired that the anchor not hold but merely act as a drag on the bow, we can keep it at short stay and it will not dig itself into the bottom. An anchor at

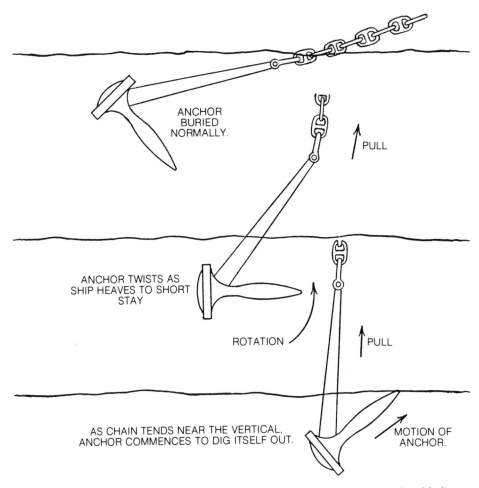

ANCHOR BURIED NORMALLY.

PULL

ANCHOR TWISTS AS SHIP HEAVES TO SHORT STAY

ROTATION

PULL

AS CHAIN TENDS NEAR THE VERTICAL, ANCHOR COMMENCES TO DIG ITSELF OUT.

MOTION OF ANCHOR.

FIGURE 6–3. Digging out when weighing. (The anchor digs itself out as the ship heaves in on the anchor chain.)

short stay is often very useful for holding the bow against the wind while twisting in a harbor, and at times it can be used to control the bow when going alongside to moor.

Therefore, if we wish to anchor securely—and this is the reason for anchoring—we should insure that no appreciable strain is put on the chain until sufficient chain is out to insure that the pull on the anchor is horizontal. We must be sure that the pull is steady so that the anchor buries itself, and, once the anchor is dug in, we should avoid excessive yawing. To set the anchor securely it is worthwhile to lay out the chain and dig in the anchor by use of the ship's engines. This must be done smoothly and without too much power or the anchor is likely to capsize and come out of the bottom. If the ship is yawing considerably and the anchor is tending to drag, it is often very useful to drop a second anchor at short stay under the forefoot so as to snub the excursions of the bow and thus insure that the pull on the holding anchor will be from a nearly constant direction.

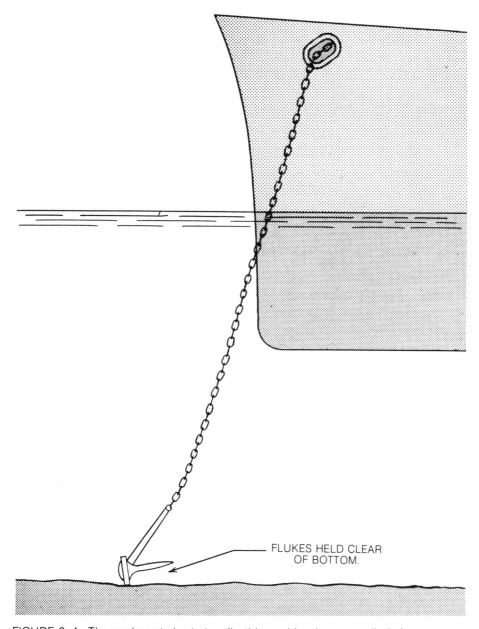

FLUKES HELD CLEAR
OF BOTTOM.

FIGURE 6–4. The anchor at short stay. (In this position it cannot dig in.)

Another consideration in anchoring is to use the proper scope of chain. When at anchor, the bow of the ship moves considerably owing to wave motion, yawing, gusts of wind, and current eddies. As a result of this motion the ship tends to come up against the end of the chain with a jerk; and if jerks thus created were applied directly to the anchor, it would soon break free from the bottom. If, however, we use sufficient chain, the weight of the catenary applies an increasing force on the ship as it pulls the chain taut, and this smoothes out the jerks that would otherwise tend to disturb the anchor. Thus, in addition to having enough chain out to insure that the pull on the anchor is horizontal, we must have a sufficient weight of chain out to smooth out the jerks caused by the ship's motion.

The criterion used by the U. S. Navy in the selection of the anchors, chains, and windlasses for a given ship is the following:

"The ship must lie to a single anchor in a steady 70-knot wind and a 4-knot current, in 40 fathoms, with firm sand bottom."

The calculations employed to ensure that this criterion is met include both light and full load conditions for the following combined forces:

a. Wind force due to a 70-knot wind acting dead ahead.
b. Hull friction forces due to a 4-knot current from ahead.
c. Propeller drag due to a 4-knot current.

The above criterion is very comforting for, certainly, the conditions specified are seldom exceeded. Experience, on the other hand, tells us that even U. S. Navy anchors drag with alarming frequency. We must look elsewhere for the reason. The equipment is good; it must be for other reasons that an anchor drags.

In the first place, there is no such thing as a "steady" wind blowing over a parallel "steady" current flowing over a standardized sand bottom. The wind, waves, and current conspire to produce uneven and unpredicted stresses. The ship yaws, the chain jerks, the ship inclines to the wind and current, and all the careful calculations are voided. The Navy criterion is probably the best that reasonable men could ask for, but take care—even on a "firm sand bottom" nature will conspire to cause your ship's anchor to drag at well below the criterion values.

If the bottom is not firm sand, and such is frequently the case, the following factors can be used to determine the relative holding power of an anchor:

Firm sand	1.00
Stiff-dense clay (plastic)	1.50
Sticky clay of medium density	0.66
Soft mud	0.33
Loose coarse sand	0.33
Gravel	0.33
Hard bottom (rock-shale-boulders)	0.00*

Using the anchor

Having considered the general action of the anchor, let's look into the use of this tool by the shiphandler.

Whenever we use the anchor in a destroyer, we must remember the sonar

*Value applies if anchor is unable to dig in. If anchor were set or hooked under rock, holding power would increase greatly.

dome. This vital equipment is easily damaged, and if the anchor chain ever gets under the keel and against this gear, it will probably mean dry-docking to repair the damage. It is normally quite easy to maneuver so that this danger is eliminated, but, the general rule is, "Don't drop an anchor while moving ahead." If there is little wind and current, this problem is solved by surging slightly past the anchorage and then dropping the anchor while backing through the "let go" bearing. If the rule is followed to anchor only when moving astern, the chain will always be payed out clear of the ship, and it will thus be laid out nicely on the bottom without fouling the anchor. Backing down upon anchoring will also expedite digging in the anchor firmly when the desired scope has been payed out.

It is difficult at times to determine when the ship ceases to move ahead and begins to move astern. Often the landmarks being used to fix the ship's position are so far away that small movements of the ship have no measurable effect on the bearing. If the forecastle has been provided with some small pieces of wood, these can be thrown into the water and the ship's movement readily determined by observing her motion with respect to the "chips." We must remember that our movement over the bottom can differ from our movement with respect to the surface of the water by the amount of the current, but "throwing a chip over" is very useful in determining the ship's motion through the water at low speeds.

Occasionally, because of wind and current or because of restricted maneuvering room, it is desirable to drop the anchor while moving ahead. In a small or congested harbor it is often necessary to approach the anchorage going down wind or current. In this case, since the ship will be carried down by the wind or current, the chain could tend back under the ship before she swings. The situation should be studied and the anchor used on that side which will insure that the wind and current will carry the ship *away* from the anchor, and that the chain will pay out clear of the ship. If we are approaching our anchorage directly down current, it is very useful to head for a point about 50 yards to one side of the center of the berth as shown in Figure 6–5, and, as we arrive at the berth, twist the bow towards the berth with the engines and rudders. If this maneuver is done correctly, the ship will have considerable inclination to the current as the bow passes over the center of the berth. Once this position is reached, the anchor can be safely dropped and the chain will pay out directly up current and clear of the ship.

When anchoring in a cross wind, it is often impractical to pass through and then back across the center of the berth because the wind may carry us off course during the period when we are dead in the water. In this case, since the wind will tend to move us broadside away from the anchor, the only precaution necessary is to use the upwind anchor and have as little headway as possible when we "let go." The same is true when anchoring in a cross-current.

If the situation gets out of control and the chain tends back under the ship or under the bow, we should keep the chain slack and back clear with our engines. Remember that we have at least 105 fathoms (210 yards) of chain available before the "bitter end," and if we keep it slack it will lie on the bottom and clear of the underwater projections. A lot of maneuvering can be done within the 210 yard radius of our shortest anchor chain.

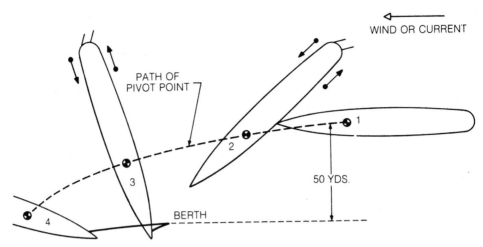

FIGURE 6–5. Anchoring downwind or down-current.

The question of whether to let the anchor go from the hawsepipe or to "walk" it out with the anchor windlass often arises. Certainly, if an anchor were dropped repeatedly from a great height onto rocks or coral heads, it could damage the anchor, and in any case the weight and momentum of a long scope of chain running out is a factor to be considered. On the other hand, walking the anchor out takes time, and the anchor might catch on something as we move about the harbor. A compromise can be reached by making it a rule to drop the anchor only the last 10 fathoms. Thus, if we are going to anchor in 25 fathoms of water, we would walk the anchor out 15 fathoms, disconnect the wildcat from the windlass, leaving the chain held by the brake or by a stopper, then drop the anchor for the last 10 fathoms. This is a relatively safe system because the charted depth should be sufficiently accurate to keep the anchor well clear of the bottom, and it is quite safe to drop an anchor 10 fathoms. We must not forget the "bending shot," and we must be sure that all concerned know the point from which the chain is being measured. It is very convenient to measure the length of chain "at the hawse" since this can be checked visually from the bridge.

The question now arises, "How much chain should we use?" In addition to the considerations mentioned above, we must take into account the size of the berth, the character of the bottom, and the expected weather. In any case the longer the scope of chain, the less likely the ship is to drag. The following amounts of chain have been found to be quite satisfactory for a destroyer under normal conditions:

Depth of water up to 7 fathoms	30 fathoms of chain
Depth of water 7 to 12 fathoms	45 fathoms of chain
Depth of water 12 to 20 fathoms	60 fathoms of chain
Over 20 fathoms of water	Three times the depth

The longer the scope of chain used, the heavier the catenary and the pull necessary to "straighten out" the chain. In strong winds and particularly when the waves begin to build up, the chain should be veered to give plenty of scope to insure the chain near the anchor remains on the bottom and the catenary weight is great enough to cushion even the most severe surges.

In bad weather it may be necessary to veer to a very long scope of chain to prevent the chain from becoming taut and applying jerks to the anchor.

When a ship anchors in a tideway she must expect a shift in her heading each time the tide changes and this, of course, means a shift in the direction of pull on her anchor. An anchor dug in in one direction may tend to dig out when pulled from another direction. In good holding ground the readjustment takes care of itself quickly with no serious shift in the anchor's position, but in a strong tideway where the size of the anchorage is limited, the use of a two-anchor moor should be considered.

As the wind and current shift, there may be slack moments when the ship tends to ride up over her anchor and, when the stress comes on anew, the chain may tend back under the ship, endangering the sonar dome. To minimize this hazard, some ships habitually utilize an anchor pendant, usually an eight-inch nylon with a large shackle to attach it to the anchor chain, led out through the bullnose and attached to the chain when the desired scope is reached. The pendant is secured and the chain slacked further so that the ship rides to the pendant through the bullnose rather than to the chain through the hawsepipe. Thus the anchor is effectively attached to the forwardmost point on the ship and the chain has the best chance of keeping clear of the sonar.

Weighing anchor is normally a simple evolution if certain basic rules are followed. First, we must handle the ship so that the anchor chain does not get under the keel. The ship can be maneuvered at low power, if necessary, to back away from the anchor and straighten the chain out forward. Due to wind and current it may be necessary to spin the ship on her anchor before weighing, but we should not do this until we have heaved short. A long scope of chain can be deceiving. Finally, we must be careful not to get way on the ship until the anchor is in sight and we have received the report, "Clear anchor." For, until we actually sight the anchor, it is impossible to tell what it may have hooked onto.

The approach

Anchoring precisely is often important, yet at times precision is difficult to achieve. Generally speaking, a destroyer shiphandler should be able to place his anchor within 25 yards of the designated anchorage. If the anchor misses by more than 40 yards, he should weigh and try again. Remember the Golden Rule here, for there is nothing more annoying than having to worry about a ship that has anchored haphazardly in an adjacent berth.

The secret to accurate anchoring is careful planning ahead of time. Once the anchorage has been assigned, the conning officer should study the anchorage carefully to select the most advantageous approach course and the most useful landmarks. Generally speaking, a straight run for the last 1,000 yards is very convenient, and if this can be made directly towards a known landmark, the problem is greatly simplified. A prominent landmark on the beam should be selected upon which to "let go" when we arrive at the anchorage. The selection of bearings on both a landmark ahead and one on the beam can establish the desired "let go" position of the ship, and the conning officer's job is simplified to conning until these bearings are reached.

The navigator should lay out distance back along the track on the chart so during the approach he can rapidly report the remaining distance to the anchorage. Marks at 1,000, 500, 300, 200, and 100 yards are especially desired, and it will often be useful to establish bearings for these points ahead of time. It is almost customary for a destroyer's gyro to act up just as the anchorage is approached. Since a few erratic fixes are usual before the navigating team begins to function properly, thorough advance preparations are very comforting.

When making a normal approach to anchor with a destroyer, the following system has been found very useful:

Yards to Berth	Action
500	Be making 5 knots through the water
200	STOP
100	BACK ONE THIRD

This should allow us to surge slowly through the "let go" bearing and the anchor can be dropped as we back through the bearing the second time. As in all other maneuvers, however, each skipper must calibrate his own ship and modify the above figures to suit his own situation.

Often it is not possible to make a steady 1,000-yard approach because of the shape and size of the harbor and the presence of other ships at anchor. If a short approach must be made as a result of congestion, it is usually feasible to establish the location of the assigned anchorage by eye with respect to the other ships or to landmarks. Having identified the location, the conning officer should keep his eye on this spot and maneuver the ship so that the anchor is over the spot selected. In this type of approach, we should approach slowly and check our estimate with fixes before dropping the anchor. In a naval anchorage it is relatively easy to locate one's berth because the other warships can normally be depended upon to anchor with precision. On the other hand, the average merchantman exerts little effort to anchor in the center of his berth, and his position can be considered to be only approximate.

Emergency use of the anchor

In addition to the above considerations on its use, the anchor should be looked upon as the "emergency brake" of the ship. When maneuvering in shoal water or in a harbor, the anchor should be ready for use on a moment's notice. In case of an engine casualty or a steering casualty, it can stop and hold the ship to keep her from running aground. While a ship is proceeding at normal speed she is normally quite controllable, regardless of the state of the weather, but when she is required to lie to for any reason, she is largely at the mercy of the elements. If something prevents proceeding to our destination in a harbor, and we are forced to stop, the anchor is the only means through which we can secure the ship and prevent her drifting with the wind and current.

General

As the shiphandler learns to use his anchors he will learn that they are more than portable moorings. For instance, he will save time and effort by spinning on his anchor instead of laboriously twisting with the engines. He will use his anchor to control his approach when making a downwind landing, and he will leave an anchor out in the stream when he thinks it may be useful later. The anchor of a good shiphandler spends a lot of time on the bottom serving a useful purpose, rather than just rusting in the hawsepipe.

MOORING

Frequently, destroyers are required to moor to buoys. These buoys are firmly anchored with multiple anchors, and the chain leading up from the anchors to the mooring ring is very large and strong. The actual buoy is simply a float to hold the end of this mooring chain above the surface so that a ship can be secured to it. Mooring to a buoy is safer than anchoring because the ship is thereby secured to heavier and better anchors. The berths can be smaller in a harbor where buoys are used, because a buoy, having both upstream and downstream anchors, is practically stationary, and ships (moored with a short scope of chain) swing in a circle of smaller diameter.

A destroyer normally moors to a buoy with her anchor chain, and it is this practice that makes "picking up" or "snatching" the buoy somewhat difficult. The anchor chain is so heavy that a man can scarcely displace the lower end of the chain as it hangs from the bow. Heavy manila line can be run fifty yards to the buoy if necessary, because it nearly floats as the water bears most of its weight, and even relatively heavy wire can be run several yards. But from a practical point of view, we should consider that the end of an anchor chain cannot be moved by hand. Consequently, the end of the anchor chain *must be placed* directly on the buoy when mooring.

There are many methods of snatching a buoy, but all of them require that men be placed on the buoy to handle the lines and shackle the bitter end of the chain to the buoy. It is occasionally possible to put the bullnose directly over the buoy, lower the men and the chain to the buoy from the ship, and secure directly to the buoy. This, needless to say, is a precision maneuver, and it is very difficult if there is any wind or current. It is much safer, if less spectacular, to use the ship's boat to get the men onto the buoy and to use another method to secure the chain to the buoy (Figure 6–6).

The first step in any good method of snatching the buoy is to secure the bow to the buoy by some temporary means, such as a "hook rope," to hold the ship and to give us time to get the chain to the buoy. A 6-inch manila mooring line is not strong enough to withstand the strain as the ship is snubbed into the buoy, and a heavy wire is very difficult to run for any distance. In a strong wind or current we have only seconds to get our hook rope secured to the buoy before our bow is carried out of range. This is where the spring-laid wire rope mentioned earlier is again worth its weight in gold. It is strong enough to hold the bow under almost any wind condition, and it is relatively easy to handle. Once a destroyer is secured to a buoy with a 1⅝-inch "spring lay," only the most drastic abuse will cause the buoy line to part.

FIGURE 6–6. The Special Sea and Anchor Detail moor the ship to the buoy.

Thorough knowledge by the conning officer of the details of the mooring arrangements is essential to a successful evolution. The bridge, forecastle, and engine room must work together as a team more during this operation than during almost any other. The conning officer must know beforehand where the first lieutenant will want the buoy with respect to the bow at any given time, and the throttleman must have a feel for the delicacy of the maneuver.

Rigging for the trolley method

The "trolley method" of sending the chain to the buoy will be described because it is the quickest and surest method. This method uses a minimum of lines and men, and has a maximum safety factor at all times. As in most seamanship evolutions, the secret of success is thorough preparation.

In rigging for the trolley method of snatching a buoy (Figure 6–7), we first break the anchor chain, connect the buoy shackle to it, and lead the chain to the bullnose. Then we pass the buoy line out through the bullnose and back to the lifeline on the side on which the boat is to be lowered. Next, using relatively large shackles (1-inch are good for this), place them over the buoy line and secure them to the chain a few feet above the big buoy shackle and at intervals of about 6 feet

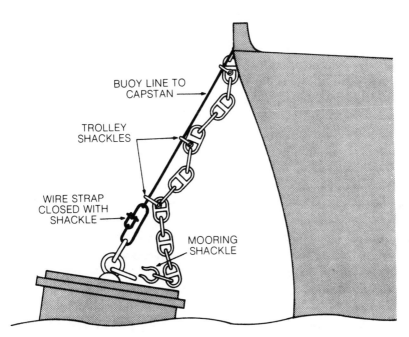

FIGURE 6–7. Trolley method of snatching a buoy.

along the chain. These shackles act as trolleys for running the chain down the buoy line. Finally "21-thread" handling lines on the buoy shackle and a short messenger on the buoy line will be found useful. When all has been rigged, pass the end of the chain out the bullnose and rouse out enough chain so that the buoy shackle just clears the water. Make sure that the buoy line runs free through the trolley shackles.

Approach and mooring

Now we are ready to approach the buoy (Figure 6–8). When about 500 yards from the buoy and making about 5 knots, put the buoy party in the boat, lower it, and have it come up under the bow. The boat can be put in the water safely by a competent crew at speeds up to 10 knots, but since the boat can make only about 6 knots, we must proceed slowly enough to allow the boat to gain its position on the bow and ahead.

At 200 yards, stop the engines, pass the buoy line and messenger to the boat, and send the boat out ahead with the buoy line. The boat should reach the buoy about 50 yards ahead of the ship, and the men can be on the buoy securing the buoy line by the time we bring the ship gently to a stop.

A strong wire strap and shackle is excellent for securing the buoy line to the buoy since it will fit any size or combination of rings and links. This is especially important when mooring to an unfamiliar buoy which might have an oddsize ring. Do not use a buoy hook for securing the buoy line. Not only are these hooks large and unwieldly, but they have been known to straighten out and fail just when they are needed most.

The ideal buoy approach puts our bullnose *abreast* the buoy, about 10 yards to one side, with the ship heading into the wind or current so that she can be maintained in this position while the buoy line is being secured to the buoy. Bringing the buoy up abreast the bow is absolutely essential in many ships if the maneuver is to be controlled from the bridge, because the high flared bow of some of the newer ships completely masks the surface of the water ahead for a hundred yards or more. As soon as the buoy line is secured to the buoy, we should heave in until the buoy is close to the bow.

By keeping the buoy abreast the bow instead of dead ahead, the conning officer can see the buoy at all times and thus can handle the situation easily. Once the line has been secured to the buoy, it is usually advisable not to use the engines again until the chain has been securely shackled to the buoy, as the bow can generally be heaved to the buoy with the anchor windlass alone. There are times, of course, when the engines must be used to keep the bow close to the buoy, but the use of the engines should be kept to a minimum.

Throughout the maneuvering the ship must be handled with great care. It takes two seamen to handle the line and the mooring shackle at the buoy, and while these men are on the buoy the ship must not be allowed to surge against the

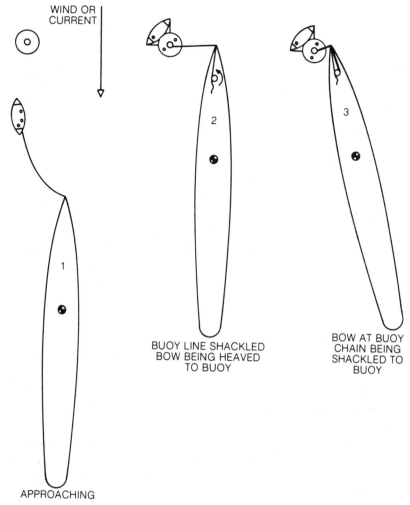

WIND OR CURRENT

2

BUOY LINE SHACKLED
BOW BEING HEAVED
TO BUOY

3

BOW AT BUOY
CHAIN BEING
SHACKLED TO
BUOY

1

APPROACHING

FIGURE 6–8. Maneuver in snatching a buoy by the trolley-line method.

buoy line or to brush against the buoy. It is surprising to see how readily a ship can pull a buoy under. It takes only a slight brush to spin the buoy and endanger the men on it.

Never allow the boat to get *between* the buoy and the ship. A sudden surge or a parting line here could spell tragedy. *Always* remove the men from the buoy before taking any considerable strain. Under normal conditions the ship's bow will be drifting gently in toward the buoy while the buoy line is being secured, and so can be easily brought to the buoy with the men on the buoy. If more than a light strain is needed to work the bow to the buoy, get the men off first before taking the strain, and then put them back on when the bow is snubbed up to the buoy and the chain is ready for shackling.

When making a buoy downwind or down-current it is usually feasible to hold the stern up into the wind or current with the engines until we are secured to the buoy, and then to let the ship swing, keeping the buoy out from the bow by use of the engines.

Making a buoy crosswind or crosscurrent is the most difficult way to make it. Under such circumstances we should, if possible, approach to the position described above with the wind or current dead ahead; but if this is impossible, it will be necessary to make a "flying snatch." The speed of the men on the buoy is the key to this maneuver. Approach so as to put the bow well upwind and slightly short of the buoy (to insure that it will pass clear of the buoy as the ship is blown downwind). Use the engines and helm to twist the bow upwind throughout the operation. This will keep the bow as near the buoy as possible as the stern is swept downwind, and will give the men on the buoy a maximum opportunity to get the buoy line secured. Once the buoy line is secured, we can swing to it and eventually heave the bow up to the buoy. Care must be taken while swinging, because a parted buoy line at this time will require another approach at the very least.

Mooring to two buoys

Making both bow and stern buoys offers certain new problems to the conning officer. Generally, the problem is readily solved by concentrating on making one buoy at a time and simply avoiding the other buoy until we are secured to the first one. Normally, in an uncomplicated situation, make the bow buoy as described above. If two boats are available, the stern wire can be run to the other buoy while the bow is being secured, but no strain should be taken aft until all is secured forward. When all is ready, walk out the chain forward and move the stern towards its buoy with the engines until the stern wire can be heaved in to the desired scope. When the stern wire is secured at the desired length, tauten the moor by heaving in on the chain, forward, to the desired tautness.

Making two buoys when heading downwind or down-current requires securing to the stern buoy first. In this case we should avoid getting the stern buoy dead astern until the stern wire has been run and then secured at the desired scope. A buoy dead astern cannot be seen from the bridge, whereas one slightly on the quarter can easily be seen. Running out the chain forward is relatively simple except that, in this case, the chain probably will not slide down the buoy line because of the long scope of the buoy line out forward, and it will be necessary to pass a messenger through the forward buoy mooring ring and back to the capstan to haul the chain out to the buoy.

Mooring fore and aft to buoys in a crosswind or crosscurrent is a problem frequently encountered (Figure 6–9). As before, the solution is to moor to one buoy at a time. Once the ship is secured to the forward buoy, we can walk the stern up to the stern buoy with the engines. This can be done in all but the strongest winds, but since it puts considerable strain on the forward buoy, we must not attempt it until the chain has been secured to the buoy forward.

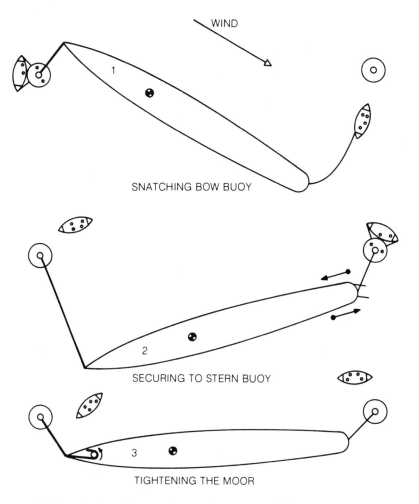

WIND

1

SNATCHING BOW BUOY

2

SECURING TO STERN BUOY

3

TIGHTENING THE MOOR

FIGURE 6–9. Snatching two buoys in a crosswind.

Mooring to two anchors

Though seldom seen, because piers and buoys are usually available to Navy ships, mooring to two anchors provides the greatest safety available from the ship's own equipment. A classical moor is to drop two anchors a substantial distance apart and then adjust the scope of chain to each until the ship's bow is held securely midway between the two anchors. If the ship may be moored for a considerable time and may swing around her moor with the change of tide, it is normal with naval ships to insert a mooring swivel in the rig to prevent the chains from fouling. Most merchant mariners, however, don't bother with a swivel, feeling that it takes no longer to clear the chains before getting under way than it does to rig and unrig the swivel, and they are correct in most cases.

The advantage of mooring in this manner is that the bow of the ship is snubbed to one place. When assigned to a small anchorage, if the ship is moored so that her mooring swivel is over the center of her berth, she can swing with the tide and wind and her stern will never extend much more than a shiplength from the center of the berth. She might require twice this radius of clearance were she to anchor normally.

More important than the capability to ride within a small radius of the center of the berth is the increased security of the moor versus normal anchoring. As pointed out in Figure 5–5, a ship riding to a single anchor tends to yaw; the stronger the wind, the greater the yaw. The frequent change in the direction of the pull on the anchor combined with the jerks on the anchor when the ship "comes about" while yawing is the most frequent cause of dragging anchor. If a ship has her anchor dug in, has adequate chain out, and does not yaw, there is little danger of dragging. Mooring to two anchors very nearly assures such safety.

In the average situation, while moored as indicated in Figure 6–10, the pull of the ship is divided between the two anchors in accordance with the geometry of the moor, but the pull on each anchor is always along the line from the anchor to the mooring swivel, which direction never varies more than a few degrees from that from the anchor to the center of the berth. This is in sharp contrast to the situation when anchored to a single anchor where the pull on the anchor changes with the direction of the wind and current. Furthermore, under a given combination of wind and current, a moored ship is very stable. Since the two-anchor arrangement provides restraints to keep the bow from moving to the side, the ship does not yaw and the pull on each of the anchors is constant.

When the ship swings in line with the two anchors, however, the restraining side forces do not come into play until the bow has moved appreciably to one side. In this case, the two-anchor moor does not eliminate yawing, but it does tend to reduce the amount of yaw considerably. In a situation where maximum security of the mooring is the prime objective, the line between the two anchors should be appreciably different from the direction in which the ship is expected to head in response to the combination of the wind and current.

One should not conclude, however, that mooring with the anchors in line with a reversing tidal current, for example, is a useless evolution. On the contrary, in addition to reducing the diameter of the berth by an amount equal to twice the scope of chain which would have been used, the alteration in the direction of pull on the anchors is avoided. As the direction of the tide shifts, the ship shifts from riding to one anchor to riding to the other, and the pull on each anchor is always in the same direction, i.e., towards the center of the berth. If the ship is moored during several changes of tide, the anchors dig in more and more securely instead of being uprooted and replanted at each change of the direction of current.

The operation on the forecastle when mooring and unmooring is one of the grand evolutions of deck seamanship. In mooring to two anchors, if we wish to use a mooring swivel (and the major difficulties in mooring surround the rigging and unrigging of this swivel), we must arrange that the chains to the two anchors meet

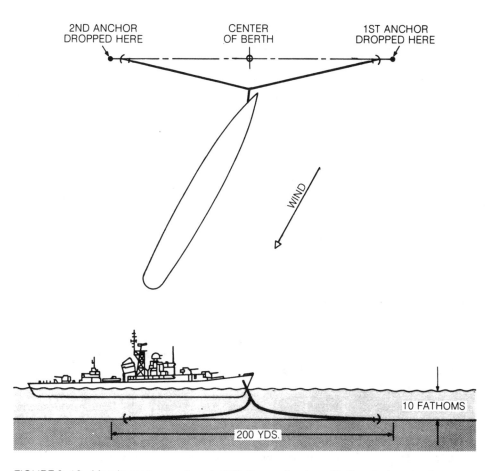

FIGURE 6–10. Mooring to two anchors in 10 fathoms of water, with the wind across the moor.

at a place where the chains can be broken, that we can hold the chains securely while attaching the swivel, and that, after the chains are attached, the swivel can be eased out of the hawse and the two chains run clear. The essential difference between the Eldridge and the O'Neil methods is that in the former both chains are run out of the same hawsepipe *before* the anchors are dropped, and in the latter the anchors are each dropped from their own hawse, and, after the ship has been adjusted to the center of the berth, the chains are re-rigged so their ends enter the same hawse for rigging the swivel. In a destroyer, the O'Neil method, modified to suite the particular forecastle installation, is probably the more practical.

The conning officer's problem in mooring is to place the two anchors correctly and maneuver the ship as necessary while adjusting to the center of the berth. Obviously, the easiest method of placing the anchors is to pass through the center of the berth heading into the existing combination of wind and current, dropping one anchor the desired distance short of the center and the other the desired distance past the center of the berth. If the conning officer drops his first anchor before passing through the center and carries on to drop the second, the evolution is known as a "flying moor." If, on the other hand, he passes through the center and drops the upstream or "riding" anchor and then eases back through the berth to drop the downstream or "lee" anchor, the maneuver is called an "ordinary moor." Since a destroyer has only one anchor windlass and must drop one of her anchors from a chain compressor (and thus cannot heave in on this anchor without re-rigging the chains), she should always drop the anchor connected to the wildcat first, pass through the center of the berth, drop the second anchor from its compressor, and then heave back to the center of the berth with the chain to the wildcat while gradually paying out chain from the compressor. This procedure dictates the use of the ordinary moor except when there is so little wind or current that there would be no concern about riding to a chain held only by the compressor.

Let's consider the problem of mooring a destroyer in 10 fathoms of water with a mud bottom. Because of the depth of the water we would like to have 45 fathoms of chain to a single anchor, so we might decide to insert the mooring swivel at the 45-fathom shackle in each of our chains. Taking into account the five-fathom, bending shots this will give us 50 fathoms or 100 yards of chain from the mooring swivel to each of the anchors. Since the swivel will be about two fathoms below the surface, this amount of chain will give a scope-to-depth-of-water ratio of greater than six to one.

In 10 fathoms of water, our hawsepipes are about 14 fathoms from the bottom and simple triangulation indicates that each anchor should end up 96 yards from the center of the berth with the chains taut. The chains, however, will never be completely straight and about four fathoms of slack in one chain is necessary for dipping around the bow and connecting to the swivel, so we will have about as taut a moor as possible if the anchors actually end up each 90 yards from the center of the berth. On the other hand, we wish to be sure the anchors are well dug in in their final position, so we should allow about 10 yards of movement for each anchor for this purpose. In summary then, our calculations show that we should drop the anchors 200 yards apart and then heave them in until the two 45-fathom shackles are on deck (with chains through the same hawsepipe) so the mooring swivel can be inserted.

In approaching such a moor, we should have both anchors ready for letting go, one from the wildcat and the other from its compressor. Heading into the wind and current, we should pass through the center of the berth and drop the anchor from the wildcat exactly 100 yards beyond the center of the berth. We should then back through the center of the berth, veering chain as we go, and when 100 yards back from the center, let go the other anchor from its compressor. We can use the first anchor chain to measure the distance between the anchors, letting go the second anchor when we have veered to 100 fathoms on the first one (the movement of the anchor in digging-in will just about cancel the sag in the chain). We can then heave ourselves to the center of the berth with the riding chain and go through the evolution of connecting the shackle.

The above procedure is for achieving a very taut moor for riding in a small berth in a tideway, for example. Under such conditions the tighter the moor the better, and the moor is properly made heading into the existing current. On the other hand, if the ship is being moored to be more secure in the face of strong winds, it is not desirable to have the anchors in line with the expected wind, and it is neither desirable nor possible to keep as taut a moor. In such a case, the line between the anchors should be at right angles to the direction of the wind, and the anchors should be dropped about 80 yards to each side of the center of the berth. In any case, the strain on the chains as the wind picks up will cause the anchors to dig in further and will cause the geometry of the moor to adjust to the wind condition. Under severe conditions the anchors might drag until they are sharp on either bow, but as long as the ship is prevented from yawing, the shiphandler can feel sure he is getting about as much holding power as possible out of the two anchors.

Mooring is neither difficult nor extraordinarily time-consuming. The added security of a two-anchor mooring, especially in light of the frequent mishaps caused by dragged anchors, should be very appealing to the careful mariner. It is much wiser to put that second anchor on the bottom in a manner planned to produce maximum security for the ship, than to leave it resting in its hawsepipe. When the first anchor has already started dragging, it is usually too late to do a good job with the second.

The Hammerlock moor

Riding out a very severe storm or hurricane at anchor requires the utmost skill on the part of the shiphandler, and he must extract the last measure of safety from his preparations. A planned mooring is much better than the haphazard dropping of two anchors, but even a well-planned normal moor can be improved upon for a heavy blow. The "Hammerlock moor" was discovered by skillful accident by the skipper of an AKA riding out a hurricane in Chesapeake Bay, but it is equally applicable to any type ship equipped with two anchors.

A normal moor using a mooring swivel has several disadvantages for use during a severe storm. First, if even a short scope of chain is allowed between the hawse and the mooring swivel, the bow is not held rigidly and the ship may commence to yaw. Second, the entire strain is placed upon a single length of chain, the parting of which would cost the ship all capability of anchoring. Last, the anchors cannot be worked individually or weighed without disconnecting the mooring swivel, and this may be nearly impossible during a really bad storm. The Hammerlock avoids these disadvantages.

The Hammerlock moor can be executed by dropping the first anchor, veering to the desired scope of chain, and then maneuvering towards the side from which the anchor was dropped until the chain is hard around the bow and laid out directly across the direction of the wind. The second anchor is then dropped and, as chain is veered to this second anchor, the ship will move back to an intermediate position with an anchor broad on each bow and the chains tightly crossed on her stem. In this position her bow will be fixed, she will not yaw, and the full holding power of both anchors will be utilized in securing the ship. Either anchor can be worked at will to adjust the moor, and the only disadvantage, besides a bit of paint scraped from the bow by the chains, is that we must be careful to weigh our anchors in the correct order to avoid fouling them.

The advantage of crossing the chains on the stem instead of using each anchor to its own bow is that the foremost point on the ship, the stem, is firmly fixed by the action of the two anchors and the tendency to yaw is thus minimized. If the two chains lead normally off their respective bows from their hawsepipes, the point at which their lines of action crossed, which determines the point about which the ship would tend to pivot, would be farther aft than the stem, the amount depending upon the physical location of the hawsepipes. In a normal warship the hawsepipes are so far forward and so close together that there is probably little practical gain in crossing the chains and the chains would be least likely to fail because of chafe when leading directly from their own hawsepipes. Consequently, if the hawsepipes are well forward and close together, the chains should not be crossed.

In a hurricane the wind veers as the center of the storm passes, and the direction to which it will veer is usually known in advance. If wind shifts can be predicted, the moor can be kept properly oriented to the wind by riding to a shorter scope of chain on the anchor towards which the wind is expected to veer. As the direction of the wind changes, a larger share of the load will fall on this "weaker" anchor; it will consequently drag until its share of the load diminishes, and the whole mooring will be reoriented to meet the new direction of the wind.

Using the engines to ease the strain

It would seem that in any case when the ship is being forced back against her moorings by the wind or the current that the engines could be used to ease the strain. This theory is true in principle, of course, but if a ship is yawing severely, it is very difficult to put it into practice. The use of engine power when yawing often accentuates the yaw and worsens the situation instead of easing it. The amount of wind force exerted on the ship increases as the ship becomes inclined to the direction of the wind, and as the ship yaws her inclination to the wind varies constantly. The engine power which might ease the strain at one moment might cause the ship to surge ahead and slacken the moor a few moments later.

If the bow of the ship is held steady by a normal moor or a Hammerlock, on the other hand, the use of the engines to reduce the strain is simple and straightforward. We should use a little less power than that required to overcome the effect of the wind on the ship, thus the ship will ride back nicely against her moorings but without excess strain. Figure 6–11 is a chart indicating the engine speed required to offset the effect of the wind for various types of ships in the Navy. If, in using this chart, we select an engine speed of two knots less than that

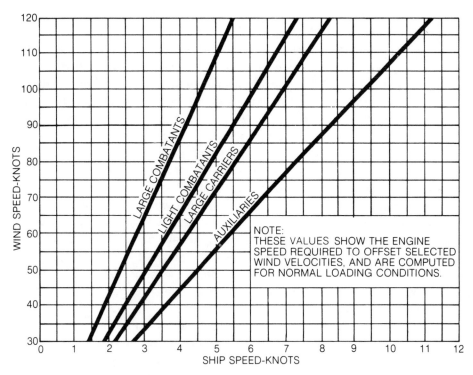

THE VALUES SHOWN WERE DEVELOPED USING THE BASIC FORMULA:
WIND LOAD = R_wAV^2
WHERE R_w IS EQUAL TO WIND FRICTION FACTOR. (R_w IS GENERALLY TAKEN AS 0.004.)
V IS EQUAL TO WIND VELOCITY IN KNOTS.
A IS EQUAL TO PROJECTED AREA ABOVE THE WATERLINE IN SQ. FT.
THREE SETS OF CALCULATIONS WITH VARYING R_w WERE USED. THE PLOTTED VALUES
ILLUSTRATED REPRESENT THE MEAN OF THESE VALUES.

FIGURE 6–11. Engine speed vs. wind velocity for offsetting force of wind. (Prepared by Bureau of Ships, Navy Department)

required to offset the wind being experienced, the strain on the mooring will be the same as though we were moored on a calm day in a current of two knots. This, of course, is a very acceptable situation, but we must watch the velocity of the wind and adjust the engine speed as necessary to keep the strain on the moorings constant.

Mediterranean moor

The "Mediterranean moor" is a method that most ships are nowadays being required to use frequently. Mooring with the stern to the mole or pier allows more ships to be moored within a given amount of dock space, and furthermore allows each ship to have her own brow to the mole. It is an excellent way to moor in small, well-protected harbors where space is at a premium, and many of the troubles experienced in nesting are eliminated (Figure 6–12). The European navies use this method extensively.

Essentially the "Med moor" is mooring one end of the ship to a mole or pier and anchoring the other end. Since the ship can't swing to the anchor, it is necessary to put two anchors out, one on each bow, so that the bow can be held in place with a wind from either beam. If the anchors are well separated, the chains will tend sufficiently out to the side to hold the bow even in a strong wind. Actually, an optimum arrangement for security of the moor would be to have the chains tending 60° out from each bow, but the harbor situation seldom allows such separation. In case the congestion of the harbor does not allow good separation, the method outlined for cruisers in Chapter 12 should be used.

In preparing to make the Mediterranean moor we must decide how far out from the mole to drop the anchors. It is advantageous, when clearing, to have the anchors well out from the mole, because, since we have but one capstan, we must work the anchors one at a time, and it is more comfortable to accomplish this time-consuming task as far out in the stream as feasible. Since our shortest anchor chain is 105 fathoms, we might pick 75 fathoms as a good scope of chain and thus allow a 30 fathom margin for error.

As indicated in Figure 6–13, for a *Gearing*-class destroyer, with 75 fathoms of chain, a 390-foot ship, and our stern close to the mole when secured, we should drop our anchors 280 yards out from the face of the mole. In order to accomplish this and to separate our anchors adequately, an approach parallel to the face of the mole is advantageous. We drop our first anchor when the hawse is about 50 yards short of a position abreast our berth, and then we drop the second anchor when the bow is about 50 yards past the berth. By putting the rudder over full and twisting the engines as we let go the first anchor, we can keep the chain from getting under the ship. The anchor which will be upwind as we back into our berth should be handled on the wildcat, and the other anchor can be handled from its compressor.

When both anchors are down, we commence twisting the ship and backing her into her berth, veering out chain proportionately as we proceed. As soon as possible we should run our stern line to the mole. As the stern approaches the mole it is advisable to shift the conn to the fantail where the situation can be seen firsthand. The stern is ultimately moved into place by backing slowly and gradually easing the chains. If the anchor on the wildcat has been dug in firmly, the motion can be controlled by slowly walking out the chain while backing steadily at a low power.

The stern is secured to the mole with a stern line and two quarter lines. Crossing the quarter lines under the stern insures a more secure moor, but on some ships this is difficult because of obstructions on the stern. It is wise to use our "strong mooring line" or even the towing hawser for the stern line.

After the stern has been secured, the moor is tautened by heaving in and equalizing the anchor chains. When the ship is finally secure, the anchor chains should both be taking a moderate strain and standing well out of the water.

FIGURE 6–12. The Mediterranean moor consists of mooring one end of the ship to the mole and anchoring the other end.

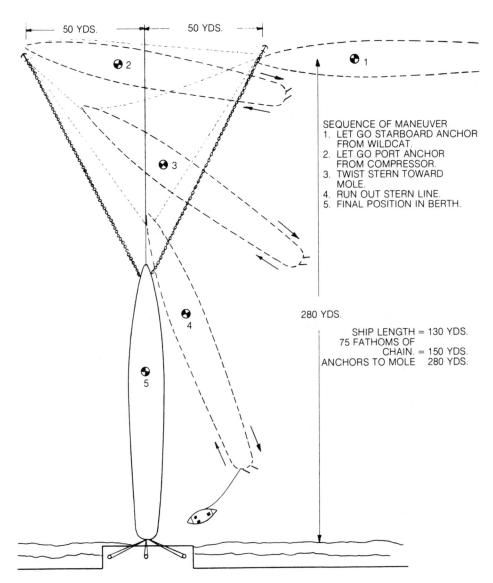

FIGURE 6–13. The Mediterranean moor.

Remember that no margin astern has been allowed in case of a wind from ahead, so there must be *no* slack in the chains.

Conning the ship while making a Med moor is one of the most interesting challenges to the shiphandler. The approach, initial turning of the ship, and the placing of the anchors can be managed from his regular station on the engaged wing of the bridge, but the final maneuvers required to bring the stern close enough to the mole for the remaining distance to be spanned by a short brow require such precision that there is no substitute for on-the-spot observation. It is therefore recommended that as soon as the anchors are down, the ship twisted to the desired heading and the stern lines run to the mole, the conning officer shift his station to the fantail. Here he can observe the distance to the mole directly, be completely abreast the status of the usually multiple stern lines, and still exercise complete control of his engines, rudder, and anchors through his telephone circuits. Moving the ship the last few feet needed to complete the Med moor requires the finest judgment and control.

7
single-screw ocean escorts

Now that we have examined the handling of a twin-screw, twin-rudder destroyer in port, we should take a look at the handling of a single-screw, single-rudder ship in the same situations. At sea, where the ship is almost always moving ahead at plenty of speed for good steering control, there is little difference between single- or multiple-screw ships from the viewpoint of the conning officer. In port, however, the differences are substantial.

A ship is controlled by controlling the force vector acting on her stern. In a ship with twin screws and twin rudders, it is possible to control the direction of that vector at will and obtain magnitudes of the force sufficient to meet most needs. In a ship with a single screw and single rudder, moving below steerage-way, side forces can be produced to either side only with the screw turning ahead; with the screw turning astern, only forces moving the stern to port can be achieved. To produce any side forces at all when the ship is below steerageway, it is necessary to simultaneously produce a propeller thrust ahead or astern. It is impossible to produce a force directly abeam, permitting the ship to twist in her own water; any side force in a single-screw ship is always accompanied by a strong force forward or aft.

Figure 7–1 is a polar plot of the locus of the boundary of all possible thrust vectors obtainable from combinations of engine and rudder orders in a single-screw, single-rudder ship compared with that of a twin-screw, twin-rudder ship. By choosing the appropriate combination, a conning officer can obtain any thrust vector he desires which falls within the boundary locus. Though the magnitude of the side thrust component may not be all that is desired, the conning officer of a twin-screw, twin-rudder ship can obtain thrust in any direction. The conning officer of the single-screw, single-rudder ship, on the other hand, has a very much more restricted choice. Only in the ahead sector is his choice comparable to that of a twin-screw equipped shiphandler, and even there he finds a definite skew to starboard. He has no possibility of producing pure beam thrust to either side, and his backing thrust is limited to a narrow sector on the port quarter. Obviously the conning officer of a single-screw ship is quite limited in his ability to move her stern about with the single propeller and rudder.

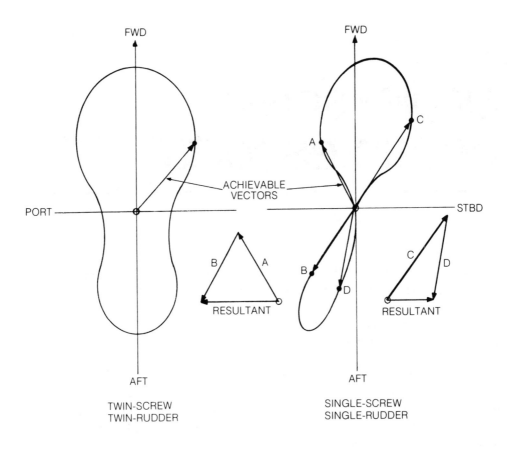

FIGURE 7–1. Typical locus of maximum possible combined rudder and screw thrust vector.

He can, however, obtain the equivalent of side thrust by alternately "kicking" his engine ahead and astern for short periods with rudder hard over in the appropriate direction. From Figure 7–1 we can see that by using kicks to alternately produce Vectors A and B for a force to port, or Vectors C and D for a force to starboard, the fore-and-aft components cancel out, leaving a resultant thrust to the side. Of course the successive "bells" must be left on long enough for the propeller to get up to speed and produce the necessary wash over the rudder, and this will result in a certain amount of surging forward and astern, but the stern can be moved steadily to port and even haltingly to starboard through use of this method. Though side forces are possible through "kicking" the engine, this is not at all comparable to the smooth controllability of a twin-screw, twin-rudder arrangement.

As a consequence of his ship's limitations, the single-screw shiphandler simply avoids situations where he must move the ship's stern to starboard while dead in the water. He can work the stern to port quite nicely if he has some room to surge back and forth a bit, and he can "back to port" quite handily. Even backing straight astern can't be undertaken unless there is enough room for a veer to port before enough sternway has been built up for the rudder to be effective. The secret of success with a single-screw ship is to plan ahead carefully, avoid situations where the stern must be moved to starboard or where the ship will have no fore-and-aft room to maneuver, and to learn to look for help from wind, current, anchors, lines and, last but not least, tugs to compensate for the ship's limitations.

THE OCEAN ESCORT*

As can be seen from the characteristics listed on page 63, the *Knox* Class ocean escort and her predecessors in the *Garcia* Class are not small ships. Though less powerful than destroyers or frigates, they are nevertheless large, powerful ships, as their top speed of 27 knots attests. In fact, the quick response of the powerful engine driving a single screw and the effectiveness of a very large rudder do much to offset their limitations (Figure 7–2).

*The remainder of this chapter is drawn almost verbatim from *Shiphandling in a* Garcia *Class Ocean Escort*, a booklet by Commander Felix S. Vecchione, USN, 13 September 1968. Comments on the handling of the *Dealey* Class are from a paper on "Shiphandling of the *Dealey* Class Ocean Escort," by Lieutenant Dana Peckworth, USN, July 1961.

FIGURE 7–2. Ocean Escort USS *Garcia* (DE 1040).

The *Knox* is a big ship by any standard, but the huge SQS-26 sonar built into her bow is a dominating factor. In addition to added draft, special care must be exercised to insure that nothing is ever permitted to come into contact with the sonar dome. This requires care in the selection of berths and constant concern when barges and other craft are brought alongside. To permit testing and calibration of the sonar while the ship is in port, ocean escorts are moored "bow out" whenever possible. With a tender bow and well-protected propeller and rudder, the ocean escort is the opposite of most ships—the conning officer keeps the bow away from contact while having much more freedom than normal with the stern. Shiphandlers experienced with twin-screw, "hard bow" techniques will be surprised to see the conning officer of an ocean escort snub the stern in towards the pier in order to get the tender bow out and away from danger.

Getting under way

Getting under way from a bow-out berth offers an excellent opportunity for an unassisted maneuver. On those occasions when the combined forces of wind and current tend to set the ship away from the pier, there are virtually no shiphandling problems at all (Figure 7–3). Lines 2, 3, 4, and 5 are taken in. Lines 1 and 6 are slacked. The ship moves out 25 to 30 feet. Lines 1 and 6 are taken in and an ahead bell takes care of the rest.

If the bow comes out faster than the stern, line 1 can be checked until the desired inclination is reached. Similarly, if the stern comes out too fast, line 6 can

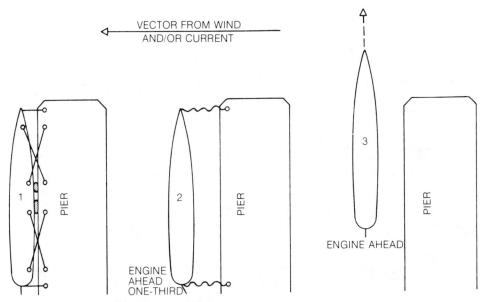

FIGURE 7–3. Getting under way from a bow-out berth.

be checked. The fore-and-aft position of the ship is maintained by a momentary ahead or back bell until 1 and 6 are cast off.

Figure 7–3 shows a ship getting under way from a starboard-side-to moor. The procedures are the same for getting under way from a port-side-to moor whenever the vector of environmental forces tends to move the ship away from the pier.

If there are no wind or current forces acting on the ship or even if a slight vector exists in the direction of the pier, getting away from alongside is still quite easy (Figure 7–4). In this instance lines 1, 2, 3, 4, and 5 are taken in. Line 6 is led to the capstan and a slight strain is taken on it. The bow will move away from the pier slowly as the ship pivots on the camel or aft fender. When the proper inclination is reached, line 6 is cast off and taken in smartly. The rudder is put over 10 to 15 degrees in the direction of the pier. An ahead one-third bell will push the stern clear as it imparts headway to the ship. As soon as daylight can be seen between the fantail and the pier, the rudder is returned amidships and thereafter used as necessary to steer clear.

The same maneuver can be accomplished from an outboard berth in a nest of ships just as it would be from alongside the pier. It can be accomplished in either direction, port or starboard. Getting under way from a starboard-side-to moor as shown in Figure 7–4 requires a little more rudder to push the stern clear, but, other than that, the techniques are the same.

Getting under way forward unassisted is also quite simple when the ship is moored parallel to the wind or current (Figure 7–5). In the case of current, with the

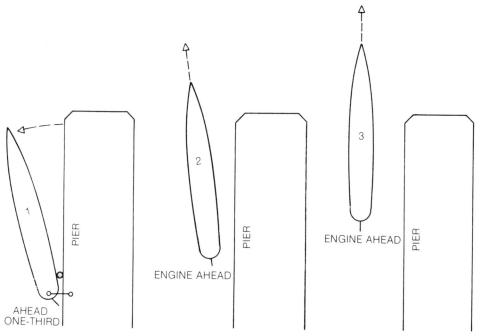

FIGURE 7–4. Getting under way when no wind or current forces act on the ship.

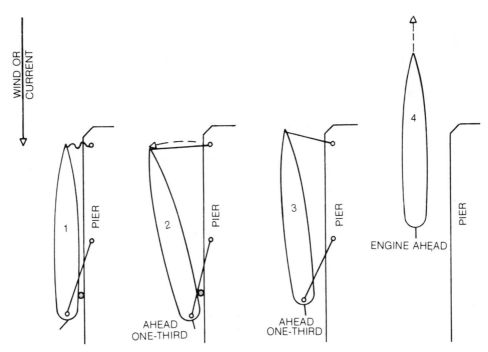

FIGURE 7–5. Getting under way forward when parallel to wind or current.

ship's head stemming the current, the rudder is put over in the direction away from the pier, line 5 is held, line 1 is slacked and the rest of the lines are taken in. The ship's head will fall off in the direction of midstream. As this happens, the rudder is returned amidships, line 1 is checked momentarily, line 5 is slacked, and an ahead one-third bell will move the stern out away from the pier. The final step is to take in lines 1 and 5 and go.

Backing away from a berth unassisted is little more complex than moving out in a forward direction. If the ship is being set away from the pier, the principal difference between backing out and going out forward is in selecting an appropriate angle between the ship and the pier before casting off—one that will allow sufficient room for the ship to back to port safely (Figure 7–6).

Under no-wind conditions and assuming the berths astern are clear, we can back away unassisted from a flat starboard-side-to moor with a little risk of damage (Figure 7–7). All lines are taken in and the rudder is put over right full. A back two-thirds bell will move the stern out from the pier and at the same time start the ship moving aft. If there are no other forces involved, the sonar dome will not strike the pier. As soon as a speed of 3 to 5 knots of sternway is attained, the engine is stopped and as the ship coasts back, movement in either direction can be controlled by the use of the rudder.

Backing straight away from a flat port-side-to moor under the above conditions is not recommended, because the ship's tendency to back to port will force the stern against the pier. Instead, where berthing conditions permit, it is recommended that the ship spring the bow out; put the rudder over in the direction of the

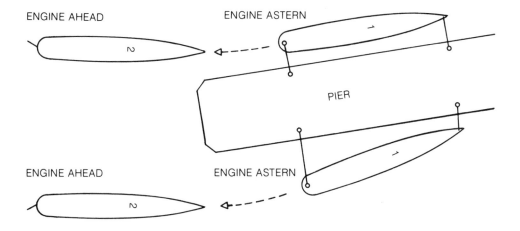

ENGINE AHEAD   ENGINE ASTERN

PIER

ENGINE AHEAD   ENGINE ASTERN

FIGURE 7–6. Backing to port when ship is being set away from the pier.

pier; come ahead to clear the pier, get the stern out, and arrive at a proper angle; then back away from the berth (Figure 7–8).

An unassisted backing maneuver should generally not be attempted in an ocean escort under conditions where the environmental forces tend to set the ship on to the pier. Unless the urgency of the situation warrants accepting the risk of damage, the conning officer should wait until a tug becomes available or until the environmental conditions change.

Casting

Once the ship has backed clear of the pier, the next maneuver is to turn around and stand out of the harbor. Although it is not possible to twist a single-screw ship, it is possible to turn it unassisted in considerably less space than that required by the ship's turning radius. If our very short turning radius is still too much, we must usually resort to casting to starboard, "kicking" the stern around as described above, for a right-hand turn; or pivoting on the port anchor for a left-hand turn. The ship is equipped with only a bower anchor on the centerline and a port anchor, and neither is suitable for pivoting to starboard. If the port anchor were snubbed under-foot, it would tend to work against the right-hand turn and if the centerline anchor were used with any headway on at all, the dome might be damaged.

Casting to starboard makes use of the ship's natural tendency to back to port. Initially, the rudder is put over right full and an ahead two-thirds bell is ordered. When the ship begins to move, the engine is reversed to back two-thirds. The rudder is kept right until the ship becomes dead in the water, at which time it is shifted to left full. Once the ship begins to move astern, the procedure is again reversed, and an ahead bell is ordered, but this time, as soon as the rotation of the screw

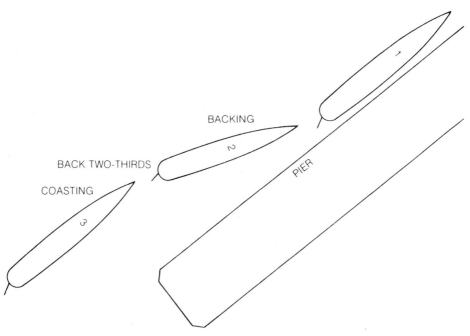

BACKING

BACK TWO-THIRDS

COASTING

PIER

FIGURE 7–7. Backing away from a starboard-side-to moor under no-wind conditions.

changes, the rudder is shifted back to right full. From this point on, the process is repeated as many times as are necessary to turn the ship to the desired heading.

To pivot on the anchor, the anchor is prepared and about fifty yards short of the intended turning point the anchor is let go, and a scope of chain 15 fathoms greater than the depth of water is payed out. For most bottom conditions this length of chain is necessary to get the 2,500-pound lightweight type (LWT) anchor to dig in. As soon as the chain picks up the strain, the rudder is put over left full and the speed of the engine is increased slowly. Depending on the type of bottom, 35 rpm is usually sufficient to pivot the ship without causing the anchor to drag excessively. The result will be a tight circle to the left of 150 to 200 yards in diameter.

Landings

As a general rule for both port and starboard landings, the final approach should be planned so that the ship stops parallel to and 30 to 40 feet outboard of the assigned berth. The last few feet are taken care of by pulling on lines 1 and 6, adjusting as necessary to keep the dome away from the pier as the bow comes in.

A port-side-to landing under conditions where there is no set from wind or current is a relatively simple maneuver (Figure 7–9). The ship makes the approach at an angle of 10 degrees with the pier and a speed of 2 to 3 knots. As the headway is killed by backing, the stern will slide in alongside the pier.

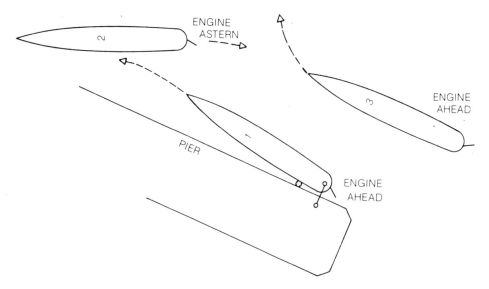

FIGURE 7–8. Leaving a port-side-to moor.

The speed of the approach has a lot to do with the final heading of the ship. The faster the approach, the more backing power will be needed to kill the headway, and the greater will be the swing of the stern to port. To counteract this, the angle of approach should be increased or decreased an appropriate amount whenever the speed of the approach is changed.

If the ship is being set off the pier, an approach for a port-side-to landing should be made at a speed of about 5 knots from an angle of 15 degrees. In this instance, smart line handling fore and aft is important. If the stern is blown away too far before the after lines can be made fast, we must back clear and approach again.

Starboard-side-to landings are more of a shiphandling problem. The movement of the stern when backing hinders rather than helps the conning officer. Under no-wind/ current conditions, an unassisted maneuver is possible with a flat approach at bare steerageway (Figure 7–10). In a calm, the ocean escort will answer her rudder at speeds down to approximately one knot. At this speed, the approach course should parallel the heading of the pier as closely as the location of ships astern of the berth will allow. Just prior to reaching a position abeam of the assigned berth, the rudder should be put over left full and a momentary backing bell ordered to stop the headway. Lines 1 and 6 can be used to haul the ship in against the pier.

Unassisted starboard-side-to landings with wind and current tending to set the ship off the pier are the most difficult of all. A faster approach must be made. Timing must be perfect, for little or no room is left for error. The conning officer may want to give some thought to dropping the port anchor underfoot to help deceleration and control of the bow. He may also want to use a line-throwing gun to get lines 1 and 6 over.

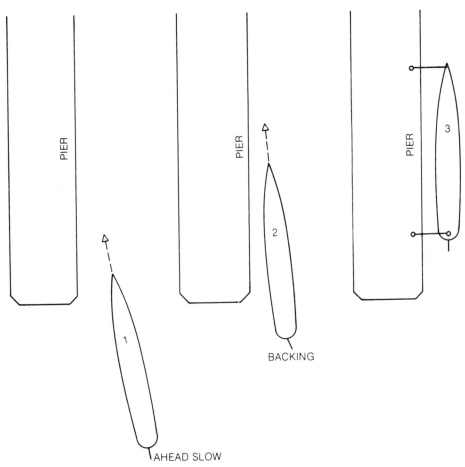

FIGURE 7-9. A port-side-to landing with no set from wind or current.

When the wind and/or current is setting the ship down against the pier, an anchor or a tug should be used to stabilize the bow. Without such assistance, especially starboard-side-to, the bow may blow down and our precious sonar dome be the first point to contact the pilings. With a single screw we have little control of the stern when nearly dead in the water and no control of the bow.

Anchoring and mooring

When the single-screw, large sonar escort is backed to a stop while anchoring or picking up a buoy, at the last minute her stern moves to port and her bow moves to starboard. If the backing is continued to permit dropping the anchor while moving astern, the stern will continue to port, and chain will be laid out at an angle some 20 to 30 degrees from the approach course. The tendency of the ship to swing her stern to port and her bow to starboard when backed to a stop can be played to the advantage of the shiphandler.

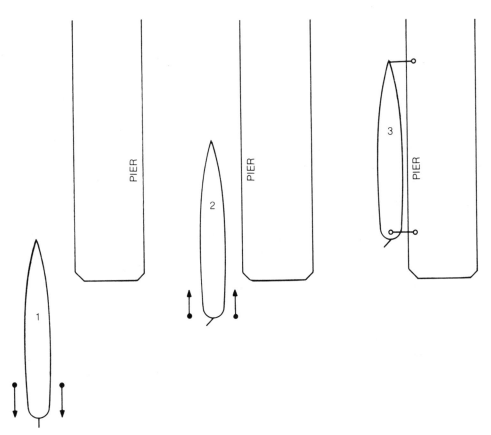

FIGURE 7–10. Starboard-side-to landing with no set from wind and current.

In the normal, uncomplicated approach to an anchorage or to a buoy, the ship should be headed towards a point about 10 to 20 yards to the left of the desired final position of the bow. By the time the ship is backed to a stop from about 5 knots, the bow will have swung about that distance to the right of her original course. If the wind is blowing from either side, the heading should be shifted an appropriate amount to windward to compensate for the "dead-time" in the evolution. These large escorts all have high, flared bows which blow downwind rather rapidly. We should remember that after we have killed the escort's headway and are working the anchor or buoy, we can move her bow to starboard to counteract wind or current to a limited extent, but we can't move it to port at all.

The Employment of Tugs

Ninety percent of the real meaning of good seamanship is the exercise of good judgment. In an ocean escort, when a chance of damaging the ship or her sonar dome exists, the decision not to attempt an unassisted maneuver is good judgment. Good seamanship requires the use of a tug as necessary in order to assist in the successful completion of the maneuver.

There is nothing tricky or particularly difficult about handling tugs. It is a matter of the conning officer being aware of all of the forces that he has available to him or that he must contend with and then using these forces in whatever combination is necessary to do the job.

If it is necessary to use a tug on the bow, the threat to the dome is the first thing that should be determined. It is possible to damage the sonar dome by hitting it with a tug's screw or rudder, but there is no reason for concern whenever Navy YTB or YTM tugs are used. The YTB 752 class comes the closest to the dome, but there is still sufficient clearance for safety. Assuming the dome is flooded and the ship is properly trimmed, Figure 7–11 shows the separation that will result. The nearest point of contact occurs with the tug's screw abeam of frame 8 of the escort. In this position, with the tug on an even keel snubbed in along the shear of the bow, approximately four feet of clearance remains between the dome and the tips of the blades. With this amount of clearance, there is no need to restrict the placement or employment of the tug in the vicinity of the bow.

Orders are given to the tug to get the desired direction and amount of force just as if the tug were a second shaft. Hand signals are the most convenient method of directing a tug, although commands may also be given by police whistle or voice radio. All commands, no matter how they are given, are acknowledged by an appropriate signal on the tug's whistle.

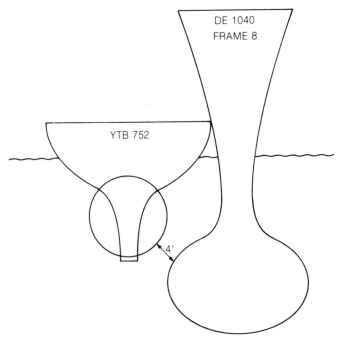

FIGURE 7–11. Clearance when employing a Navy YTB tug at the bow of an escort.

The *Dealey* Class

Escorts of the DE 1006 or *Dealey* Class differ from their larger sisters mainly because they are provided with twin rudders for their single screw instead of the conventional single rudder. Their two large rudders are mounted just to the sides of the propeller discharge race and are thus not in the propeller discharge current when the rudders are amidships. This probably results in less drag from the rudders and certainly resolves the problem of the inefficiencies of helical screw current impinging on the rudders, but it certainly results in a very excellent steering system. The response of the ship with her screw turning ahead is reported to be remarkable and when backing, the rudders are effective enough to overcome her natural tendency to back to port after the ship has moved about one ship-length astern, i.e., is moving astern at 5 knots or greater.

Summary

Single-screw ships are probably going to be seen even more frequently in the future than in the past. They present a special challenge to the shiphandler, but since he understands the particular characteristics of his ship he will probably feel as capable of meeting the requirements of fleet operations as any skipper in a twin-screw ship. If his ship has limitations, he will compensate for them in his planning, preparation, choice of berth, and alertness to outside forces. There is essentially no shortcoming of the single-screw ship (other than the lack of operational redundancy offered by the second screw) that couldn't be fully compensated for by a bow thruster of sufficient power.

8
handling at sea

When we leave the calm but congested environment of the harbor and head for the open sea, we must readjust our thinking. At the harbor entrance, as the ship's bow first rises to the swells of the open sea, we shift to an environment where 2,000 yards is a short distance and speeds up to 30 knots are the normal operating speeds. Our ability to estimate distance and to judge motion is greatly reduced as the familiar checkpoints of the harbor slip behind us. We must be ready to meet the extremes of weather and sea condition in a world where the environment can shift from a distant passing situation to an urgent collision situation in an extremely short time.

We clear the harbor and normally move into our place in a tactical formation. As we join the forming, reorienting, turning, wheeling, and all of the other intricate maneuvers of a complex formation, we begin to see the need for a system of maneuvers to apply to our individual ship.

Superheat

One of the most irritating problems which faces those handling the older classes of destroyers is the problem of superheat. In the newer classes with their 1,200 psi steam systems, the designers have gone back to the pre-World War II arrangement of boilers with integral superheaters that are always in use. In the *Forrest Sherman* and later classes, superheated steam is used for all purposes, so adequate steam flow is always assured and the conning officer need not be concerned about the superheat problem. In such a ship the conning officer can ring up maximum speed for the boilers on the line or he can ring up STOP without any great preparation or warning. For recovering an object in the water, the ship can approach at maximum speed, back to a stop, and then stop all engines and lie to with no hazard to the engineering plant. This is not so in the older classes, and close coordination must be maintained between the bridge and the engineers to prevent damage to the boilers.

From an operational point of view in the older destroyers then, we can consider that we have the choice of the following steaming conditions:

Boilers in Use	Speed Range with Saturated Steam	Speed Range with 850°F Superheat
1	0 to 17 knots	8 to 20 knots
2	0 to 22 knots	10 to 27 knots
4	0 to 29 knots	15 to 35 knots

Having selected one of these speed ranges, it takes time to shift to another. To increase the number of boilers in use, the temperature of the steam in the steaming boilers must be lowered to "saturated" to permit the new boilers to be cut in. In order to stop quickly from a high speed, we must steam with saturated steam and more boilers may be required than for the same speed using superheat.

Rather than ring up STOP with superheat on, it is better to "rock" the engines back and forth from AHEAD ONE-THIRD to BACK ONE-THIRD to maintain the flow. This can be done frequently enough so that no appreciable way will be gotten on the ship. If the engineers have been notified promptly, they can reduce the superheat and maintain the flow so the ship can be safely stopped after a few minutes.

To meet the normal operational requirements and also largely to remove the necessity of special orders concerning superheat in the older destroyers, the following system has been found useful:

1. The captain designates how many boilers shall be in use and whether they shall be steamed with or without superheat.
2. If "with superheat," and the speed is sufficient, the boilers are brought up to 700°F without further orders. (Saturated temperature is 600°F.)
3. If the ordered speed requires it, the superheat is raised without order; but as soon as the requirement is removed, the superheat is again lowered to 700°F.
4. If the speed is lowered too low to maintain the necessary flow, superheat will be reduced or cut out as necessary without order; but when the speed is raised again, superheaters will be lighted and the superheat raised to 700°F without further order.
5. Should the conning officer be required to stop without sufficient notice, he will "rock" the engines instead of ringing up STOP, until the engineroom reports that the superheat has been lowered to saturated.

The above procedures offer a satisfactory system which will meet the normal operational requirements of a destroyer. The moderate superheat can be quickly lowered with little chance of damage to the boilers, yet the superheaters are lighted and the ship has the ability of building up to the maximum speed for the boilers in use without having to slow even momentarily.

The destroyer's role

In a destroyer we are always required to perform the most difficult maneuvers. When the large ships change course by a simple turn, we must reorient through the entire arc of the turn. If the turn is large, we must countermarch or split the screen and reorient. When the course is fully set, the signal flags flutter again and we are shifted from a circular to a bent line screen, but as soon as an air attack threatens we are called back. These formation maneuvers are laced with a liberal dose of plane guarding, mail passing, fueling at sea, and general messenger work. A destroyer spends a large part of each day and night skirting around the edges or knifing through the center of the formation, and she must do it smartly and precisely or the most serious consequences can occur.

Because of the power and maneuverability of the destroyer (and the normal courtesy to seniors), it has become accepted that the destroyer will keep out of the way of heavy ships. Although the rules of the road apply in a naval formation as well as upon the high seas, the destroyer conning officer is considered to have blundered if he allows his ship to get into a position where a heavy ship is forced to maneuver to avoid him.

This subordinate position of the destroyer occasionally leads to awkward situations with heavy ships. At times, destroyers have literally to flee for their lives because an officer of the deck on a large ship has too liberally evaluated the destroyer's ability to keep out of the way. Nevertheless, it has always been a point of pride among destroyer officers that they could always accord the heavy ships the privilege of right of way and still maneuver with them effectively.

Maneuvering through a formation

The trick of maneuvering through a formation is to handle the ship so that not only will we pass clear of the other ships in the formation, but also we will convince the OODs of these ships that we are doing so. This requires that we make our intentions clear to everyone at the earliest possible moment. In a crossing situation, a course which points our ship 30° ahead of the other ship's beam may actually be sufficient to carry us astern of him, but if we alter course sufficiently so that we are actually *pointing* astern of him, the conning officer of the other ship knows at a glance that we will clear him. So we should make it a rule to change course boldly enough so that our intention is clear from the first moment.

In keeping clear of other ships, the question naturally arises, "How much is *clear*?" Certainly if a collision does not occur, the ship has cleared. On the other hand the record of a carrier skipper's blood pressure while a destroyer cuts under his bow might be a better measure of the "closeness." Actually it is well to draw an imaginary "keep out" boundary 2,000 yards ahead, 1,000 yards abeam, and 500 yards astern of each heavy ship, as shown in Figure 8–1, and stay well outside of it. If we are approaching on an opposite course, we should push the forward boundary out further ahead, or if we are on a parallel course, we can shave the boundaries a little. These arbitrary boundaries have proved very satisfactory in practice, and if we stay clear of this "keep out" area there will be no cause for criticism of our actions.

A very useful rule for safe maneuvering when close to another vessel and heading towards her is to keep our bow on the same side of the line-of-sight

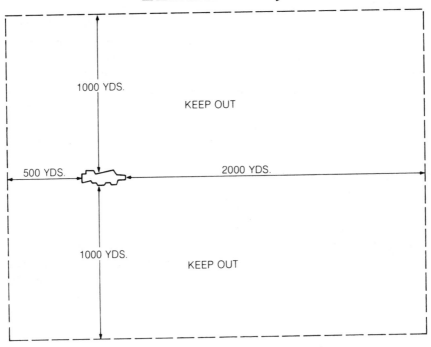

FIGURE 8–1. The "keep out" area around a large ship.

between us as the other ship's stern, as illustrated in Figure 8–2. This will insure that we will pass astern of her, if she continues her present course. If she unexpectedly turns toward us, it also allows us to clear by turning in the direction we had originally offset our bow from the line-of-sight. In this case we have a head start in the turn, and, by holding our turn, can insure that a collision will not occur.

Another cardinal rule for safe maneuvering is, "Always turn *away.*" This rule means to keep our bow pointed out from the formation toward clear water as much as possible during a maneuver, and under no circumstances to get caught on the *inside* of a turn. When beginning a maneuver calling for an initial radical turn, we should make the turn to the side *away* from the formation. If we are on the wing of a bent line screen, this may require a turn of nearly 270° to come to the first course, as shown in Figure 8–2, but it will pay dividends in undamaged nerves. If the maneuver requires a terminal radical turn, we should make it outboard also. When approaching from ahead, if this would require passing too close to some other ship, we should first pass at a safe distance from the other ship, then turn outboard to come up abreast of the station, and finally ease in to the correct station on a course nearly parallel to that of the formation.

The beauty of the turn away is not always immediately apparent to the

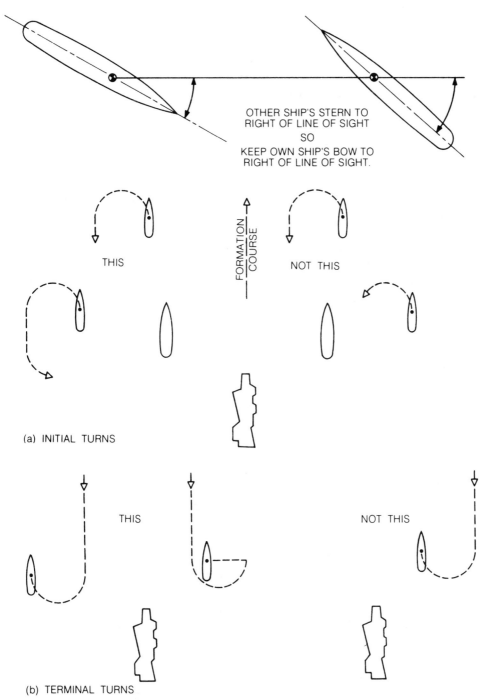

OTHER SHIP'S STERN TO
RIGHT OF LINE OF SIGHT
SO
KEEP OWN SHIP'S BOW TO
RIGHT OF LINE OF SIGHT.

FORMATION COURSE

THIS   NOT THIS

(a) INITIAL TURNS

THIS   NOT THIS

(b) TERMINAL TURNS

FIGURE 8–2. Principles of safe maneuvering.

uninitiated. However, it is only necessary to sweat out one shuddering turn with one's mind undecided between BACK EMERGENCY or AHEAD FLANK (because we miscalculated the situation) to make one appreciate this rule.

Destroyers are expected to maneuver smartly at all times. In many cases they must commence their maneuver the moment the signal is understood, and under any circumstances they are expected to "get up and go" the minute the signal is executed. FLANK SPEED should be used unless another maneuvering speed has been specified, and the largest practical rudder angle—up to 30°—should be used for all turns unless executing a precision turn with the formation. Using plenty of rudder for the initial turn may put us on our new station minutes earlier than if we execute a slow turn, but if our ship is already making 20 knots or more when the signal is executed, we should use a bit less rudder to avoid throwing men and equipment—not to mention the captain's breakfast—against the nearest bulkhead.

The exactness of station-keeping is a good measure of the smartness of the ship (Figure 8–3). It is a good rule to define "on station" as being within 100 yards of the assigned station. The OOD should initiate corrective action at any time the ship exceeds this limit. On some ships, basic station tolerances are defined as a definite range tolerance and a certain bearing tolerance. This is not a very good system, because it requires different excellence in station-keeping at different ranges. Modern equipment allows very accurate measurement, and it is relatively simple to convert a distance tolerance to bearing limits when on station.

To produce really good station-keeping on a given station, the relationship between range and bearing and own ship's course and speed should be known. The fore-and-aft and athwartship components of incremental changes of course and speed should be determined. For instance, if the formation speed is 18 knots (600 yards per minute), a 5° course change will give a 50 yard per minute athwartship component of motion, whereas it will take a 15 rpm change in speed to produce the equivalent fore-and-aft component. Thus, if our station is 45° on the bow of the guide and we wish to decrease the range while keeping the bearing constant, we can accomplish this by dropping our speed 15 turns and changing our course 5° toward the guide as shown in Figure 8–4(a).

If we are 70° on the bow of the guide and wish to decrease his bearing while keeping the range constant, we can solve our problem by visualizing a 70-20 right triangle. By the Radian rule, the leg opposite the 20° angle is one-third the length of the leg adjacent to this angle, so we see that we must keep our athwartships component one-third of the fore-and-aft component if we are to change the only bearing. As Figure 8–4(b) shows, an increase in speed of 45 turns while steering *in* 5° will do the trick.

If the conning officer will analyze each correction he makes in order to know exactly what motion to expect, he will soon acquire the habit of exact station keeping. He will be able to adjust more rapidly in a new station and quickly calibrate the performance of the guide. As soon as the mystery of relative motion has disappeared, he will be able to accurately forecast the effect of incremental changes of course and speed.

The reputation of a ship in a formation is rapidly acquired and is hard to

FIGURE 8–3. Exact station-keeping is a good measure of the smartness of the ship.

change, once acquired. There are good ships and bad ships. The good ships are dependable and predictable; the bad ones must be kept under surveillance to avoid a catastrophe. It is not necessarily a measure of the captain's shiphandling ability, but rather a measure of the reputation of the whole regime of the skipper and his OODs. If a ship can be depended upon to "get up and go" when the signal hits the air, if she is maneuvered with decision and prudence at any hour of the day or night, and if she can take her station rapidly and maintain it with accuracy, the ship will always be marked as a *smart* destroyer.

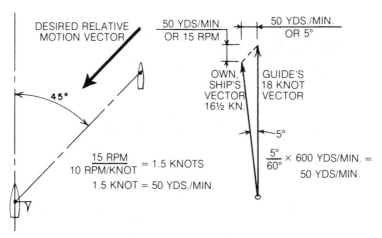

DESIRED RELATIVE MOTION VECTOR

50 YDS/MIN. OR 15 RPM

50 YDS./MIN. OR 5°

45°

OWN, SHIP'S VECTOR 16½ KN.

GUIDE'S 18 KNOT VECTOR

5°

$$\frac{15 \text{ RPM}}{10 \text{ RPM/KNOT}} = 1.5 \text{ KNOTS}$$

1.5 KNOT = 50 YDS./MIN.

$$\frac{5°}{60°} \times 600 \text{ YDS/MIN.} = 50 \text{ YDS/MIN.}$$

(a.) STATION KEEPING BROAD ON THE BOW. DECREASING THE RANGE WHILE KEEPING THE BEARING STEADY.

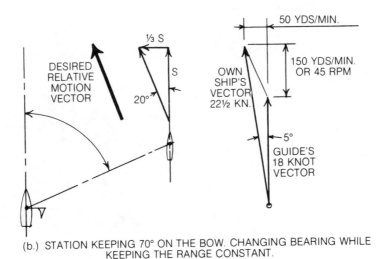

DESIRED RELATIVE MOTION VECTOR

⅓ S

S

20°

50 YDS/MIN.

OWN SHIP'S VECTOR 22½ KN.

150 YDS/MIN. OR 45 RPM

5°

GUIDE'S 18 KNOT VECTOR

(b.) STATION KEEPING 70° ON THE BOW. CHANGING BEARING WHILE KEEPING THE RANGE CONSTANT.

FIGURE 8–4. Keeping station by approximating the relative motion.

Heavy weather

The above discussion has dealt with operating at sea in company with other ships, and with maneuvering in formations. Though the complex evolutions of modern naval formations pose difficult problems, the sea itself presents the gravest and most trying test of the shiphandler's ability. The annals of the sea are full of moving tales of the seaman's fight against the elements as he dares the mighty ocean in his relatively frail craft. As the wind changes the sea from a pleasant calm to a refreshing swell, to a troublesome chop, to a pounding sea, and finally to the brutal crushing fury of a full gale, the shiphandler's attention shifts from the niceties of perfect maneuvers to the problem of simple survival. There is no more awe-inspiring sight than to see a tremendous wave towering above our bridge, combing and curling as it crashes toward us (Figure 8–5). There is no greater moment of incredulous relief than the moment we perceive that the ship is being borne up and over the menacing mountain of water instead of being buried beneath its immensity. If we are to be able to cope with the sea in its ugliest moods, we must study the mechanism of waves and see how they act upon the ship.

The formation of waves

We will not investigate the causes and peculiarities of the different types of storms because the meteorological aspects are adequately covered in the literature on weather. Rather than probing into the reasons why the storm came into being, we will consider *what to do about it* once it is upon us. We will look into the character of the wind and the waves and find out how to handle the ship safely in spite of them.

When the wind blows, the friction of the air against the surface of the water tends to drag the water along with it. When the air stream begins to play upon the surface of the water, it accelerates the particles on the surface; but as these

FIGURE 8–5. The sea itself presents the greatest challenge to the shiphandler's abilities.

particles of water begin to move, they "pile up" in certain areas ahead because the particles in these areas have not been accelerated as much. The individual particles soon find their motion opposed by a "piled up" mass of water, and the motion of the individual particle is reversed as the gravitational result of the piling-up overcomes the wind action. Then, after the initial pile of water particles has moved on, the motion of the individual particle is reversed a second time by the front slope of the following pile. The piles of water particles, or waves, formed by the action of the wind move along quite rapidly across the surface of the water. The movement of the individual particles in the pile is oscillatory due to the action of gravity as they are alternately on the front slope and the back slope of the wave. There is also the unidirectional average movement called the surface current, resulting from the drag of the wind. In a typical situation the wind might be blowing at 30 knots, the waves moving in the direction of the wind at 20 knots, the individual particles of water on the surface surging forward and backwards a total of 5 feet, and an average surface current due to the wind of 2 knots.

Normally, the stronger the wind, the higher the waves will be. The higher the waves, the faster they will move, because the particles on the leading face are carried higher and will reach a higher velocity as a result of the greater distance to accelerate. Also, the higher the waves, the greater will be the distance between crests. Thus, as the wind increases we can expect the waves to grow larger, to move faster, and to have a greater distance between crest and crest.

It takes an appreciable time for a wave system to be set up, and, because of the movement of the waves, it also takes a considerable distance. The highest waves for a given wind velocity are found where the wind has been blowing steadily for days across hundreds of miles of deep, unobstructed sea. Under these circumstances a 40-knot wind might produce waves averaging 20 feet in height from trough to crest, and 30-foot waves would be encountered frequently. Under more severe conditions much higher waves are occasionally encountered, but it is quite difficult to judge the height of waves from a ship because of the severe plunging and rolling encountered in such seas. For a complete discussion of the formation and character of waves, refer to Hydrographic Office Publication No. 602—*Wind, Waves at Sea: Breakers and Surf*, by H. B. Bigelow and W. T. Edmonson.

Handling the ship in rough seas

We can thus consider that in rough weather the surface of the water is a series of troughs and crests moving along at some mean velocity, but that except for a small surface current, the surface of the water is not moving along with the wind. The force that a moving fluid can exert at a given velocity is proportional to its density, and since water is so much denser than air, the combined effect of the wind and the waves on the ship is almost solely that due to the waves. The wind becomes an important effect in the survival of the ship only at hurricane velocities where the wind is so strong that it can cause a ship to carry a large list to leeward.

Each type of ship reacts differently to the action of the waves. According to its mass distribution and righting characteristics, each ship has a natural frequency in roll and pitch. This is the frequency at which the ship would tend to roll in calm water if she were listed slightly to one side and then released. A ship will tend to roll at this frequency under all conditions of wave motion, and the most severe rolling will occur when the frequency of the wave motion approximates the natural frequency of the ship. Actually, this frequency is usually measured by its period (the time required to go from even keel to extreme right, to extreme left, and back to even keel), and a ship's natural period of roll is a matter of interest to the shiphandler. The normal period of roll for a destroyer is about 9 seconds.

The greater the righting moment for a given inclination (the moment tending to return the ship to an even keel when inclined), the shorter will be the period of roll. If a ship is losing its righting moment due to the free surface effect or a change in its mass distribution due to flooding, its period of roll will increase. If a ship's period of roll increases, it is losing its stability.

The first action of the ship which should be examined is simple rolling. When heading into or running with a sea, destroyers frequently roll 20° to a side. This is considerably increased when heading diagonally across the seas, and the maximum rolling normally occurs when the sea is on the beam or the ship is "in the trough" of the waves. If the period of the waves approximates the natural period of the ship, a resonant condition exists and the ship will roll severely with deep, steady rolls. The list caused by a turn at high speed, coupled with the normal wave motion, can produce an augmented roll which can be quite large. There are few destroyers which have not experienced a roll of 40° to 50° at some time during their service.

Obviously, rolling of the magnitude mentioned above is of concern to the conning officer of the ship. If the ship were to take a single roll of 30° unexpectedly during a meal, great damage could easily be done in broken crockery and glassware alone. The damage to spare parts and stores mounts with each roll unless such gear has been stowed perfectly. The damage to office machines, furniture, instruments, etc., is always great during severe rolling as these objects get away from the grip of the user. When a ship rolls deeply, she dips her side under the water, and a destroyer will occasionally submerge her lifeboat at the davit head. Such rolling is not only uncomfortable and fatiguing to the crew, but it is dangerous to life and limb, and it is almost always accompanied by material damage to the ship and her equipment. The good shiphandler is always alert to minimize the ship's roll, and he makes sure to warn all hands ahead of time to make preparations for rolling when it cannot be avoided.

Usually the best way to minimize the roll is to run with the sea at a few knots faster or slower than the waves. This means we will have a low, but steady, relative motion with respect to the waves, and thus will avoid the unsteady motion experienced when going at about the same speed as the waves. When traveling about the wave speed, we are alternately accelerated by the front slope of the wave and retarded by the rear slope. Since the water at the crest of a wave is momentarily traveling at about the velocity of the wave, we will have less rudder effectiveness due to the low relative velocity at the rudder when our stern is on the crest. This, combined with the tendency to "skid" as we hang on the crest of the wave, makes it desirable to go at a speed different from that of the waves.

Heading directly into the waves also minimizes the roll, but this usually makes the pitch a maximum. This is not quite as good a solution as running before the sea, because the general action of the waves on the ship is more violent. The momentum of the waves is opposed to the motion of the ship in this case.

The more the sea is brought to the beam, the more the ship will roll. The athwartships inclination of the surface of the water is greatest in this orientation, so the amplitude of the force which is initiating the roll is at a maximum. The period of the initiating force is also important, and if the period of the waves is nearly the natural period of the ship, maximum rolling will be experienced. On the other hand, if the period of the waves is much longer than the natural period of the ship, the ship may ride quite comfortably parallel to the trough as she rides up and over the waves with little inclination.

The most severe pitching is experienced when headed directly into the seas. In this case the bow is carried up by the oncoming wave, and then the ship plunges into the trough as the wave passes. The resonant period of the ship in pitch is often matched by the waves, and, from the point of view of possible damage, pitching is equally as important as roll. When a ship buries her bow under tons of water while bucking into a rough sea, there is a tremendous stress on her hull.

In rough weather, severe damage can be done to our ship by the action of the waves. In addition to damage simply from the violent motion of the ship, deck equipment can be bent and torn loose by the impact of the water as the waves sweep over the deck. Plates are sprung and warped, and whenever a leak occurs, water damage follows. The more our ship is punished by the seas, the less efficient she is. The crew, though veterans of the stormiest weather, become fatigued by the struggle to exist, because they must continually hold on to keep from being thrown from their feet and hence can get no real relaxation, day or night.

Obviously, we must learn to operate in rough weather or our ship will be useless in a storm. On the other hand, the ship will be of no service to anyone if she is lost because her crew did not take sufficient precaution. How rough can the weather be without severely damaging our ship? Where is the point at which we must cease thinking of the operations and take steps to protect the ship from the storm? These are important questions that must always be borne in mind.

These are certainly matters of degree, and the point of decision must change with the operation. The risk taken must be justified by the importance of the mission. It is imperative, however, that the shiphandler know when his ship is in danger, and it is vital that he know what to do about it.

Simple rolling up to 30° to the side is acceptable as one of the normal problems found at sea. As long as the gear which has been stowed in the proper manner in the proper place is still secure, we must recognize that any damage caused by loose gear is caused by improper securing. On the other hand, when gear is breaking loose from its regular stowage, when lifeboats are dipping, and when the decks are being swept by combers, it is time to search for means of reducing the effect of the weather. Heading into the sea or away from it will normally reduce the roll to an acceptable level, and changing speed will often alter the rolling by changing the frequency with which we are cutting the waves.

Destroyers can be driven into the seas until their keels come clear of the water all the way back to the bridge, and they can disappear in their own spray as they bury themselves into the waves. They can do this occasionally with little apparent damage, but abuse such as this will eventually cause extensive damage in buckled bulkheads, lost deck gear, cracked plates, etc. Any weakness on the forecastle will be searched out as the waves cave in the gun mount, rip off the fire plugs, and sweep away the hose and line reels.

There are two good indications when the ship is being driven into the sea too severely. The first is the pounding experienced when the bow comes clear of the water and crashes into the next wave. This produces a shock that can be felt throughout the ship and is an indication of the severity of the force of the waves. The second effect is a vertical vibration of low frequency which is set up as the whole ship bends longitudinally under the weight of water picked up by the forecastle as the ship plows under the waves. Unless there is an overbearing operational need to do otherwise, the course and speed should be set so that neither this pounding nor vibration is encountered.

In selecting the course and speed for the easiest riding, it is usually necessary to try a few experiments before a completely satisfactory combination is found. Generally, downwind courses are much more comfortable courses than those into the wind. Avoid courses near the trough, unless the seas are long and steady. If pitching is the problem, try courses inclined to the direction of the seas; this will make the wave fronts appear less abrupt. In most cases, when heading into the seas, the ship will ride better at a low speed. A difference of only two knots may be the difference between severe pounding and acceptable pitching.

Survival in mountainous seas

We have discussed means of making the ship ride more easily in a rough sea, and we have discussed how to avoid the relatively minor damage caused by rolling and pitching. However, when the ocean goes wild during a hurricane, these relatively minor factors are set aside and we are faced with stark survival. A full gale in the North Atlantic or a typhoon in the South China Sea can toss the mightiest ship about as though she were a toy boat. The waves lose their normal form as their tops are sliced off by the howling wind, and the air is a mixture of rain and spray. Visibility drops with the barometer. The waves dwarf a destroyer, and they seem intent on the destruction of everything living.

If we are to survive these extreme storms, we must have the principles of heavy-weather shiphandling foremost in our minds. If we lose electrical or propulsive power, we lose our ability to control the ship and then we are at the mercy of the seas. A ship without her engines and rudder will soon broach and expose her vulnerable sides to the onslaught of the waves. The seas will find her weaknesses as they cascade over her helpless form, and she will soon begin to take on water. Finally, with her stability reduced by the free surface of the water in her hull, she will succumb to a mighty wave, will capsize, and be lost to the storm. Sea anchors and oil bags still have their place in modern seamanship under specialized circumstances, but by the time it is apparent that the ship is *in extremis*, the weather is usually much too severe for men to work on the decks streaming gear of any kind.

The guiding principles of survival in a severe storm are: *maintain power, maintain buoyancy,* and *maintain stability.*

To preserve these vital properties we must make certain of the watertight integrity of the ship. At the first sign of a severe storm the ship should be secured for heavy weather. All topside gear should be secured with extra lashings, inboard lifelines should be rigged, and all watertight hatches should be battened down and checked. The most common cause of loss of power is the "grounding" of the main switchboards when salt water gets to them. We must make sure that all hatches or ventilation ducts in the vicinity of the generators or switchboards are firmly secured.

The buoyancy and stability of the ship go hand in hand. To keep the center-of-gravity down, the ship should be properly ballasted. Free surface should be avoided wherever possible, and all tanks should be either completely full or completely empty. All compartments which should be dry must be kept that way. Bilges should be pumped, and if water leaks into any normally dry compartment, it should be pumped out immediately. If we are properly ballasted, if we have kept the free surface to a minimum, and if we have maintained our buoyancy, we should come through any storm with flying colors.

The trick of controlling the ship in a typhoon is to keep out of the trough. As indicated in Figure 8–6, if the ship is proceeding at an angle to the seas, there is a tendency to force her to align herself parallel to the trough as she crosses the wave fronts. When she goes up the forward face of a wave, gravity tends to force her bow down into the trough. As she goes down the trailing face of the wave, gravity again tries to twist her into the trough by skidding her stern down the face of the wave.

If our ship gets caught in the trough, the waves will crash into her broadside and she will roll wildly. Once in the trough, it is very difficult to get out, because any control we can exert on the ship is overwhelmed by the action of the waves. The side forces available from the engines and rudder are small compared to the force of the sea. Our best chance lies in going ahead at maximum speed to insure maximum rudder force and in seizing any opportunity to turn out of the trough. In most cases it is advisable to turn *downwind,* because this allows us the greatest interval before being struck by the next succeeding wave.

Once we are heading nearly parallel to the wind and seas, it is possible to maintain our heading if the helm is handled skillfully. The choice whether to head into or away from the wind is an important one. Our ship is built to take the most severe waves from ahead. The bow is shaped for it, and, generally speaking, the

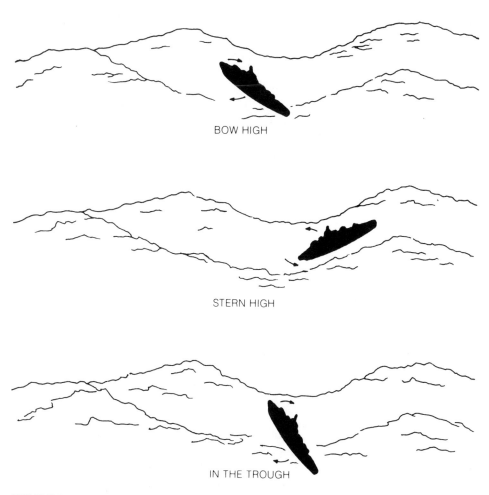

BOW HIGH

STERN HIGH

IN THE TROUGH

FIGURE 8–6. In heavy seas the ship always seeks the trough.

rest of the forward structure is designed to take heavy seas. On the other hand, if we head into the wind, we add our own velocity to that of the sea, and the resulting impact is greater. We must maintain an adequate speed ahead to insure that we can steer or else we will lose control of our heading and broach, so we cannot slow below a certain minimum.

If we head downwind, on the other hand, we reduce the relative velocity of the waves by the amount of our speed, but we are exposing our stern to the wave fronts and it is neither shaped nor reinforced to resist the direct action of the waves. However, if we can maintain a speed so that the relative velocity of the waves is low, the stern will be able to stand up under the reduced action of the waves. As long as the waves do not crash down upon our fantail and "poop" our ship, running before the wind is the most gentle method of riding out a severe storm.

The choice of whether to head into the seas or to run with them will also depend upon the location of the center of the storm. In a cyclonic storm the wind blows nearly toward the center of the storm except in the vicinity of the "eye," where it blows tangentially, and our selection of the direction in which to ride out the storm must be modified by our desire to get out of the storm as soon as possible. A less advantageous inclination to the seas can be accepted if it will carry us out of the path of the storm and away from the most intense portion.

As in most phases of shiphandling, safety in a severe storm depends upon forehandedness. The ship that is properly ballasted and carefully secured for the storm will have a minimum of trouble riding out the most severe storm. The skipper who has studied his ship and is alert to the signs of the sea will be able to handle his craft in spite of the weather. A sound ship handled on sound principles of shiphandling can weather any storm. The shiphandling skill of the officer at the conn is the keystone to safety at sea.

The do-nothing theory

It was stated in an article, "Typhoon Doctrine—All Engines Stopped," by E. W. Malanot, *U. S. Naval Institute* PROCEEDINGS, July 1955, that the best way to ride out a typhoon is to stop all engines and let nature take its course. This radically unusual approach has been used with proven success in the case of ships of the merchant type, and it is suggested that it might be utilized by all classes of ships when facing the fury of a typhoon. There has been sufficient discussion in naval circles of this method of riding out a hurricane to warrant a careful evaluation of its merits.

Actually the central thesis of the proposal is this: "at the center of a hurricane or typhoon the seas come from any and all directions and under such confused conditions the best thing to do is to stop the engines and let the ship drift with the forces." Certainly any action we might take with the engines and rudders should be aimed at minimizing the action of the seas or the wind. Obviously such action should be planned to counter a certain direction of the wind and sea, but if there is no fixed direction of the wind and seas, how can one logically select a course and speed? At the center of the storm, therefore, where the seas are confused and the wind has died down or is variable, the recommendation to stop the engines and let the ship drift seems completely sound.

The extension of the proposal, however, calls for stopping the engines and letting the ship drift throughout the duration of the storm. The theory seems to be that if the ship can ride through the "eye" of the storm (which is the worst part), in this manner, she can ride out the whole storm with her engines stopped. This was actually demonstrated on several occasions by merchant type ships.

This last is a dangerous suggestion. What may be safe in a large bluff merchant hull with high freeboard and great metacentric height, might be the greatest folly in a low, sleek destroyer. Destroyers, especially the newer ones with their deckhouses extending nearly to the sides, are very vulnerable to beam seas, and the prudent conning officer will do well to do all within his power to avoid taking hurricane seas on the beam. Of the four modern destroyers that were lost in such storms in World War II, all available information indicates that the ships got into the trough of the seas and were unable to extricate themselves. The severe rolling and force of the waves on their sides caused material failures, and in a very short time the ships were capsized by the action of the wind and the waves. Though lack of proper ballasting and other factors played their parts, the fact remains that once in the trough, though the ships had taken relatively little water aboard, the wind and seas literally bowled them over.

No, the do-nothing theory is not advisable for a destroyer and should be attempted with caution in any type ship. At the center of the storm (or at any other time when a situation is confused and there is no logical basis for selecting a course and speed) it is reasonable to stop the engines and wait for the situation to change. But under the normal conditions outside of the "eye," where the direction of the wind and the seas is all too definite, the shiphandler should use his engines and rudders to keep his ship oriented so that the impact of the forces of the storm is minimized. This ordinarily calls for the conning officer to head his ship into the approaching seas and to hold her there with whatever power is required. A hurricane is the most savage of storms and one should not risk the damage of being "pooped" by a hurricane sea. The ship is constructed to withstand more safely the force of the waves from ahead, so the ship should be conned to keep her bow into the seas, but with as little headway as possible, since the energy of such forward motion would just be added to that of the onrushing waves.

Practicing for heavy weather

It is one thing to pass the word, "Secure ship for heavy weather," and another to actually have it done effectively. A wise skipper will have a thorough inspection made each time the ship is prepared for a storm. Hatches, lifelines, storerooms, and engineering spaces should get special attention. The more effort spent in preparing for heavy weather, the less damage can be caused by the storm.

As the opportunity permits during bad but not dangerous weather, experiments should be made to determine the best courses and speeds for the ship during very rough weather. The average and extreme rolls of the ship during similar periods on courses into and with the seas should be compared and any tendency to pitch severely or to pound should be noted. The skipper and the crew should prove to themselves the capabilities and limitations of their ship so when they are actually faced with a hurricane they can have confidence in their ability to cope with it. Having determined the storm characteristics of his ship by experiment, the skipper should firmly decide the best method of handling his particular ship in a hurricane and make sure that all conning officers are acquainted with his decision.

9
special maneuvers at sea

Although the most satisfying shiphandling is usually done in restricted waters where the ship must be positioned with precision in the vicinity of a number of obstacles, there are many very demanding and delicate evolutions required at sea. The more the fleet becomes self-sustaining at sea, the more often ships are required to go alongside one another (Figure 9–1). Fueling and provisioning at sea have long been commonplace on extended cruises, and today deployed fleets are entirely dependent upon transfer at sea.

Replenishment at sea

Replenishing of fuel, stores and communication at sea is an evolution frequently performed, and at times conducted even under adverse weather conditions (Figure 9–2), though potentially dangerous since the ships must steam very close to one another for a long time and a steering casualty, a momentary engine breakdown, or a misunderstood order could cause a collision. The techniques are so well developed that accidents are very infrequent.

When approaching alongside another vessel, it is best to control the ship's heading by giving the "course to steer" to the helmsman. Select the best helmsman on board, and limit his task to keeping the ship's head on the course ordered. It is generally unsatisfactory to try to give rudder angles to the helmsman while maneuvering alongside, because not only would that be attempting to do the helmsman's job for him, but, depending upon the fore-and-aft position with respect to the other ship, as much as 15° right or left rudder may be required just to keep the ship's head steady.

When commencing an approach to go alongside it is desirable to start from between 500 and 1,000 yards astern, and, if the situation allows, to take a few minutes to check the other ship's course and speed. Usually we will find it necessary to steer a few degrees from the signalled course, and to steam at perhaps

155

FIGURE 9-1. USS *Enterprise* (CVAN 65) and USS *Shasta* (AE 33) take replenishment stations.

five turns from the signalled speed. These are not large differences, but knowing exactly what the other ship is doing allows us to make a more accurate approach.

Our intention is to arrive abreast the supply ship on a parallel course at exactly her speed at a convenient but safe distance from her side, and to do so in a minimum of time. A practical way to arrive abreast at the desired distance is to make the approach parallel to the other ship's wake at the desired distance to the proper side and have the opportunity to check the accuracy of the chosen course continually during the approach. This parallel approach from astern is not absolutely necessary and a safe approach can be made by a skilled shiphandler with little or no parallel run, but if the operations permit the luxury, it is convenient to make the last 500 to 1,000 yards of the approach on a steady course parallel to that of the supply ship.

What is the desired distance between ships when we complete the approach? Some shiphandlers consider it daring to approach very close to the supply ship to facilitate the passing of lines and rigs, and they like to stay "in close" to shorten the transfer time. Such daring may be satisfying to the ego, but it

FIGURE 9–2. USS *Massey* refueling from USS *Leyte* in heavy weather.

seldom actually has any beneficial effect on the time required for the evolution, and it is rather foolish to get close unnecessarily since the only *serious* mistake one can make when replenishing is to get so close to the supply ship that a collision results.

When all is ready, the conning officer, on the engaged wing of the bridge, increases speed and begins the approach (Figure 9–3), so as to put the side of his ship about 90 feet from the supply ship. From the engaged pelorus we sight along the course we have ordered to see where the engaged wing of the bridge is heading. When our ship is at the proper distance to the side, sighting along the same bearing as the other ship's course should intersect a spot in the water 90 feet from her side.

Another useful check when making the approach is to compare the wake with that of the supply ship. When in the correct position to the side during the approach, there should be about 5 yards of blue water between the white foam of the wakes of the two ships.

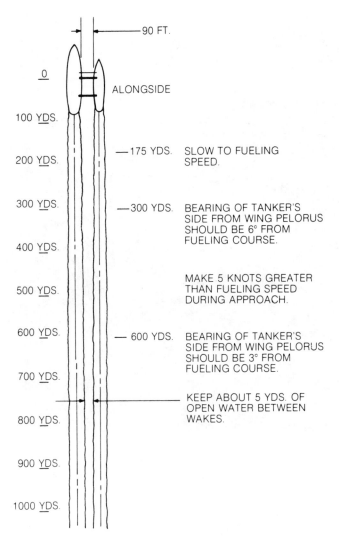

FIGURE 9–3. "Coast-in" approach for fueling.

As we approach, we commence using the Radian Rule. At 600 yards astern, the supply ship's side should bear 3° from the course if we are approaching correctly. At 300 yards, her side should bear 6° from the course. By checking the bearing continually, we can adjust our final distance from her side on the approach.

Using the "coast in" method, the engines should be slowed to replenishment speed when the ship reaches a point 175 yards astern of the abreast position (5 knots at 35 yards per knot surge). Using the "back down" method at 25 knots, the engines should be ordered BACK TWO-THIRDS when about 100 yards astern of the desired position and shifted to AHEAD TWO-THIRDS and to replenishment revolutions just before the ship has actually slowed to the speed of the supply ship. If one is *behind* position, shift the engines *ahead* while still a few knots above replenishment speed; if *ahead*, *back* to a few knots below replenishment speed before shifting the engines ahead.

Throughout the deceleration it is very useful to have someone in position to read the speed by pitometer log. As a result of the major speed change and possible corrections, it may be difficult to predict the actual speed through the water, but the "pit log" will give the true speed.

Once alongside, the combination phone and distance line will be quickly rigged and the conning officer can measure his distance from the supply ship with accuracy.

The best position to ride alongside is a matter of debate. Most publications on the subject speak of distances from 60 to 100 feet, but all agree that it may be necessary to adjust these distances. The basic thought that should be borne in mind is that danger of collision lies on the side *toward* the oiler, and only the embarrassment of parting the hoses lies away from the oiler. The riding position should be selected not only to provide the margin necessary for the anticipated conning errors, but also to take into account the possibility of a steering or engine casualty.

Using the span wire or other modern rigs, the receiving ship can sheer out to as much as 300 feet before parting the hoses, so there is no necessity to ride in too close. An average position between 100 and 120 feet has been found comfortable for a destroyer and there is plenty of margin outside of these limits for correction before damage to the rig or the ships becomes imminent. For a destroyer an initial position with 90 feet between ships for passing lines and a mean distance of 110 feet while replenishing has been found safe and efficient.

The more modern replenishment rigs are designed for greater separation, which is sometimes required by the difference in height between the supply and receiving points. When using the new refueling probes, separations of up to 160 feet have been found necessary to insure a good connection.

Many of the newer replenishment ships are equipped with constant tension highline rigs which exert a constant force of several tons, tending to pull the ships together. With several of these rigs connected, the conning officer of even a large ship may have to steer out by several degrees to counteract the tension. He should be especially alert to compensate for the force when the highlines are being tensioned or de-tensioned. Should he have trouble holding his ship out against the tension, he should request an increase in replenishment speed of several knots to increase the effect of his ship's inclination. The older rigs, such as a normal highline, housefall, or Burtoning rig, exert a closing force only when a load is in the span and this force is scarcely noticed at normal replenishment speeds.

In rough weather or with a short approach run it is safer to approach wide. We can come always up to a point abreast our fueling station and then move in to the desired distance. This is particularly recommended if the supply ship is yawing badly.

One of the sharpest debates among modern mariners is that concerning the proper approach speed when going alongside another ship. The "conservative" school recommends approaching at 5 knots greater than the supply ship's speed, slowing to the replenishment speed at the proper distance and "coasting" into position abreast the supply ship. The "radical" school recommends approaching at 25 knots and backing the engines to reduce speed at the required moment. The "conservatives" speak darkly of engines backing unevenly, causing a veer to one side, and they are concerned about possible damage to boilers and machinery resulting from such "rough" use; the "radicals" speak of simplicity, efficiency and smartness.

The author has been converted from "conservative" to "radical." Experiments with both *Forrest Sherman* and *Springfield* showed that no combination of engine power (including such as STARBOARD, BACK FULL with PORT, AHEAD ONE-THIRD) had any significant effect on the helmsman's ability to steer a precise course when backing from 25 knots, as long as the ship was making 8 knots or more through the water. Since replenishment speeds are normally 10 knots or greater and the approaching ship never slows much below replenishment speed, concern for the effect of uneven engine response can be dismissed. (It is suggested, however, that any shiphandler with lingering doubts on this point take time to test his ship to observe her behavior under such conditions.) As for damage to the engineering plant caused by backing at high speeds, the plants are designed for such power changes and there is little in the history of the many ships which have used the "back down" approach for years to support such fears.

To deny oneself the use of backing power while going alongside another ship at sea would be similar to denying himself backing power when making a pier in port. Certainly such a landing can be made, but it is so much easier to use the engines to bring the ship to a stop. The same is true under way: it is much easier to reduce the ship's speed quickly to the replenishment speed when close to the desired position by the use of backing power than it is to estimate the moment to reduce the engine revolutions to replenishment speed and depend on water resistance to slow her.

As for the approach speed, any speed greater than the replenishment can be used, but obviously the higher the speed the more quickly one arrives alongside. Replenishment speed plus 5 knots is recommended when using the "coast in" method, and 20 or 25 knots is normal when using the "backdown" approach: 20 knots when first getting used to the system or for night approaches, 25 knots for most normal daylight approaches.

While riding alongside, it is often convenient to divide the station-keeping duties between two officers. By giving one officer control of the ship's course—that is, the distance from the supply ship—and the other officer control of the ship's speed—that is, the fore-and-aft position—we can control the ship very nicely. These two factors are almost completely independent when a ship is alongside, and each officer has only one factor to consider. It may also be desirable for the conning officer to wear a sound-powered telephone set connecting him directly to the helmsman and annunciator man. His orders will be heard more clearly, and this vital control trio will be isolated from the administrative hubbub which accompanies replenishment.

Following course and speed changes by the supply ship while we are alongside is not as difficult as it might seem. As long as the changes are made gradually and with complete exchange of information, it is only slightly more difficult to maintain station alongside during a maneuver than while steaming steadily. For course changes, it is usually advisable to change course in 10° to 20° increments, with the oiler using a small amount of rudder. We can follow the turn by ordering successive courses-to-steer to the helmsman.

At the completion of each increment, a slight pause should be made to allow the destroyer to catch up, and at the end of each 45°, a couple of minutes should be allowed to let the destroyer settle down again. The only difficulty in making a large course change in one steady movement is that once the destroyer conning becomes erratic, it is apt to become more so by over-correction. Stopping momentarily at each 15° gives a series of check points, and the pause at 45° allows complete steadying.

Speed changes while alongside are relatively simple, because supply ships accelerate very slowly. Again, incremental changes and complete exchange of information are essential. In this case, changes of a knot at a time are easily followed.

Helicopter operations

All fleet units operate with helicopters today and most of the major ships have permanent helicopter platforms or "flight decks" suitable for launching and landing helicopters. Helicopters carry the mail, transfer personnel and stores, act as life guards, and participate in exercises to the extent that they are an integral part of nearly all fleet evolutions (Figure 9–4). As a matter of fact, replenishment of general stores by helicopters conducting VERTREP has become the standard method of distributing these supplies in our deployed fleets. The helicopter has become an important factor in the shiphandler's life.

Seemingly of unlimited versatility, the helicopter responds instantly to the slightest change in wind direction and speed. When maneuvering close to a ship, the helicopter pilot is handling his craft in one moving and occasionally turbulent medium while endeavoring to position his craft with respect to a ship moving in a different medium with different turbulence. To land on deck he must position his craft within a foot or so of the desired position on deck, and even to make a pickup or drop by hoist he must control his craft to within a few feet. The bumpy air and general environmental difficulties provided by nature require great skill and intense concentration on the part of the pilot; the shiphandler should not add to his problems.

The helicopter pilot sits in the front of his aircraft looking forward, so he would naturally like to be able to see his points of reference and any hazardous obstacles in his forward sector of view. But he would also like to have a relative wind of at least several knots to head into, and he wants to avoid buffeting and

FIGURE 9–4. The helicopter plays an important part in modern shiphandling.

turbulence at all costs. The problem for the shiphandler, then, is to provide a relative wind over the ship's flight deck which permits the pilot to make an approach into the wind with the least turbulence possible, but at the same time from such a direction that he can see the major portion of the ship's superstructure in his forward hemisphere of vision. Since the "flight deck" on most ships is aft, this usually requires a relative wind of not less than 10 knots but not more than 25 knots from forward of the beam, but not so sharp on the bow that the turbulence from the superstructure, particularly stack gas from the funnel, flows across the flight deck area within the rotor span of the helicopter. To accomplish this is not as easy as one might think. In fact, the shiphandler very frequently cannot produce the most desirable conditions and has to offer the pilot the best compromise he can manage to work out.

For example, if there is no true wind, the shiphandler can produce relative wind only from dead ahead, so to reduce turbulence he may have to slow to 15 knots or less to assist the pilot. If the wind is blowing more than the upper limit, the shiphandler must head in the downwind sector to reduce the relative wind below the limit. In a 25-knot wind, to get the wind forward of the beam but less than the 25 knots, he would have to make more than 25 knots downwind. Actually in such a situation, a wind on the beam or quarter usually has to be accepted.

In addition to his concern for the wind, the shiphandler must minimize the roll of his ship and, to the extent possible, the heave of the deck while the helicopter is landing and until it has been firmly secured. If the ship is rolling more than 10° to a side, a helicopter should not be permitted to land. During the moments that its wheels are on deck, its rotor up to full rpm, but it has not yet been lashed down, the pilot will continue to fly it. If the ship rolls to one side, the helicopter will start to skid downhill and the pilot must compensate with cyclic pitch to hold the craft in place—the rotor blades will then pitch down toward the deck, endangering anyone within their arc and perhaps even striking the deck. A rolling deck is incompatible with an unrestrained helicopter and the conning officer must make sure that the ship's roll will not exceed a few degrees during the critical period of landing before the craft is firmly on deck and secured.

Finally, because of the danger of the blades getting out control, the rotor of some helicopters cannot be started or stopped in a relative wind greater than some arbitrary limit, such as 35 knots so; even with the craft on deck, it may be necessary to maneuver to obtain a wind suitable for starting or stopping the rotor.

Handling the ship for helicopter operations can often be a rather complex problem of balancing the wind and the sea conditions. The conning officer should make sure he is adept at solving relative wind problems on the maneuvering board, and the situation should be well thought through before the helicopter approaches. Even though the helicopter pilot may be ready to conduct operations under marginal conditions, the skipper of the ship shares responsibility for safe operations, and with helicopters, a bit of bad luck converts to instant tragedy!

Plane guard

Plane guarding is a duty frequently assigned a destroyer. In this role, as rescue destroyer she not only stands by to assist in case of an accident, but also serves as a marker pylon for the approaching aircraft. For this reason, when plane guarding, the destroyer conning officer must keep his station accurately.

The primary rescue destroyer station is the one astern of the carrier (usually 165° relative, 1,000 yards). This distance was selected to allow the destroyer ample room to stop before running past any crash occurring near the carrier. The station is slightly on the quarter to allow the destroyer's bridge personnel to see across the bow of the carrier in case a plane "goes in" over the bow. This also moves the plane guard out of the "landing pattern," which is to port of the carrier.

Other rescue destroyer stations may be assigned, especially at night when it is desirable to establish a visual horizon for the pilots by using the trucklights of the rescue destroyer to provide this reference. When a number of rescue destroyers are assigned, the group is handled as a small Task Group, with complete signals for the stationing and maneuvering desired. When a single rescue destroyer is assigned, she is expected to assume her station and maneuver properly with little or no further instruction. The conning officer of a rescue destroyer is expected to anticipate and follow whatever move the carrier may make.

Obviously the proper position for the rescue destroyer during flight operations is 165° from the true wind, so upon being ordered to assume her station, she should proceed to a station 1,000 yards from the carrier, with the true wind on the proper bearing. Once on station, she should parallel the carrier and follow her movements by simple turns. The problem has been further simplified by the current fleet practice of predicting the flight course well beforehand and allowing the rescue destroyer ample time to get on station. Difficulty arises, however, when the wind is light and the carrier does not desire to use the predicted course for her actual operations.

Should the carrier commence to turn unexpectedly, we should head for her wake to insure that we will be able to follow astern as she maneuvers. Our objective is to gain our proper station as quickly as possible once she settles on a course, and from 1,000 yards dead astern we can slide out to our proper station very quickly. We must not make the mistake, though, of assuming too early that the carrier is on course or we will end up on the inside of the turn and have to sheer away for safety's sake. In very calm weather carriers often turn radically when searching for the almost non-existent breeze.

If we are on station on the quarter, and the carrier makes a change of course, it is a useful practice to change course approximately an equal amount but in the *opposite* direction until the bearing has been corrected, and then swing parallel to her, as shown in Figure 9–5. For example, if the carrier changes her course 10° to the right, we should change our course 10° to the left until the bearing to the

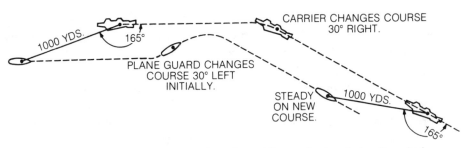

FIGURE 9–5. Keeping on plane guard station while carrier hunts for the wind.

carrier has changed the required 10°, and then we should come 20° to the right to parallel her. For left turns, we might turn right a smaller amount than the carrier turned (or even hold our course), but for small adjustments of course it is a useful rule.

Plane crash

If a plane crashes, head directly for it at best speed, as shown in Figure 9–6. The conning officer must station men on the pelorus and on a stadimeter (used as described in Chapter 1) to obtain ranges and bearings to the scene of the crash. It is a good rule to drop our speed at the last minute so as to be making 15 knots through the water at 500 yards from the crash, and with 450 yards to go, BACK TWO-THIRDS. This should bring the ship dead in the water abreast the crash, but we still have BACK FULL or BACK ONE-THIRD should we need adjustment. When about 100 yards from the downed pilot, we should change course slightly to *windward* to bring the pilot along the *lee* side. When the ship is dead in the water it will drift with the wind, while a man in the water is practically unaffected by the wind; therefore, from a windward position, the ship will drift *down on* the pilot. Once the ship has been brought to a stop with the man close aboard, it is easy to work him to the survivor's net with lines and swimmers.

Don't be afraid of running the man down as we approach. In the first place, the chance of being able to actually hit him with the stem is quite remote, and, even if we did, our speed through the water is so low that it probably wouldn't hurt him. It is an unfortunate fact that in crashes of carrier-type planes at sea, the occupants are either in good shape or they don't survive, so we can expect that if the pilot is afloat, he can paddle around a bit and will avoid the stem. The biggest

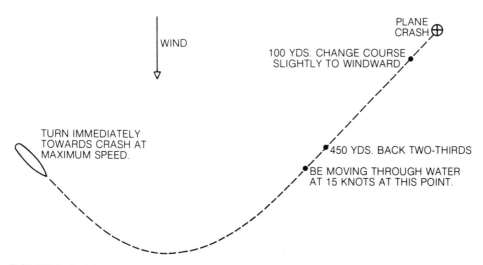

FIGURE 9–6. Maneuver for a plane crash.

trouble we will experience will be that the fliers swim away from the ship because of lurid tales they have heard about being "sucked into the screws." The effect of the screws on a man on the surface is usually overrated, and in case the man in the water should get close to the screws, we can order STOP SHAFT until he is clear.

The 15-knot and 450-yard figures mentioned above were derived by calibrating a 2,100-ton destroyer in calm weather with no wind. A slight adjustment is necessary in case of wind, but the figures work out remarkably well. Backing TWO-THIRDS at 600 yards for an approach speed of 20 knots worked out very well also, but each skipper should calibrate his own ship. Approach speeds greater than 20 knots need not be figured, because the speed can be knocked down to 15 or 20 knots rapidly just before the final approach is made.

In a destroyer a boat is not normally used in the rescue operation unless the approach is so poor that we have completely missed the man in the water, or unless there are so many men in the water that it would be advisable. Of course we would use the boat at any time it would offer a speedier or safer method of rescue, but in practice the ship itself can be the primary rescue vessel. However, the boat is normally maintained manned and ready at the rail to be lowered when needed.

The helicopter is a magnificent rescue vehicle and can normally effect the rescue of a single man before a destroyer can change course to head for the man. With more than one man in the water, sometimes both are needed and the helicopter's presence then presents an additional problem to the destroyer. As the helicopter hovers over the wreck trying to pick up survivors, it blocks the destroyer's approach, and it must clear before the destroyer can safely move in. It is a command function of the carrier to call off the helicopter or to direct the destroyer to keep clear, but since the destroyer's conning officer must initiate his clearing action several hundred yards before the ship arrives at the scene, late instructions can cause an awkward situation. If no orders have been received by the time the ship is about 500 yards from the crash, it is best to sheer out to the side, stop abreast of the scene, and send the boat to the survivors. A whaleboat and a helicopter can work together with no undue danger.

Man overboard

Maneuvering for a man overboard is similar to the situation at a plane crash, except that it is assumed that the man in the water is initially just astern of the ship. If the situation allows, the stern should be swung away from the man in the water and the screw on that side stopped, but normally the bridge is not aware of the man in the water until too late for such action. The initial turn is usually made *toward* the side to which the man fell, in hopes that a turn in that direction will help clear him by moving the stern *away* from him.

A good approach for recovering the man in the water can be made with a continuous full rudder turn in one direction, as shown in Figure 9–7, until the bow is pointed at the man. The speed should be adjusted to 15 knots during the last half of

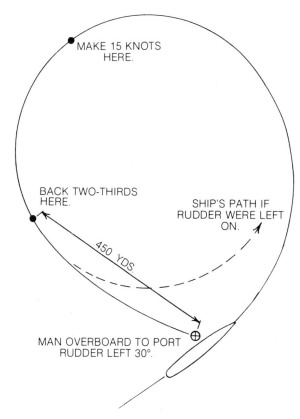

MAKE 15 KNOTS
HERE.

BACK TWO-THIRDS
HERE.

SHIP'S PATH IF
RUDDER WERE LEFT
ON.

450 YDS.

MAN OVERBOARD TO PORT
RUDDER LEFT 30°.

FIGURE 9–7. Maneuver for "man overboard."

the turn, and the engines should be ordered BACK TWO-THIRDS when 450 yards from the man in the water. If the man is in sight, this continuous turn in one direction promises to bring him back on board in the shortest time.

If the man is not in sight, or if conditions are such that it would be difficult to find him should we lose contact, a "Williamson turn" may be a better approach. As indicated in Figure 9–8, this calls for continuing the initial full rudder turn until 60° from the initial heading, and then *ordering* the helm shifted and reversing the direction of the turn. The ship's heading will normally just reach 90° from the initial heading as she commences to swing in the opposite direction. We continue turning in this new direction until we can steady up on the opposite of our initial course. Upon completion of a Williamson turn, we will find ourselves heading back along the ship's initial track and about one turning diameter from the point at which we commenced the turn. This allows us to search carefully back along our former track until we locate the man in the water.

Locating the man in the water is often the most difficult part of the operation. The life buoy watch should be equipped with and instructed to throw over a package of marker dye and a float light (which gives off both flame and dense smoke) as close to the man in the water as possible. Even though he does not see the man, the

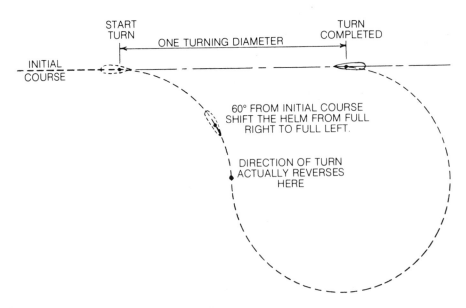

START
TURN

ONE TURNING DIAMETER

TURN
COMPLETED

INITIAL
COURSE

60° FROM INITIAL COURSE
SHIFT THE HELM FROM FULL
RIGHT TO FULL LEFT.

DIRECTION OF TURN
ACTUALLY REVERSES
HERE

FIGURE 9–8. The "Williamson turn."

life buoy watch should throw these markers over to assist in establishing the ship's former track for reference, in order to return to the exact area after completing the turn.

CIC can be of great assistance during "man overboard." If a mark is made on the plot at the moment that "man overboard" is reported, CIC, by use of the dead reckoning tracer, can always report the bearing and distance to this spot and can advise in maneuvering the ship back to the place where the man fell over. If he is still in sight during the first part of the maneuver, CIC should be kept informed of the actual ranges and bearings to the man in the water, so that they can correct their plot and have better information in case contact is later lost.

Handling boats at sea

Though we have pointed out that it has become the practice in the fleet to use the ship itself to perform most of the functions required, there are times when it is necessary to lower a boat at sea. Rescuing large numbers of people from the water and recovering torpedoes are typical evolutions in which a boat is used. The problem in employing a boat at sea is getting it *into* and *out of* the water safely.

Lowering a boat is relatively easy, even when using the older crescent davits, because the falls can be lowered rapidly; and the boat, once waterborne, can be quickly disconnected by using the quick-release feature of the hooks. We must, of course, be sure that the stern hook is released first and the the falls are pulled clear of the boat quickly, but these are relatively simple matters. It is hooking on and hoisting a boat at sea that is difficult. The heavy lower block of the standard whaleboat falls is nearly unmanageable if the boat is bobbing up and down and the ship is rolling. One moment the lower block is resting in the boat with the slack of the falls draped over the bowhook's shoulders as he struggles to engage the hook, and the next moment it is jerked high above the heads of the boat's crew as the ship rolls away from the boat. This lower block is a man-killer. Because it has inflicted so many injuries on boat crews over the years, skippers are reluctant to lower a boat at sea unless absolutely necessary.

The constant tension modification to the Welin-type gravity davits in *Forrest Sherman* eliminates to a large extent the difficulty and hazard of lowering and hoisting boats at sea. As illustrated in Figure 9–9, a freely rotating arm is added to each davit which holds a weighted sheave on the bight of the wire just inboard of the

FIGURE 9–9. Lowering a boat using Welin gravity davits on USS *Forrest Sherman*.

head sheave. The downward weight on the bight is selected in relation to the weight of the hook on the end of the fall so that there is a net pull of about 20 pounds tending to pull the hook upwards. The free rotation of the arm between its stops is sufficient to allow a total pull-out of about 10 feet with this slight upward pull. In operation, when the boat is lowered into the water, this upward force keeps the falls taut and the hook engaged while the boat can bob freely through a range of up to 10 feet without coming up hard against the falls or having the falls go slack. To unhook the boat, the crew needs only to pull down with a force of a little more than 20 pounds, trip the hook, and let go—the tension feature will pull the hook up and clear smartly. For hooking on, the falls are lowered until the hooks are about 5 feet above the mean level of the boat, the men in the boat reach up and pull the hooks down against the tension until they can be hooked into the hoisting rings, and in a few seconds the boat is ready for hoisting. With this rig, even in difficult weather, the lowering and hoisting of boats at sea becomes a safe evolution which can be accomplished both quickly and efficiently.

Regardless of the type davit being used, the fundamental difficulty in handling boats at sea is caused by the rapid changing of the distance from the davit head to the surface of the water alongside the ship. The most capable boatswain's mate in the world can't control this as he struggles to hoist his boat; it is the shiphandler only who has this under any control.

To assist the deck force in their task of lowering and hoisting the boat, the conning officer should select a course to provide a minimum roll and the slowest changing of the level of the water alongside. Running downwind at the speed of the waves would provide a perfect solution, but unfortunately the boat cannot make such a speed and thus could not come under the falls. Consequently, since the ship's speed through the water is limited to the maximum speed that the boat can make, our ship's speed must be not more than five knots when handling a standard motor whaleboat. The best solution with this limitation is to take a downwind course at a low speed in order to minimize the ship's roll and to reduce the relative velocity of the waves as much as possible. If it does not increase the roll, a course which brings the wind to the quarter on the opposite side from the falls will assist further by making a lee in the vicinity of the falls.

When handling a boat while running with the seas, care must be taken that the boat does not broach as she runs down the face of a following wave. The higher the speed at which we are conducting the operation and the more the tension on the sea painter, the less trouble we will have with the boat. In very high seas it may be advisable to pass a stern line led well aft on the ship to hold the boat in her fore-and-aft position in spite of the overtaking waves.

If the wind and the sea are not from the same direction, a compromise course may be required. Usually, however, it will be the direction of the wave motion that dictates our course. The hazards of lowering and hoisting boats at sea are minimized if we have minimized the ship's roll and have reduced the relative motion of the waves as much as possible. The longer the interval between wave crests, the longer is our opportunity to hook on and hoist away.

Towing

Towing another vessel at sea is a maneuver that has been made difficult by too much planning and discussion. Actually it is a relatively simple evolution under good sea conditions, and in no case is it any more difficult than fueling at sea. Fundamentally, the ship to be towed is lying dead in the water; the towing ship passes close and sends over the messenger for the towing hawser. The towing ship then stops and maintains her position sufficiently close to allow the hawser to be run, and finally, after the hawser has been secured and the towed ship's chain has been run out the towing ship slowly sets taut and commences towing.

In the first place, much of the complicated preparation which is normal practice is not necessary. There is no reason for running the messenger up to the forward part of the ship. Since the stern is going to follow along after the bow, we can shoot our "shot line" or heave our heaving line just as well from the stern as from the bow. Next, draping the towing hawser in bights about the stern is inviting trouble. It can easily get out of hand, and it has been known to foul a screw. On a destroyer the towing hawser can be stopped down on deck and run out of the stern chock very handily. An "easing out lizard" can be used for easing out successive bights, and this same lizard will be useful in retrieving the hawser later.

We should make the approach nearly parallel to the ship to be towed, as shown in Figure 9–10, so as to pass about 100 feet to windward of her forecastle; next, send over the messenger, and then bring the ship to a position where her stern will be about 100 yards ahead and 100 feet abeam of the other ship's stem. This position allows us a clear view of the situation from the bridge and insures safety in case the other ship should surge ahead or we should surge astern.

The secret in passing the towing hawser is to maintain the proper distance from our ship's stern to her forecastle. If we send a junior officer to the fantail with a stadimeter set for ten times the height of the other ship's bullnose, by dividing his

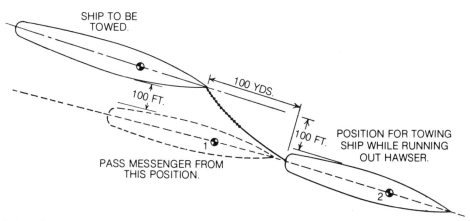

FIGURE 9–10. The approach for towing.

reading by ten the JO can send us the exact distance from our ship's stern to the other ship's sterm. This is most important during the time the other ship is shackling her chain to our ship's hawser, because if we open the distance too much, the hawser may be lost and the whole operation must be started again.

As soon as the hawser has been run and the other ship's chain run out, we can begin the delicate operation of "taking the strain." If our towing hawser is 100 fathoms long, and if the towed ship has 80 fathoms of chain out at her bullnose, our stern will be 360 yards from the other ship's bullnose when the hawser is straightened out. The stadimeter on the fantail will be of great help during this part of the evolution, but we must remember that accuracy of the ranges depends upon accurately setting for the other ship's bullnose height. By nudging our ship with the engines, we can slowly open until the hawser begins to tend *aft* instead of up and down. From this time on we must watch the distance carefully and allow it to open only gradually. Until the strain has been taken and is steady, there is a real danger of parting the hawser, because an almost indiscernible forward motion will end in a severe jerk. As the hawser straightens out, the towed ship will begin to move until finally a state of equilibrium is reached, with the hawser taking a steady strain.

Once the tow has been gotten under way and the first "steady strain" condition reached, the difficult part of taking a ship in tow has been completed. From this point on, the speed can be gradually increased in one knot increments until we are towing at about 10 knots. This speed represents about the maximum that a destroyer can tow another ship with the conventional rig. Higher speeds could probably be made in deep water by leaving an anchor rigged at the end of the towed ship's chain, where it is shackled to the towing hawser, to give more weight to the catenary. This would provide greater cushioning action and allow greater stresses before the towing hawser is straightened out.

When towing for an extended period, the scope of the tow may have to be adjusted to suit the sea conditions. If the towing ship is being *slowed* by the front face of an oncoming wave at the same time that the towed ship is *accelerating* down the back slope of a wave that has passed, the towed hawser will go slack. As the situation reverses and the towing ship *increases speed* down the back face of a wave and the towed ship *slows* on the front face of a wave, the towing hawser will be pulled taut with a jerk. Such a situation can part the tow even under mild sea conditions.

The ideal situation is to adjust the length of the tow so that the two ships are experiencing the same wave action at the same time. This will be the case when the distance between bridges is equal to the distance between wave crests, or a multiple of this distance. The scope of the tow can be adjusted most easily by having the towed ship vary the amount of chain she has out. If the towed ship has no power, it may be necessary to change course until the two ships are "in step."

When ready to cast off, we must reduce speed gradually so that the towed ship will not run up on the towing ship. We must remember that the weight of the catenary is always pulling on the towed ship, so, until we have cast off, the towed ship will continue to move ahead slowly. It is necessary to maintain a constant distance, such as 100 yards, between the ships during the disconnecting.

Plan ahead

The special maneuvers required at sea can all be made simple by having a pre-selected plan of action and knowing the calibration of our ship. Though a special situation may require a departure from our plan, we will have a firm basis from which to proceed to meet the requirements of a particular case. The conning officer should insure that he has a complete plan for meeting *all of the normal emergencies* encountered at sea. For the schedule evolutions, such as fueling or towing, he can make more elaborate preparations. Forehandedness includes solving as much of the problem ahead of time as the situation permits.

10
restricted waters

When our ship is under way within the confines of the harbor, we are faced with different problems from those we have faced in the open seas. The channel narrows until at times it is scarcely wider than the ship itself. The depth of water decreases until the bottom is only a few feet from our keel. Landmarks are so plentiful that any single one tends to be lost in the multitude. Even the buoys and beacons appear to have been scattered haphazardly as the various channels meet and intertwine.

When moving about in such waters our first concern is to make certain we know our position and to insure that the course we are following is in safe water. This sounds like a statement of the navigator's duty, but the conning officer also has a share in this task. In a restricted harbor, the navigator has his hands full just keeping track of the ship's location. With a well-trained team, he can plot the ship's position accurately about once each minute. Thus he can tell us where we *have* been a few moments after we have been there, and he can lay out the major segments of our track ahead and tell us when to turn. But when we begin threading the buoys in a narrow channel, when we are required to maneuver to pass other shipping, or when we are making complex turns using the engines, the ability of the navigator to keep abreast of the situation is strained. He can no longer keep the position accurately plotted and lay out the maneuver of the moment, and still advise the conning officer in sufficient time for this officer to depend entirely on the navigator's advice.

In a busy harbor we must leave the realm of formal navigation to a certain extent and enter the realm of visual piloting. Consequently, the conning officer in the harbor must at all times navigate by eye. He should do this not only to guard against the possibility of a navigator's mistake, but also to be ready to meet the situation when the scene moves too fast for the plotting team.

Conning chart

To keep track of the ship's position, identify buoys and landmarks, and check the charted depth of the channel, the conning officer must have access to a harbor chart. It often interferes with the navigational plot if the conning officer must use the navigator's chart for information. This officer has enough to do without stepping aside every few moments to let someone have another look at the chart.

It will pay big dividends if we provide an extra up-to-date harbor chart for the exclusive use of the conning officer, with the latest recommended track for passing through the harbor; and, if the ship's berth is known ahead of time, the navigator's recommended courses and speeds should be laid down on it.

Some officers like to have this chart mounted on a convenient desk or surface immediately in front of their conning position so they can check off the ship's progress as she moves to her berth. Others prefer to have the chart mounted on a thin board or else simply folded conveniently so that they can orient the chart to the ship's heading and sight across the chart when identifying landmarks. The first system has the advantage of having the conning chart oriented to true north (as is normal when using charts), and thus minimizes the chance of ordering an incorrect true course. The second system maintains the relative picture oriented correctly with the ship's head. Either system gives the conning officer fast access to a harbor chart without interfering with the navigating team.

Preparation for handling in port

Before any officer conns a ship in a restricted harbor he should carefully study the chart. He should trace the intended course with the navigator to insure that he is aware of all of the dangers he might encounter. He should check the charted depth of water throughout the track to make sure that he has not overlooked any shallow spots. He should select his turning points and plan his speed while he has ample time to study the situation. He should make note of any dangerous spots, and should select "danger bearings" on prominent objects to mark the separation between danger and safety. The safety with which he handles the ship in the harbor is dependent to a large measure on the thoroughness with which he has studied the harbor chart.

It is not sufficient to study the chart by itself, because important features might thus be overlooked. The chart should be studied with the help of the applicable Coast Pilot to make sure that all of the important points are ferreted out. The Coast Pilot gives not only the salient features of the harbor but also the recommended routes that should be followed. The Coast Pilot describes the tide and current conditions which will be encountered in the harbor, and if these are significant, the conning officer should insure that he is provided with complete and accurate data from the appropriate Tide and Current Tables.

Navigating by eye

Having completed our study of the harbor and having provided ourselves with a conning chart, we are ready to handle our ship in these restricted waters. As mentioned, our first task is to determine the ship's location on the chart.

Navigating by eye is neither as difficult nor as inexact as one might think. Because of the extreme care taken in Navy ships in the matter of navigation, there is a tendency to depend upon the navigator's chart to the exclusion of all else. Actually, in a well-marked harbor, the ship can be moved in and out of port by visual piloting without referring to the navigator and his carefully marked chart. This does not lessen the need for the navigator, for he must be at all times ready to take us through the unmarked sections of the harbor, but it does indicate the capability of visual piloting in handling the ship in the harbor.

We make our first rough location of the ship's position by identifying enough landmarks to decide the general area in which the ship is located. Then by checking bearings, estimating ranges, and utilizing pairs of landmarks as they come into line and establish a range, we refine our position until we are confident that it is correct within relatively narrow limits. As we approach the more restricted part of the harbor, our estimating becomes more exact, because we are getting nearer to the navigation markers upon which we are fixing our position. We can frequently check our position as we pass buoys close aboard, leave headlands abeam, or steer for known objects ahead.

For the simple entry into or departure from a harbor we usually have the assistance of the *harbor ranges*. There is normally a series of ranges marking the center of the main channel, and we simply shift from one range to the next as we proceed through the harbor. It is quite simple to steer so as to keep the range markers in line and thus proceed accurately along the track marked by the ranges. If the ship is exactly on the range, we have a very good fix each time we pass a channel buoy.

In the absence of a harbor range, we can establish a similar piloting aid by selecting courses that head directly for prominent objects in the harbor. We can easily follow the track thus selected by adjusting the ship's head so that the bearing to the selected object remains constant and equal to the course of the selected track. In this manner we obtain the equivalent of a range by substituting a single landmark and the ship's gyro compass for the two landmarks of a range.

Gauging the set

Whether steering the harbor range or following a constant bearing to a fixed object ahead, we have a good check on the cross-channel *set*. This may be due to wind or cross-current, and it is helpful to have an estimate of how much of each we are feeling. This information may come in handy later, since the wind effect is usually felt to about the same extent all over the harbor, but the current at any point is dependent upon the channels in the vicinity.

The set we are experiencing *parallel* to the ship's head is more difficult to estimate. However, since the effect of wind from dead ahead or dead astern is usually negligible except when handling alongside, we can attribute all fore-and-aft set to current without being far wrong. This can be found by comparing our ship's speed through the water, measured by pitometer log or rpm, against the speed actually being made good over the ground as reported by the navigator.

Though we can measure the set we are actually experiencing, we must also be able to *anticipate* the current we are going to encounter. The most obvious means of determining the current in the channel is to observe the current wake at a buoy or past some pilings. A one-knot current causes a definite ripple, a three-knot current will cause swirls and eddies for several yards, and a five-knot current will cause a boiling wake to stretch out downstream for fifty yards.

The angle of lean of the harbor buoys is also a good indication of the direction and strength of the current. Spar buoys are designed to assist in estimating the current, but one must be careful in using them to estimate the strength of the current. Some are so delicately balanced that they lean heavily to the side even in very light currents. It is a good habit to make a mental note of the current indicated at each channel buoy as we proceed along our way.

Following the channel

In a tortuous channel it is often impractical to mark the channel with ranges, so the edges of the channel are marked with channel buoys. These are usually placed in pairs on opposite sides of the channel, so the channel can be followed by simply steering for the midpoint between the next pair of buoys. Along difficult sections of the channel the buoys are placed more frequently and they clearly outline the edges of safety.

As the channel widens into the open sections of the harbor, the need for paired channel buoys no longer exists. Here only the shoal water and submerged dangers are marked, and only an occasional *fairway* buoy is added to indicate the recommended channel. Under these conditions the pattern is not so easy to follow, and it is necessary to take extra care in identifying each buoy.

When only one side of the channel is extensively marked, or when following one side of a wide channel, we are faced with the problem of adjusting our course to markers *on one side only*. We must follow the channel by keeping an appropriate distance out from the line of buoys marking the side. As the channel winds, we must adjust our course to the new line of buoys.

It is usually safe to proceed directly from one channel buoy to the next if we insure that we remain *inboard* of the line connecting the two buoys. If we lay down a track parallel to the line connecting successive buoys and at a convenient distance, such as 50 yards, inboard of the buoys, it will be an ideal track to follow. Between buoys we can check our position by fixes and can catch our drift readily by watching the bearing on the next buoy ahead. This buoy is nearly dead ahead and should draw to the *off-channel* side as we approach it. If the bearing draws to the *channel* side, we are being set out of the channel and must take corrective action.

The only difficulty in following a channel marked on one side only is to make the turns correctly. We know the new course in advance as we turn into a new leg of our track, because it is the line connecting the next successive buoys. Our problem, therefore, is one of deciding how much rudder to use and when to order it.

Turn diagram

To make our turns accurately we can prepare a *turn diagram*, as shown in Figure 10-1, from the ship's turning data. This turn diagram is a plot of the ship's track when making 10 knots through the water and turning with 10, 15, 20, and 30 degrees of rudder. It is assumed that the ship was proceeding steadily on course 000° at 10

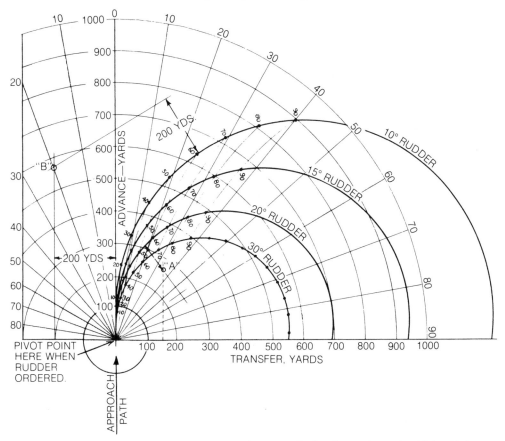

FIGURE 10-1. Turn diagram for speed of 10 knots. (Indicating points at which ship's heading has changed the indicated number of degrees from the initial approach course.)

Example of Use:

Problem   To determine how to approach and when to order rudder to pass 100 yards abeam of a Buoy "A" on a course 55° from present course, using 20° rudder.

Solution   From 55° point on 20° rudder curve, lay off Point "A" 100 yards 145° (90° from a track of 55°).

This indicates that we should approach on a track which would pass 160 yards abeam of Buoy "A", and we should put the rudder over when the buoy bears 35° from our approach course and is 270 yards away.
(Note: This diagram is for illustration only and is not accurate for any certain ship).

knots and that the rudder was ordered over as the pivot point passed through the center of the plot. The numbers along each track show the points at which the ship's heading changes each successive ten degrees from the original heading. Though this diagram is exact only for 10 knots, small differences in speed do not make any appreciable difference in the track of the ship, so the diagram is usable throughout the range of speeds normally used in the harbor.

To use the diagram, we measure the amount we are about to change our course and then locate this change in ship's head along the curve for the amount of rudder we intend to use. This locates the *range* and *bearing* to the point at which our course change will be completed from the point at which we order rudder. If we then select the point on the navigating chart at which we wish the turn to be completed, we can plot back from this point to determine *when* to order the rudder. If we wish to reference our turn to any other point, we can plot such a point on the diagram in the same manner in which point A was plotted in the figure.

Another use of the diagram is to select the *rudder angle* to be used for a certain turn. If we are running 100 yards inboard of a line of buoys, and the next leg of our track is 80° toward the buoys from our present course, we can locate the position of the turning buoy on the turn diagram by the intersection of the lines 100 yards on our beam before and after the turn, as indicated for points A, B, and C of Figure 10–2. From Figure 10–2 it is seen that 10° rudder will put us outside of the channel, and 20° rudder will put us quite close to the buoy, so we had better use 30° rudder for the turn. It is apparent that in any case of turning *toward* the buoy, the more rudder we use, the farther we will pass from the buoy. The disadvantage of using large rudder angles is that a steering error or casualty may cause us to overshoot and cross the line of buoys.

When the turn is to the side *away* from the line of buoys, we can use any amount of rudder we desire if the channel is wide enough to accommodate a slow, easy turn. The easier our turn, when turning *away*, the farther we will pass from the buoy. To determine the point at which to order helm, we plot the offset lines on the turn diagram as before, but in this case they will be *outside* of the turn circle. The range and bearing to the buoy when we should order the rudder over are indicated by the intersection of the offset lines. Point "B" in Figure 10–1 is such an intersection for a 10° rudder turn in the case where we are running 200 yards from the buoys and our turn is 60° *away* from the buoys.

When time or circumstance does not allow the careful plotting of the turn as indicated above, we can make our turn by eye. If we can be on the new course when the buoy is the desired distance on our beam, we will have accomplished the turn satisfactorily. To achieve this, the conning officer can estimate this beam position by eye, and can steer to put his pivot point through this point just as the ship swings to the new course. This is not as difficult as it sounds, because, having mentally selected his objective as a point in the water at the beginning of the turn, the conning officer can take corrective action as necessary as he approaches this point.

A typical track for following one side of the channel is indicated in Figure

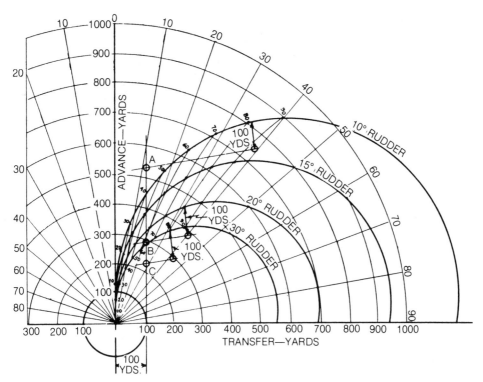

FIGURE 10–2. Using the turn diagram for selecting rudder for a turn around a buoy.

Problem   We are running 100 yards inboard of a line of buoys and desire to continue to do so. The next turn is 80° toward the line of buoys. How much rudder should we use, and when should we order it?

Solution   Plot the lines 100 yards on our beam before and after the turn for 10°, 20°, and 30° rudder, giving intersections A, B, and C. A is outside of 10° track, B is too close to 20° track. We should therefore use 30° rudder and order the helm over when the buoy is bearing 28° from approach course, distance 220 yards.

10–3. The points at which to put the rudder over were selected by using the turn diagram. Good target points for making the turns by eye are indicated, and it will be noted that they are slightly advanced along the track from the actual beam points to allow an easier turn. Care should be taken not to come too close (closer than 30 yards) to the buoys when making sharp turns.

181   RESTRICTED WATERS

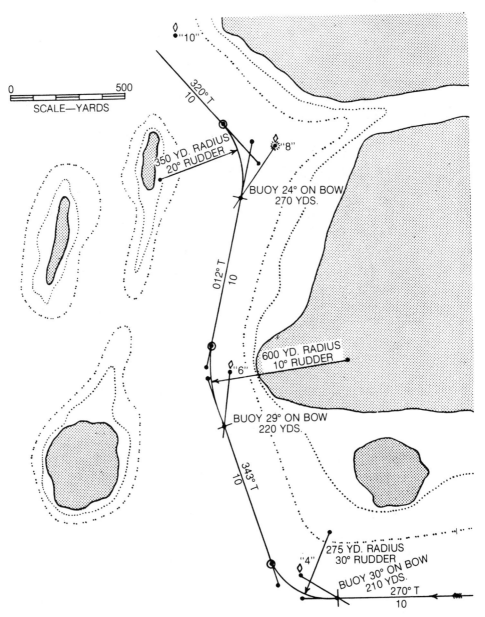

FIGURE 10–3. Following a channel marked on one side only. (Running 100 yards abeam of buoys, using the turn diagram for making turns. Target points for making turns by eye are indicated by dotted circle.)

Squatting

As a ship increases speed, she sinks appreciably with respect to the mean surface of the water. Both her bow and stern ride lower in the water as her velocity is increased (Figure 10–4), and the water level alongside, amidships, is lower than

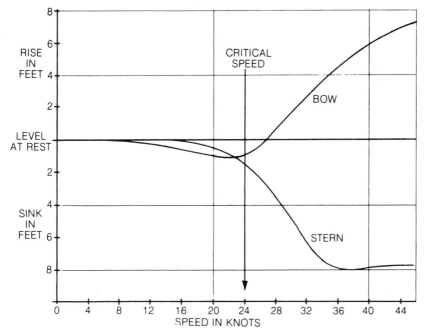

FIGURE 10–4. Change in level of bow and stern as ship increases speed. (For 400-foot, high-speed ship. Adapted from Figure 157, *Speed and Power of Ships*, by Rear Admiral David W. Taylor (CC), USN (Ret.).)

that of the surrounding water. There is a distinct bow wave and a distinct stern wave, and the water between the two is depressed. This is caused in part by the increase in relative velocity of the water as it flows under the ship, and in part by the interaction of the bow and stern wave systems. As the ship travels along, she rides in a depression created by her own passage.

If the speed is further increased past the "critical speed," the bow begins to rise abruptly and the stern sinks more rapidly, as indicated in the figure. This phenomenon is known as "squatting," and has a distinct effect on the resistance to the ship's motion and the speed resulting from a given power.

The wave system, known as a Kelvin wave group (Figure 10–5), caused by the passage of a ship, consists of curved waves that spread out sideways, nearly parallel to the sides of the bow, and transverse waves, nearly perpendicular to the direction of the motion of the ship, which follow astern at approximately the speed of the ship. It is these transverse waves that play an important part in the squatting of a ship. As the speed is increased, the crest of the bow wave moves back along the ship, and the bow tends to ride up on its own bow wave. At the same time, if the stern is riding in a depression of the transverse wave system, the stern will sink. If the first depression of the transverse wave system is at the stern, the ship can be considered to be riding on the back of its own bow wave as indicated in Figure 10–6. It is the coincidence of this first depression with the stern (and its wave system) that determines the critical speed.

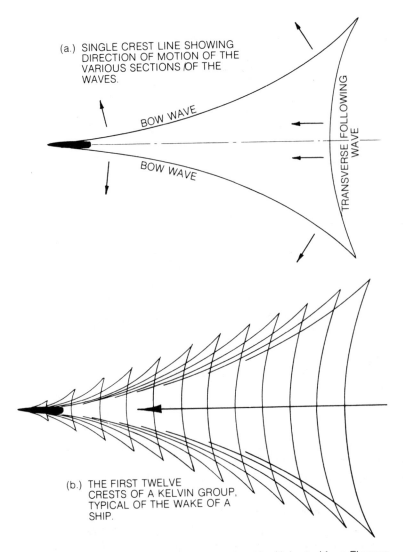

(a.) SINGLE CREST LINE SHOWING DIRECTION OF MOTION OF THE VARIOUS SECTIONS OF THE WAVES.

BOW WAVE

BOW WAVE

TRANSVERSE FOLLOWING WAVE

(b.) THE FIRST TWELVE CRESTS OF A KELVIN GROUP, TYPICAL OF THE WAKE OF A SHIP.

FIGURE 10–5. Wave systems in the wake of a ship. (Adapted from Figures 36 and 37, *Speed and Power of Ships*, by Rear Admiral David W. Taylor (CC), USN (Ret.).)

Both sinking and squatting are increased in shallow water. The proximity of the bottom causes increased relative velocity as the water flows under the ship, and the waves of the wake are more pronounced. Squatting can become a serious problem in shallow water, both from its effect on the propulsion of the ship and from the danger of the resultant wake.

In a typical situation of attempting to make high speed in shallow water, a destroyer making turns for 30 knots in 30 feet of water might only be making 22 knots over the ground. The squat would be so severe that the stern would be riding

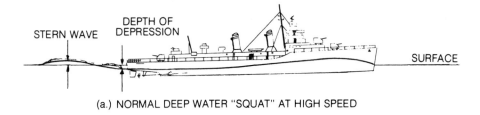

(a.) NORMAL DEEP WATER "SQUAT" AT HIGH SPEED

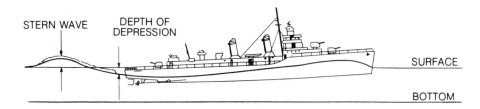

(b.) AUGMENTED "SQUAT" DUE TO SHALLOW WATER

FIGURE 10–6. "Squatting" at high speeds.

about 8 feet *lower* than normal, while the bow might be 4 feet *above* the normal level. With our ship drawing 19 feet at the propellers, this would mean that at the bottom of their travel the blade tips would be only *3 feet* from the bottom. Severe pounding would most probably be felt at the propellers as the blades passed through the area of varying velocities and eddies between the bottom of the ship and the bottom of the channel.

The severe squatting experienced in shallow water is attended by a huge stern wave that towers over the fantail of the ship. If we stand on the fantail of a destroyer while attempting high speed in shallow water, the crests of the outward moving bow waves abreast the stern would be nearly at eye level, and the transverse stern wave would stand menacingly 15 feet higher than the level of the deck at the stern.

The danger from these waves is not to our ship but to the other ships in the harbor, and to the docks and other structures at the water's edge. It is as though the ship were racing about the harbor towing a train of tidal waves astern. Such waves can lift large ships bodily and cause them to roll heavily. They can sever moorings, break up nests, and throw ships against their docks. Such waves can cause damage to beach structures as far away as 1,000 yards from the ship's track.

Consequently, though we should steam at sufficient speed to keep good control of the ship, we should limit our speed in the harbor to that which will cause no damage. Most shallow harbors have definite speed restrictions, and vessels are not allowed to proceed at more than 10 or 12 knots. Except in the deepest and most open harbors it is not wise to exceed 15 knots.

Meeting other ships

When steaming about the harbor we usually meet other vessels and are often required to pass very close to them. In order to do so safely, we must be able to ascertain the other ship's intentions before we are so close that we cannot accommodate our movements to an alteration of his course. The system of passing signals set out in the *Rules of the Road* is for this purpose, and the whistle is the main instrument for exchanging such intelligence.

Most naval officers, however, look upon the whistle as an emergency signal only, and save it for such use. Thus, they proceed with incomplete information about the intentions of the vessel they are meeting, when adequate means has been provided to easily obtain this information.

The whistle signals should be used whenever it is desirable to determine the intentions of another ship. An exchange of signals definitely establishes that the other ship is aware of our presence and agrees to passing in a certain manner. If additional use of the whistle will assist the safe and efficient transit of the harbor, the whistle should not be spared. It is certainly not smart shiphandling to proceed on incomplete information.

Four or more blasts on the whistle means "I do not understand your intentions," as well as being the danger signal. It should be used as soon as there is serious doubt as to the intentions of the other vessel. It is not intended that we wait until a situation has become dangerous before we use this signal.

Though there are only four whistle signals, it is remarkable how many problems can be solved in this four-word "language." We should recognize its limitations, though, and be alert for those times when an understanding has not been reached. At such times it is wise to sound four blasts early in the game and let everyone know that there is doubt in our minds.

A particular passing problem which is often troublesome is the encounter with a small craft not equipped with a whistle. The fishing boat, yacht, or launch may be on a collision course, but we cannot exchange signals. We may also remember that a whistle signal is not complete until it is *answered* by an identical signal from the other vessel. What should we do?

In this case, we should indicate our intentions to the small vessel by appropriate whistle signal, and then proceed accordingly. Though we have not sealed a mutual pact by a complete exchange, we have helped things by drawing his attention to us and indicating our intentions. If he does not respond correctly to the one-sided signals, we still have the four-blast signal at our command.

Actually in most situations where the danger of collision with a small craft becomes evident, the situation is caused by inattention on the part of the crew of the small vessel, or, because of the nimbleness of his craft, the skipper of the smaller vessel hasn't yet considered the problem pressing. Small vessels usually go to great pains to avoid embarrassing larger ships, and if their attention is drawn by a whistle signal, they will quickly take steps to avoid the larger ship. The four-blast signal is very handy for calling the attention of the smaller vessel to the fact that the conning officer of the larger ship considers the situation acute.

Handling the ship in a canal

Occasionally our ship must make a passage through a canal, and we must be prepared for the problems of such waterways. Because a canal is a manmade channel, it is only as wide as absolutely necessary for its purpose. We therefore find ourselves in a waterway much narrower than is our normal experience, and the ship seems to be going aground on both sides of the channel at once.

In addition to the obvious limitations to maneuvering in a canal, there are several unexpected effects which we encounter in these narrow channels. (This subject is covered in Report 601 of the David Taylor Model Basin, entitled *The Performance of Model Ships in Restricted Channels in Relation to the Design of a Ship Canal*.) As we attempt to proceed at a higher speed, the ship may appear to sink alarmingly with respect to the banks of the canal. If we stray from the center of the channel, our steering is affected. There is a tendency for the ship to move *bodily toward* the near bank, and there is an opposing tendency to force the *bow away* from the near bank. Although these effects are more noticeable in large ships, it is worthwhile for all shiphandlers to become acquainted with them.

In a restricted channel where the cross-sectional area of the ship becomes an appreciable part of the cross-section of the channel, the sinkage of the ship with speed is much more pronounced than that experienced at sea or even that experienced in shallow water. A large ship, when traveling at 12 knots in a 45-foot channel 500 feet wide, might sink bodily 8 feet *below* its normal level when dead in the water in the channel. Just before reaching critical speed (where the bow commences to rise and the stern to sink), the ship rides in a deep depression in the surface of the water that extends nearly the entire length of the ship. This "sinkage" must be considered in determining whether the channel depth is sufficient to allow the passage of our ship.

This increased sinkage is caused by the increased velocity with which the water, displaced forward, must flow aft about the ship as the ship moves ahead. This increased velocity, and the attendant decrease in pressure, causes the level of water to be lowered all along the midship section. Since the area of the passage between the ship and the boundaries of the canal is decreased, the velocity of the water moving astern must increase to "fill in" behind the ship at a given speed. The action of the propellers in taking their suction from the restricted area increases the sinkage experienced by from 10 percent to 15 percent.

As the ship strays from the center of the channel and steams closer to one bank than the other, the passage between her side and the nearer bank becomes even more restricted; the velocity of flow on that side must therefore increase, and the water level between the ship and the near bank is lowered. This tends to force the ship into the near bank, an effect known as "bank suction." If a ship is maintained on a course parallel to the adjacent bank, she will move bodily in to the bank.

As the ship approaches the bank, the bow wave on the *near* side becomes augmented and tends to push the bow *away* from the bank. This is clearly indicated in Figure 10–7, which has been drawn from actual experimental data with models. Thus, in addition to the bank suction tending to draw the ship bodily *in to* the bank, there is the bank effect which applies a twisting movement to the ship and tends to make the ship sheer *away* from the bank.

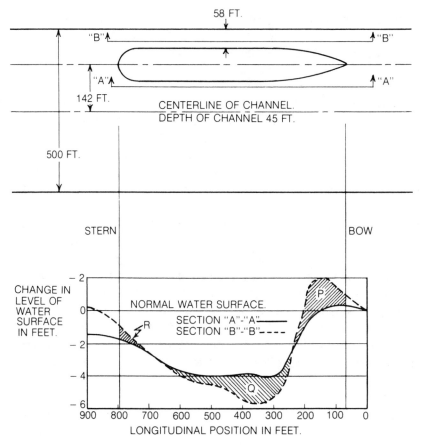

FIGURE 10–7. Water surface profile for ship located off centerline of canal.

Bank effect is felt because Area P is larger than Area R.
Bank suction is felt because Area Q is larger than P plus R.

(Data are from Figure 7.20 of Report 601, of the David Taylor Model Basin, entitled "The Performance of Model Ships in Restricted Channels in Relation to the Design of a Ship Canal." Figures are for a large tanker, 720 feet long, making 11 knots in a 500-foot-wide channel with vertical banks.)

In practice, a ship can usually steam safely near one bank of a canal, but she must maintain a slight inclination *away* from the near bank to overcome the bank suction, and she will usually require several degrees of rudder *toward* the near bank to hold the ship's head steady against the bank effect.

An insidious situation can result while steaming close to the bank of a canal when the ship momentarily gets too close to the side. The bank effect may become too large to be overcome by the rudder, and the bow may be forced away from the near bank. This will cause the stern to swing towards the near bank; the bank suction will then become stronger on the stern, and the sheer will be increased as the stern is drawn toward the near bank. The resulting sheer may be so great that the ship will cross the canal and go aground on the *opposite* bank before she can be gotten under control again.

Another problem when navigating in a canal occurs when passing sections where the bank has been cut out to form docks for mooring ships or for other purposes. The pilots of the Suez Canal, where cutouts are provided to allow large ships to pass one another, have reported a serious tendency for ships to veer *into* the cutouts as they come abreast of them. This has caused passing ships to veer toward and collide with ships waiting in the cutouts when it initially appeared that they were passing with a safe margin.

The tendency to veer into a cutout is caused by the removal of the bank effect as the ship comes abreast the interruption in the canal bank. When the force tending to push the bow *away* from the bank is removed, the rudder used to counteract it commences to turn the ship *toward* the near bank and *into* the cutout. Unless this rudder angle is removed immediately, the ship will turn in response to her rudder. When passing interruptions in the canal bank, the shiphandler must be alert to detect and counteract any changes in the forces on his ship.

The severe sinking, the bank effect, and the bank suction described above are usually troublesome only to very large ships in very restricted canals. A destroyer can maneuver safely quite close to the bank of a canal with little noticeable effect. These effects are dependent on the ship's speed through the water, and, as with most hydrodynamic effects, the strength of the force on the ship varies generally as the square of the ship's speed. *Moderate speed should be the rule when navigating a canal*.

Normally a canal is just as easy a place in which to handle the ship as is a narrow marked channel in the harbor, but the proximity of the banks makes it seem more confined. The canal has one distinct advantage, however, in that the current, if any, flows parallel to the banks, so there is no cross-channel set due to current. Further, canals are very thoroughly marked, and one is seldom in doubt about his position.

The most difficult part of handling a ship in a canal is following sharp turns in the channel when there is considerable current flowing. If we are going upstream and turn late (Figure 10–8), the current can get on our inboard bow, retard our turn, and cause us to go into the bank. If we get caught in such a position, the best action is to order BACK EMERGENCY to kill the ship's headway, and then drift downstream with the current. If we can kill the ship's way with respect to the water, the ship will

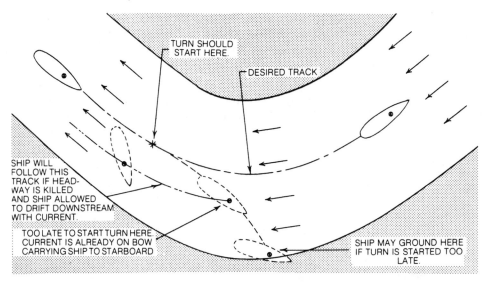

TURN SHOULD
START HERE.

DESIRED TRACK

SHIP WILL
FOLLOW THIS
TRACK IF HEAD-
WAY IS KILLED
AND SHIP ALLOWED
TO DRIFT DOWNSTREAM
WITH CURRENT.

TOO LATE TO START TURN HERE.
CURRENT IS ALREADY ON BOW
CARRYING SHIP TO STARBOARD

SHIP MAY GROUND HERE
IF TURN IS STARTED TOO
LATE.

FIGURE 10–8. Following a turn in a canal or narrow channel while going upstream.

be carried downstream at a nearly constant distance from the bank regardless of the orientation of the ship. Once straightened out, we can start ahead again and make our turn in proper fashion.

Making the turn successfully is not difficult. The conning officer should take care to insure that he starts his turn at the correct moment and that he does not get the ship across the current. The proper heading for the ship at any moment during the turn is approximately parallel to the banks at that point in the turn. It is easy to check the correctness of our heading by observing the banks, and, if deviations are detected early, they are readily eliminated by increasing or decreasing the amount of rudder being used.

Making a turn going downstream (Figure 10–9) presents different problems. The current adds to our ship's speed through the water, so that our speed over the ground is increased. On the other hand the action of the current tends to reduce rather than augment the effect of beginning the turn at the wrong time. Whether we turn too early or too late, the current tends to help our turn and carries us downstream instead of forcing us towards the bank.

Passing through restrictions in the channel

Occasionally in a canal or harbor we must pass through a very narrow restriction, such as the opening in a drawbridge or the entrance through a breakwater. Often there is cross-current or crosswind, and the opening is scarcely larger than the beam of the ship (Figure 10–10).

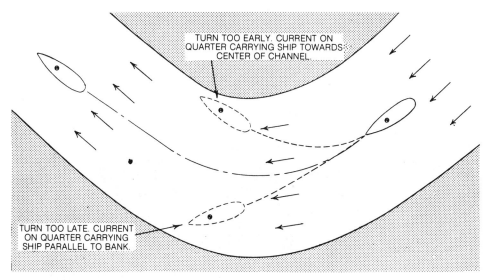

FIGURE 10–9. Following a turn in a canal or narrow channel while going downstream.

In approaching such a restriction, we should maneuver to approach the center of the opening on a constant bearing course. This requires that we alter our ship's head until the bearing on the center of the opening is steady. The difference between the bearing of the center of the opening and the ship's head when the bearing is steady determines the cross-channel angle at which we will pass through the opening. Having thus determined this cross-channel angle, we can project the extremities of the ship at this inclination to estimate whether we can safely pass through the opening. Figure 10–11 illustrates this projection and shows that with a large cross-channel angle we need a much larger opening than simply the ship's breadth.

If we find that we have too large a cross-channel angle to allow us to pass through the restriction, two courses of action are open. First we can increase our speed. Doubling our speed will halve the cross-channel angle. However, we must also bear in mind that doubling our speed will also quadruple the kinetic energy of the ship and greatly increase the damage should we strike something.

The second course of action, other than waiting for more favorable conditions, is to turn the ship as we go through the restriction (Figure 10–12). In this case we swing the ship parallel to the channel just as we arrive in the restriction, and thus we eliminate our cross-channel angle. Of course, as soon as we make this alteration, we will begin to be set across the channel, but before we have moved appreciably across the channel, we will be through the restriction. The difference between our heading and our track can be considered to be the same after the turn as before, so we will simply be altering our track over the ground by the amount of the cross-channel angle. It is necessary, of course, that the restriction be short enough and

FIGURE 10–10. With tugs assisting, the submarine tender *L. Y. Spear* (AS 36) maneuvers through a tight passage, headed for her sea trials.

that we have sufficient room on the other side of the restriction to take the attendant excursion to leeward and still return to the center of the channel.

When turning through a restricted gate, it is wise to pass the bow as close to the windward side of the opening as possible. Just as our ship's bow arrives in the restriction, we should kick the stern upwind to keep it clear of the lee side of the gate. While doing this, we allow the bow to fall off downwind as necessary, but as it is already safely through the gate, the present problem is to get the stern through. Hence, as soon as the bow has passed the windward restriction, the conning officer should move to the lee wing of the bridge to have a good vantage point for twisting the stern through.

Handling in port at night

Handling a ship in a restricted harbor at night is often required. In this case we are deprived of many of the usual visual aids, and we must depend more thoroughly on navigational aids while moving about the harbor. In preparation for handling the ship at night, the conning officer should memorize beforehand the characteristics of the important navigational lights. He should plan to accomplish his passage utilizing only the lights he has studied, and he should lay out his course accordingly.

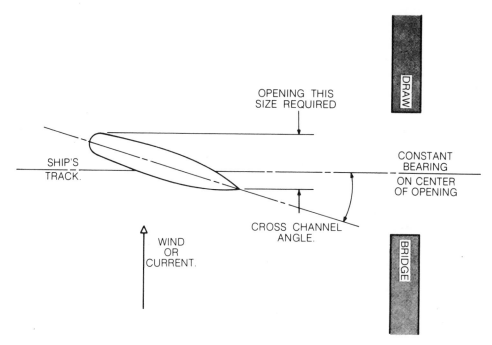

FIGURE 10–11. Passing through a restriction while being set cross-channel.

Though we are deprived in darkness of certain aids to which we have become accustomed, we still have adequate information to handle the ship safely and efficiently. The harbor ranges are lighted and most of the buoys and beacons are clearly distinguishable, once they have been identified. Though one cannot see as well as in daylight, he can distinguish unlighted objects at surprising distances even on the darkest nights. Finally, other ships are well marked with lights which can be seen clearly at all reasonable distances in the harbor. The most troublesome part of shiphandling at night is the lack of the incidental information one acquires by such actions as observing the surface of the water, checking the commission pennant of a ship at a buoy, or locating a shoal by the color of the water.

It is more difficult to orient oneself in a busy, complex harbor surrounded by a city than in a secluded waterway. In the vicinity of a city, the harbor lights must compete for recognition with the street lights, traffic lights, neon signs, and automobile headlights along the waterfront, whereas in the quiet anchorage the few navigational lights stand out clearly.

One gets an eerie, somewhat detached, feeling steaming about in a harbor at night. Although we can fix our position just as accurately as in the daylight, the familiar surface indications on the water, the buoys, and the shore line are no longer visible. One can't judge distances with any accuracy, but must rely almost completely on the distances reported by the navigator or from the radar. The

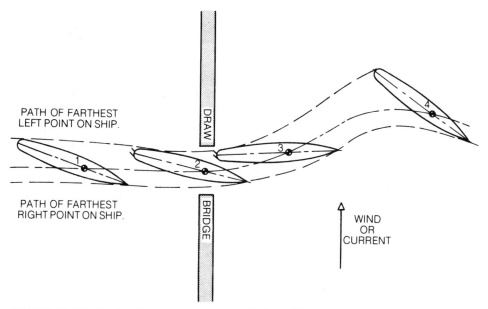

PATH OF FARTHEST
LEFT POINT ON SHIP.

DRAW

PATH OF FARTHEST
RIGHT POINT ON SHIP.

BRIDGE

WIND
OR
CURRENT

FIGURE 10–12. Turning through a narrow restriction with a strong cross-channel set.

conning officer doesn't get a *feel* for his set and drift; he hears the reports and adjusts them mentally, but his ability to doublecheck what is being reported is reduced.

Handling alongside at night

The difference between handling the ship at night and handling it in daylight comes most sharply into focus when we are making a landing. As we approach, we find we are less able to judge distances correctly or to grasp the relative orientation of the ship and its surroundings. The dock seems remote and detached, and then, suddenly, we are upon it; we had no *feel* for our approach speed.

The solution for these disadvantages obviously is caution. We should make our approach slowly and sufficiently wide to be sure that we can accommodate ourselves to the unexpected. We should seek our way with patience instead of dashing in rapidly.

The difficulty of making a pier or nest at night can be greatly reduced by the adroit use of lights. If the pier face or the side of the other ship can be illuminated by floodlights, the problem is greatly simplified. Additionally, illuminating our own forecastle and fantail with floodlights is helpful to the conning officer. It helps him keep the picture of the ship's orientation as well as making it easier for the linehandlers. Finally, we can use our searchlights to pinpoint any areas of doubt. An occasional sweep of the water between the ship and the dock tends to complete the picture and gives us a better estimate of the intervening distance.

In the use of lights at night, all hands must take steps to avoid directing the rays of any light into the eyes of the conning officer. A momentary exposure will destroy his night vision for several minutes—and these might be the crucial minutes. All floodlights should be hooded so that no rays shine toward the bridge. Reflecting objects should be kept out of the beam of the searchlight. The deck force must be trained to keep their flashlights pointed away from the bridge. Though the reflected light from the floodlit areas will also affect the conning officer's night vision, this effect is very much less than that caused by direct rays, and we can accept the results in view of the advantage of having these areas illuminated.

Handling the ship in restricted waters is one of the most interesting phases of shiphandling. We are in close proximity to the dangers and difficulties of confined waters, and we are continually facing absorbing problems. Things happen quickly and we must be well prepared for the events as they occur. As the boundaries move in, we must handle our ship more exactly. Restricted waters are not the place for dash and daring; they are the place for *care and precision*. The shiphandler's skill is tested often in the confines of busy harbors and waterways.

11
radar, sonar, and cic

The developments of modern science have increased the scope of the shiphandler to allow him to handle his ship under conditions which otherwise would have been impossible. He can maneuver his ship safely at night and in low visibility in cases previously beyond his ability. Instead of anchoring until the fog lifts, the modern shiphandler, aided by his radar and his improved sonar, can maneuver with certainty. Instead of depending solely upon the meager glimpses he might catch of shadowy landmarks, and following the advice of a navigator whose plot is a mixture of rainwater, witchcraft, and hope, the conning officer of today is supported by a specially trained, well-equipped crew who are applying all of the powerful tools of modern electronics in guiding the ship safely when the elements blind the senses of man.

But these new instruments are not foolproof and the conning officer must not follow the advice of his supporting team blindly. For each of the important gifts that the recent developments have brought us, we have an increased problem of interpretation of the electronic innuendoes. The old sea dog's eyes are wrinkled from scanning the horizon for the dangers that might threaten his vessel, and it takes years of experience to learn to evaluate what the eye can perceive. It would be foolhardy to think that the interpretation of a radarscope is any less demanding. The radar scans the same area that is viewed by the mariner from his bridge, and though the scene is neatly presented on a relatively small cathode ray tube, it contains even more information of tactical interest than can be obtained by eye. The conning officer, therefore, must be an expert at handling his radar and interpreting its presentation. He must at all times apply his experience and his direct contact with the visible elements of the situation to monitor the activity of his combat information center (CIC) and other supporting groups.

A good officer of the deck would not tolerate a set of binoculars which are out of focus, so why should he tolerate a remote radarscope that is out of focus? He would not be on the bridge if he had to ask the quartermaster to focus his glasses for him, and the same should be true if he had to call for an electronics technician to make the manual adjustments to his radarscope. An OOD should be relieved if he spends his time looking close aboard when he should be scanning the horizon, and he should also be relieved if at night, when cruising alone, he were to have his

PPI on short scale when it should be set for long range search. The radar on a ship is only as valuable as the information which is derived from it. If the conning officer cannot utilize the radar competently, he is not ready to do a competent job of conning a modern ship.

If the throttleman did not notice a drop in the oil pressure to his main bearing, he would be dealt with most harshly and he would not be allowed to continue in his position of responsibility. If a radarman does not notice and report a new contact that is showing on his scope, he is failing in his duty just as much as the throttleman. Neither the throttleman nor the radarman will produce peak performance until they know that their ability is being evaluated and their product is being utilized. As in all segments of a ship's operation, the motivation originates from the bridge. The officer of the deck should require the same quality of performance from the CIC as he requires from his lookouts or his helmsman. Though the CIC is in an advisory position, most of the other watch stations on the ship are also, and they all should be required to make excellence their habit.

CIC

On the bridge it is occasionally difficult to utilize a radarscope because of the lighting conditions and conflicting activities. The CIC, on the other hand, is arranged for ideal utilization of this instrument and sacrifices all else to this end. Thus the CIC should be able to obtain the maximum results from the radar at all times, and should keep the bridge informed of all developments.

In CIC there is space and equipment for plotting and tabulating any information desired. All applicable publications are there and ready for reference. The conning officer should therefore look upon his CIC as his source of up-to-the-minute information on the tactical situation and as a ready source for interpretation of the situation.

The conning officer should recognize that he can gain more from a single glance at his own scope than the CIC evaluator can tell him in several minutes. Though he should demand sufficient information from CIC to insure it is keeping abreast of the situation, he should use his CIC to *augment* what he can derive directly from his equipment. As a matter of practice he should acquire the habit of looking at the bridge PPI when discussing the radar information with CIC.

The capabilities and limitations of the radar and CIC must be known by the shiphandler. If he expects more than the installation is capable of producing, he may take the ship into danger without knowing it. If he demands less than the equipment can provide, he is unnecessarily limiting his ship.

CIC performs one of its most useful functions in detecting other ships and keeping track of them. From its plots CIC can inform the bridge of the location and movement of any ship on the radar screen at any time. The plot should yield the range, bearing, course, speed, closest point of approach (CPA), and time of CPA of any ship in radar range.

FIGURE 11–1. Crewmen in the CIC aboard the amphibious assault ship USS *Guadalcanal* (LPH 7) keep the boards up to the minute on the location of other ships during a Navy exercise.

The surface summary plot is the most useful plot in CIC for the shiphandler, and it must be kept up to the minute. The conning officer should frequently check the accuracy of this plot from his own observations.

Such a plot cannot be kept by simply glancing at a radarscope occasionally and sketching in the picture on another plot. The surface summary plot must accurately identify and locate each contact regardless of the complexity of the situation. Though a fixed formation steaming steadily can be sketched by eye with reasonable accuracy, the picture becomes confused as soon as the formation begins a maneuver. As the contacts merge and their tracks cross on the scope, the sketched plot loses its value, and a better method of summary plotting must be found.

An adequate summary plot must be maintained by frequent and accurate plotting of the complete presentation on the radar. Though this can be done with limited success by measuring and plotting the coordinates of all contacts, a large number of contacts cannot be handled in this way.

With modern radar repeaters, the summary plot can be kept right on the scope itself. Such repeaters are equipped with plotting heads so that all identification marks and tracks appear directly on the face of the scope. With a summary plot controller keeping the overall picture directly on his radarscope, but backed up by a more precise plotting board for measuring exact CPAs and solving maneuvering problems, CIC can maintain an accurate and useful summary of the surface situation and be a real help to the conning officer.

In addition to keeping track of the situation as presented by the radar, CIC should be ready to recommend courses and speeds during maneuvers. As soon as the signal for a maneuver is received, CIC should apply itself to solving the maneuvering problem presented. CIC should advise the bridge of the direction of the course change, and the initial course and speed, and should continually monitor the maneuver to recommend corrections if needed during the evolution.

Although the CIC is prepared to solve the maneuvering problem, it is not practical to leave this problem to them alone. Because the personnel in CIC are separated from visual contact with the situation, they frequently make mistakes that would be obvious from the bridge. Though CIC is charged with the responsibility of providing recommendations for courses and speeds during a maneuver, the maneuver should also be solved by maneuvering board on the bridge so that the conning officer has a ready picture of the maneuver. Though an experienced destroyer officer can estimate the initial course to his new station within narrow limits, he should be backed up immediately with an accurate maneuvering board solution. The CIC solution and the bridge solution will provide a check against one another. The experienced shiphandler who has mastered maneuvering board technique has the advantage of knowing, not only what is happening, but far more important, what is going to happen.

Maneuvering boards

The plotting connected with problems in relative motion in order to obtain a solution can be done on plain paper, but the work is greatly facilitated if the work is done on a polar coordinate form or "board." Three such boards are designed especially for solving relative movement problems. They are the Maneuvering Board, the Navy Mark I Mod O Plastic Maneuvering Board, and the Radar Plotting Sheet. The first two are intended to assist in the solution of all types of relative movement problems; the last is intended primarily for plotting radar contacts. Where a good deal of relative plotting is to be done, the Mark I Mod O Plastic Maneuvering Board is recommended, as its design permits an extremely rapid problem solution.

Skill in working maneuvering board problems, like skill in shiphandling, comes only with practice and long familiarity. Two helpful publications are *Dutton's Navigation and Piloting* (see Chapter 13, "Graphic Solution for Relative Motion Problems"), published by the Naval Institute Press, and *H. O. 217, Maneuvering Board Manual*, published by the U. S. Naval Oceanographic Office.

Advanced maneuvering

Destroyer officers should be the best maneuvering board operators in the fleet because their ships are required to maneuver more frequently than any others. Since it is often highly important in their maneuvering, they should be prepared to take the ship's turning circle into account. This technique is not normally covered in publications on the use of maneuvering boards, but unless it is mastered, many maneuvers will have to be made by "cut and try," since the conventional solution is inadequate.

When allowing for turns in using the maneuvering board, it is not feasible to solve the relative motion during the turn. The easiest method is to approximate the motion of our own ship and the guide during the turn, and estimate the relative position upon completion of the turn. For a maneuver requiring an initial turn to the maneuvering course and a terminal turn upon arriving on station, it is the course and speed to use between these turns that we hope to get from the maneuvering board. The following example illustrates this method of taking the turning circle into account:

Problem   To change station from 5030 to 3090 at 25 knots while guide is steady on 000°T at 15 knots.
Simple Solution (Figure 11–2)   For simple relative motion from A to B: *Steer 170°T at 25 knots.*
Advanced Solution (Figure 11–3)   A quick glance at the problem shows we will have to make a turn of approximately 180° to the right at the start and complete the maneuver with a turn of about 180° to the left. Since we will be speeding up during the first turn and slowing down during the second, we can assume that we average 20 knots during the turns.

At 20 knots, with 30° rudder, our calibration shows that we turn 2° per second with a 600 yard diameter. Therefore, during our first 180° turn, we will move 600 yards to the side and complete the turn in 90 seconds. During this time the guide advances 750 yards (1 ½ minutes at 15 knots), so our position relative to the guide upon completion of the initial turn is not A but (a) as shown in Figure 11–3. Similarly, upon arriving in the vicinity of our new station, we must execute another 180° turn to resume the formation course, and again we will translate 600 yards to the side while the guide advances 750 yards. To allow for this, we should maneuver to arrive at point (b) instead of B. Solving the relative motion problem for the move from (a) to (b), we find we must proceed on course 203°T at 25 knots. This we see is much different from the simple solution which did not take our turns into account. We also perceive that we have located a very important point, (b) the spot where we must put the rudder over and shift the engine order telegraphs to AHEAD STANDARD.

Obviously our solution is not exact because we assumed turns of 180° when in fact our initial turn is 203°. However, we are 33° closer to the correct course than we would have been had we used only the simple solution. As we complete our initial

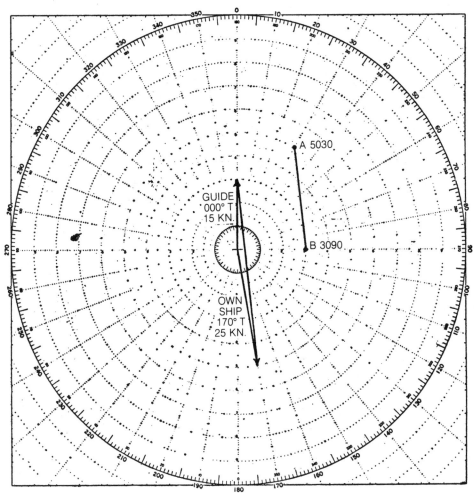

FIGURE 11-2. Simple maneuvering board solution.

turn to 203°T we can recalculate our course for point (b). If we maneuver to pass through point (b) on course 180°T, we can complete our maneuver accurately and end up exactly at point B upon completion of our terminal turn.

Radar

When on soundings or within radar range of land, CIC should be required to keep a navigational plot. By proper use of the radar and visual information, CIC can keep the ship's location very accurately, and if this plot is maintained on the dead reckoning tracer (DRT) and the NC2 plotter, the instantaneous location of the ship is always available. This is especially valuable in an emergency when the ship's location must be known immediately. There is a tendency in some CICs to use radar

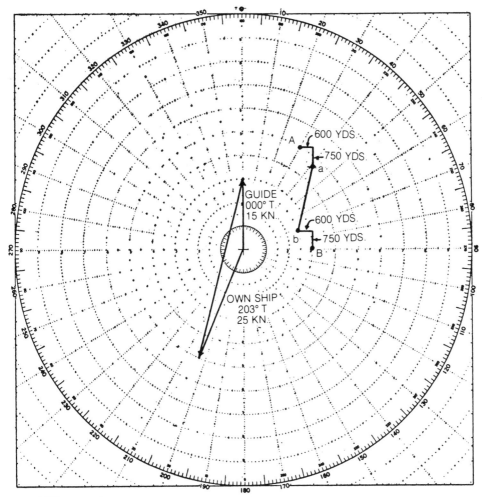

FIGURE 11–3. Advanced maneuvering board solution.

information exclusively because it would be "peeking" to use visual bearings. Although our CIC team must be prepared to navigate on radar information alone during reduced visibility, they must be impressed with the idea that they are engaged in deadly serious business and not playing a game.

We have spoken of the capabilities and limitations of the radar, and we have mentioned the necessity of the bridge stimulating the radar operators to better performance, but we have not defined our terms. As most mariners can testify, the excellence of the radar performance is dependent upon the standard demanded from the bridge. If the bridge does not require peak performance at all times, it is not likely to receive it. If the captain is easily satisfied and considers frequent radar failures an acceptable level of performance, such frequent failures will become the habit in his ship. If, on the other hand, the captain has an acute interest in the performance of his radars and accepts only high reliability, the excellence of his radars will be assured. The radars reflect the interest and effort of the men who service and operate them. If the command inspires these men to exert their best efforts, it will be rewarded by improved radar performance.

Though the radar is capable of detecting objects at very long ranges, and of indicating the range and bearing to them with amazing accuracy, it is discouraging to observe the low level of performance actually obtained unless the conning officer pays particular attention to the adjustment and operation of the radars. The surface search radars in current use in the fleet can detect a target as soon as a substantial part of its superstructure appears above the horizon visible from the height of eye of the antenna. If the radar is properly adjusted, it should give the correct range within 50 yards and the correct bearing within 1°. If the surface search radar is not producing this level of performance, it should be adjusted until it does produce these results.

In order to be able to depend upon his radar information, the conning officer must check his radars frequently. The detection range can be checked by noting the maximum range at which targets are acquired. The radar should always detect a target before it can be sighted from the bridge, and one soon learns to judge the maximum range at which a ship of a given type should be detected. If the conning officer knows that a given type ship has at one time been detected by his radar at a certain range, he should accept nothing less than this range subsequently. Although there are unusual weather conditions that allow extreme ranges to be obtained with radar, these are infrequent. The conning officer can feel confident that his demands remain within the realm of the possible if he is requiring the repetition of performance obtained previously with the same equipment. If radar ranges less than this acceptable level are experienced, the radar should be checked for failure and returned.

To determine the accuracy of the ranges being obtained, the radar's performance should be checked against other radars, and frequent "double echo" checks should be made. Though the range accuracy possible is within 50 yards of the true range, it is surprising to note how often the radar can be so badly out of calibration that the ranges reported are in error by several hundred yards. This inaccuracy will be due in part to maladjustments of the radar and in part to the improper reading of the information. Whatever the cause, it is susceptible to correction if the conning officer requires the appropriate level of performance. Ranges from all of the radars on the ship should be compared frequently and adjustments made until any radar on the ship can be depended upon to produce accuracy commensurate with the capabilities of the equipment.

The bearing accuracy of the radars is easily checked. Simply select a target at sufficient range so that it subtends a small arc, and then check the radar bearing against the visual bearing measured from the bridge pelorus. Normally the radar bearing should be within 1° of the visual bearing, but the accuracy will depend on the type of radar installed and the method used in measuring the bearing. If the radar is inherently poor in bearing discrimination, a series of bearings might fall in a small area about the correct bearing, but the average of these bearings should be very near the correct bearing. If there is any constant error, this should be eliminated by alignment of the radar.

The inherent capability of a modern radar is immense. If the conning officer does not demand high standards of performance, he will not realize this capability. Continual interest in the radar and frequent checking of its performance will go a long way toward insuring that the ship will have this tool available when needed.

Fathometer and sonar

Though the radar is the right arm of the shiphandler, the Fathometer is also an important aid. The character of the bottom of the ocean and its tributaries is as distinctive as the shoreline. The dependability and accuracy of the Fathometer makes this instrument invaluable to the mariner when he is in shoal water. The Fathometer should be used whenever the depth is of interest to the conning depth officer.

Most Fathometers measure the depth from the bottom of the ship, and thus measure the true distance from the keel to the floor of the ocean. The Fathometer can measure the depth with great accuracy from one fathom to a thousand fathoms or more; but to insure this accuracy, it should be calibrated in port and frequently checked against a lead line. If care is taken with the Fathometer it is better than the lead line when the ship is moving. Even in the hands of an expert quartermaster, the lead line readings are of questionable accuracy if the ship is moving at appreciable speed and if the interval between soundings is quite long. On the other hand, the accuracy of the Fathometer is not affected by the speed of the ship, and the soundings come so rapidly that they can be considered to be continuous.

The sonar of today is of great value in a channel and when close to other ships. At short ranges older type radars become difficult to use. Sonar, on the other hand, is at its best at short ranges, and it can do much to fill in the gap. In dangerous situations where neither visual nor radar information is available, sonar can show us all of the shoals and ships in our vicinity. It is the danger close at hand that must be avoided, and sonar gives us eyes under the water that are especially perceptive to things close aboard.

Fog

The real test of the shiphandler's ability to utilize the new electronic aids at his command comes when entering a harbor in a dense fog. Normally, radar and sonar merely assist the shiphandler and provide him with information of greater accuracy than is obtainable by other means; but in restricted waters, with zero visibility, these aids provide the *only* means of moving the ship with safety. Ferryboats may continue to operate in a fog, because their runs are short and never change. Their captains, through years of study, learn every landmark and source of sound or light along the track, and know every habit of the wind and current. "Whistle toot" ranging (timing the interval until the echo returns from the shore after a "toot" of the whistle) can be resorted to if the air is calm and the banks of the harbor are abrupt (such as found in Puget Sound). But except for such special cases, ships without modern electronic equipment are paralyzed by a heavy fog.

When proceeding at low visibility, maximum use must be made of every aid. Special fog lookouts should be posted and instructed to be alert for sounds as well as visual contacts. The best radar and sonar operators should be operating the equipment, and the most skilled CIC team should be on station. The conning officer should place himself where he can make use of all of the information that is available. Ideally, he should take a position where he can have good visibility in case the fog lifts momentarily, but at the same time he should be able to view a radar repeater. He should be in contact with the CIC, and he should be receiving the Fathometer reports directly. Above all, it is most important that the navigational plot be available so that he can be continually abreast of the navigator's best estimate of the ship's position and can have constant reference to the chart. It is a good practice to have a separate chart for the conning officer's exclusive use for identifying landmarks and for correlating the radar and sonar information with the ship's position.

It has been traditional for the conning officer to station himself on the open bridge, trying to pierce the fog by sheer force of will when poking about in low visibility. Though in this location he is well placed to observe the last moments before the collision, he can see nothing at all during the period when effective action could have been taken. Some officers propose that the captain should be in CIC where the "best" information is available, but such officers do not appreciate the importance of *visual* information in an emergency. Though 95 percent of all emergencies can be handled by efficient use of the information in the CIC, it is that last 5 percent that has kept the "Old Man" from being obsolete in this modern electronic world.

The captain should no more concentrate on being a lookout, and thus deny himself access to his other instruments, than he should bury himself in CIC and lose the information he might gain from his eyes and ears. He should study the problem and make sure that he has placed himself where he can best receive and employ all information that might become available. More can be obtained by a glance at the horizon than through a lengthy report from a lookout. More can be derived by studying a radarscope for a moment than can be received by hundreds of words from CIC. And explanations and reports are more quickly understood if the recipient is looking at the radar or sonar picture while receiving the information.

A combination conning position is therefore best, and this can be provided on most Navy ships. A position which will afford the conning officer quick access to all sources of information is best. The ability to scan a radarscope, check the navigator's chart, obtain verbal reports, maintain good visibility, and remain in communication with the helmsman, annunciators, and the commanding officer is ideal. Most of our modern men-of-war provide the "ship driver" with a physical layout which will enable him to accomplish all of the above with a minimum of footwork.

Thus, as the ship proceeds through the fog, her position can be plotted from the radar ranges and bearings on the relatively long-range landmarks, and this position can be verified by comparing the plotted position on the chart with the picture on the radarscope.

The most difficult part of "zero visibility" shiphandling is the detection and avoiding of other craft moving about in the harbor. The smaller the craft, the less easy she is to detect. However, through alert use of the radar and sonar information, we can detect even the smallest vessels. With some practice, the approximate size and speed of unseen vessels can be predicted by their propeller noise on the sonar.

Radar and sonar have made it possible for the ship to be maneuvered with safety under conditions which previously would have denied operations. If we understand our equipment and are skillful in its utilization, we can proceed, regardless of the weather or visibility. On the other hand, if we blindly accept the indications of this new equipment without understanding its vagaries and limitations, we are headed for disaster. As with other technical equipment, radar and sonar are effective only in the hands of skilled men.

12
large combatants

The bo'sun's call sounded over the amplifying system, followed by, "Now secure the special sea detail." The big man-of-war lay at rest alongside the pier, her landing completed.

Topsides, the appearance of the men matched the smartness of the ship. They were a proud-looking crew. There were grins on their faces. From heaving line distance, the lines had gone over easily, yet a narrow gap between ship and pier had preserved the sidecleaners' efforts. Below decks, the throttlemen nodded approval as they scanned an orderly series of bells in the bell book. The orders to the engines had been indicative of a conning officer who knew his business.

On the bridge a quartermaster summed it up as he looked toward the back of the conning officer, just disappearing down the ladder: "He handles her like a destroyer."

This finest of shiphandling compliments had more truth in it than the quartermaster realized. What he had meant was obvious. What he did not realize was that the principles employed had been exactly those applicable to a destroyer.

In replenishment at sea a large combatant must make the same approach as the destroyer on the vessels of the replenishment group. Thanks to a healthy appetite, she must hold alongside for greater periods of time. Tactics and formation steaming also exact a heavy demand. While reorientation of the screen may not involve the larger ship, a change in formation axis finds the destroyers of the circular screen remaining in station while the cruisers and carriers do the maneuvering. The requirement being nearly the same, and the big vessels less easy to handle under some conditions, they present a challenge to the conning officer that may be said to be the postgraduate course in shiphandling.

The instructors in this course are well qualified. The commanding officer may be a graduate of the destroyer school, and has probably commanded one or more other types of vessel as well—submarine, amphibious craft, or auxiliary. He is serving his final tour as an individual ship commander and preparing for the important step to flag grade and its responsibility for groups of ships. It is his final performance in shiphandling, and those who attain it are already well schooled in the science. He is an officer who has proved himself in handling vessels of lesser tonnage.

FIGURE 12–1. Precise shiphandling in cruisers.

In addition, our executive officer is also an ex-commanding officer. The more senior heads of department have either had a command, or are soon slated for one.

In the midst of this wealth of experience, the officer joining a large combatant might feel that his opportunity to learn shiphandling would be small. Quite the contrary. Farsighted commanding officers do all in their power to pass along their experience and knowledge. They frequently offer the opportunity to their juniors to familiarize themselves with the science of shiphandling through practice as well as instruction and observation.

The fundamentals discussed in the previous chapters are as applicable to the larger ships as they are to destroyers. This chapter will emphasize the variations in execution of these fundamentals which the tonnage, power, and configuration of these big ships require. The physical characteristics of these magnificent vessels will be discussed, and then, following the sequence of the preceding chapters, we will apply the fundamentals to these characteristics. Battleships are now out of commission, so we will deal principally with cruisers in this chapter. However, a summary section on the handling characteristics of battleships is included.

CRUISERS

In comparison with destroyers, cruisers are vessels of heavy tonnage and great length. Heavy and light cruisers were so designated because of their gun batteries, not their tonnage. With the advent of guided missiles this designation became less meaningful because all have great striking power and are heavy ships. From the shiphandler's point of view they are all similar, so for purposes of illustration we will use USS *Columbus* (CG 12), which has the following characteristics:

Length	673 ft.
Beam	71 ft.
Draft	32 ft.
Displacement	
Standard	13,600 tons
Full load	17,000 tons
Total shaft horsepower	120,000
Maximum speed	34 knots
Crew	80 officers and 1,500 men

From the photograph of *Columbus*, we note the cruiser's general characteristics from the shiphandler's point of view. She is long and slim, with a high superstructure almost equally distributed fore and aft. Her hull form is nearly identical to that of the destroyer. The most notable difference, other than the obvious difference in size, is that she is provided with four propellers instead of two.

The two inboard propellers are mounted just forward of the rudder and relatively close to the centerline. The outboard propellers are set well forward, and are offset to the side more than a full propeller diameter beyond the inboard shafts. Consequently the discharge and circulating currents of the inboard propellers greatly affect the rudder action, while the currents produced by the outboard propellers are felt very little by the rudder. A cruiser's rudder is large enough so that

FIGURE 12–2. USS *Columbus* (CG 12) steams past USS *Kitty Hawk* (CVA 63).

when turned through only a small angle, it actually enters the discharge race of the inboard screw on that side. On the other hand, though the outboard propellers have little effect on the rudder, they produce a much greater twisting moment when opposed, because of their greater lever arm. For these reasons it is sometimes desirable to handle the shafts on a side independently.

Another important characteristic is the reduced horsepower-per-ton of the cruiser in comparison with the destroyer. Our cruiser has six times the mass of a destroyer but only twice the power. A destroyer has about 19 horsepower per ton, while a cruiser has only about 6.5 horsepower per ton (total shaft horsepower vs. full load tonnage). This means that, neglecting all other factors, the destroyer can accelerate three times as fast as the cruiser.

Although the destroyer has three times the horsepower per ton of a cruiser, the maximum speed of the two types is nearly the same (about 34 knots nominally). One may wonder why the smaller vessel requires so much more power in comparison with her tonnage. A more complete discussion of the technical aspects of this problem is presented in Chapter 1.

Seaman's eye

"Seaman's eye," the expression of a conning officer's competence in shiphandling, is as pertinent to the handling of a cruiser as of a destroyer. In fact, it must be exercised with even greater skill. It has been mentioned earlier that the human eye is at its worst at sea; it is even less capable, in many respects, from a cruiser bridge than from a destroyer bridge. The height of eye from the water lends a remoteness from contact points—distance from bow to buoy, side to pier, stern to obstacle.

Handling a big ship safely requires keen judgment and a full measure of foresight. Decisions must be made early and error is often not susceptible to correction. On the other hand, a cruiser is more stable and can hold her course and speed more precisely than a destroyer, and one finds in her a wealth of talent and equipment.

Consequently the cruiser conning officer, just as his counterpart in the destroyer, must exercise excellent judgment, know his ship intimately, and understand thoroughly the principles of shiphandling. There are actually few evolutions demanded of a destroyer that are not likewise demanded of the modern cruiser.

Handling a destroyer has been likened to driving a sports car. Handling a cruiser is like driving a Rolls Royce. She is called upon for a multitude of duties— antiaircraft protection in a carrier task force, gunfire support of an amphibious landing, leader of a surface striking force, for example. But the principles learned in the sports car are applicable to driving the Rolls Royce.

Forces affecting the ship

The mass of a cruiser is many times that of a destroyer. Her inertia is greater. Consequently her tendency to resist linear acceleration is increased accordingly. Our cruiser is slow to move after the screws begin turning, and slow to come to a halt when the backing turbines have commenced their task. She resists angular acceleration as well, but here the lag over that experienced by a destroyer is less noticeable. Her turning characteristics are more nearly those of a destroyer than are her characteristics of rate of change of speed.

The physical relationship between vessel and water is more obvious in large ships than in smaller ones. For example, a cruiser in a turn illustrates quite clearly the convergence of the centerline of the ship toward the center of the turn, with the stern riding well outside and the bow inside the mean path as the ship describes the arc. In a ship of such great length it is more apparent that she is rotating about her pivot point during a turn.

The standard orders to the engines discussed in Chapter 3 apply to our cruiser even though she has four propellers instead of two. On the bridge the engine order telegraph is no different from a destroyer's. Both starboard shafts take their order from the starboard engine telegraph, and both port shafts take theirs from the port engine telegraph. The engines are controlled in pairs. Though there are some situations in which a conning officer may desire to give orders to a single shaft, special signals must first be arranged with the engine room to provide for this.

Wind affects a cruiser much less than a destroyer. The mass of a cruiser creates stiff opposition to the whims of the sea breeze. The long hull, riding deep in the water, resists the wind's attempt to move it laterally just as the keel of a racing, sloop minimizes leeway.

The distribution of the "sail area" of a cruiser gives her a further advantage with respect to the wind. It provides balance. In backing and filling in restricted waters, the tendency for the bow to work downwind is greatly decreased in a cruiser. Where the destroyer finds it difficult to turn into the wind at low speeds, and even more difficult to back the stern away from the wind, the cruiser has less difficulty. This is because her bow and stern are nearly equal in height and her superstructure is nearly balanced in its fore and aft distribution.

A comparison of the silhouette of the two types makes the difference in wind effect obvious. In proportion, the destroyer bow is seen to be higher, the stern lower than the cruiser's. The destroyer bridge structure is farther forward in relation to the overall length, and there is a lack of balancing structure aft to match that which the cruiser possesses in her after superstructure.

While the cruiser gains a degree of immunity from the effects of wind, it gains no immunity from current. When lying dead in the water, a cruiser moves identically with the current. It is floating in a fluid that is itself in motion, and is oblivious of the fact that the water which supports it is in turn moving over the ground. The current is recognizable only by a comparison with buoys, piers, or rocks, or by taking navigational "fixes." Were no object in sight and no fixes obtained, the current would be unrecognizable as such.

Current is a term used to express the movement of a mass of water over the bottom in a definite direction. It has a "set" (direction) and "drift" (velocity). A ship which is floating free, with no way on, will be carried with the current. If the current has a set of 250°T and a drift of 4 knots, the ship, dead in the water, will make good 250°T, 4 knots, over the ground. As far as the ship and the water in which it floats are concerned, it makes no difference to the ship whether the water is in motion or not, except that the motion of the water affects the motion of the ship in relation to piers, buoys, shoals, etc. A vessel lying in an 8-knot current would be unaware of any current unless it passed a buoy, or other stationary object. Since the mass of water in which the ship rests is in motion, if the ship wishes to remain stationary in relation to the ground, it must steam into the current at a speed equal to the drift and on a course exactly opposite to the set.

Handling a ship near stationary objects—piers, buoys, etc.—in a current is a problem in relative motion. The water is moving relative to the bottom. The ship can control her motion relative to the water. The motion of the ship with respect to the bottom is then the combination of the two relative movements.

In restricted waters the current at the surface and the current at various depths below the surface are not always the same. At times they differ in velocity; sometimes they actually run in opposite directions. A cruiser with her greater draft is affected by deeper currents which do not affect a destroyer. The cruiser conning officer knows that he cannot rely on surface current indications alone in predicting the net effect of current on his ship. When he is unfamiliar with the characteristics of the current, he would be prudent to take a pilot and to profit by the pilot's local knowledge.

Lines and deck equipment

A cruiser is secured to her berth or to her buoy in exactly the same manner as a destroyer. The only difference is that she moors with 8-inch nylon lines instead of 6-inch. Where a destroyer uses a ⅝-inch wire, we will find a cruiser uses a 1-inch wire. Spring lay wire rope is also popular for use in mooring cruisers.

Though the six-line mooring arrangement is the same, the equipment of handling it is more elaborate. A cruiser has two anchor windlasses on the forecastle and can thus work two lines (or two anchors) at the same time. On her fantail, a powerful deck winch can take an 8-inch line nicely. Even amidships, we may find a small winch that can be utilized for handling lines.

Even with all this equipment and the broad decks for use of the linehandlers, the lines are handled more slowly on a cruiser than on a destroyer. Part of this may be due to mental attitude, and if so, this should be corrected, but some of it has valid cause. The lines are heavier, the stresses greater. There is a communication lag as the order is passed down from the bridge through the sound-powered system. More men are required for each task, and their efforts must be coordinated if their numbers are to be effective. The conning officer on the bridge must be aware of this and consider it in his calculations.

The fenders of a cruiser are correspondingly larger than those described earlier for destroyers, and they are more difficult to shift. The conning officer should plan their location carefully and allow ample time for their placement. The long, flat sides of the cruiser's midship section are ideal places for the use of fenders, but at the bow the flare is so pronounced that it is very difficult to place a fender effectively here as the bow moves in against an object.

In general, the conning officer of the cruiser must be just as familiar with the deck equipment of his ship as his counterpart on the destroyer.

Measuring the situation

As pointed out earlier, the time lag between order and result is greater and the margin for error is less with cruisers than with destroyers. For example, to bring our cruiser to a stop from a given speed, we must BACK for a much longer time than with the destroyer, and a greater advance is made in the process. Hence, the conning officer must have the characteristics and calibration data of his ship at his finger tips. At the various speeds of approach, he must know the distance required to come to a stop, employing various backing powers; he must know the relative distance required to reduce speed when approaching another ship to replenish or pass mail; and he must know the turning characteristics of his ship. All of this emphasizes the importance of carefully calibrating the ship.

The accuracy required in handling large ships demands that guesswork be kept to a minimum. To make the calibration data of the ship readily available, it has become the practice in large ships to collect these data in a single folder on the bridge known as the *bridge folder*. Turn diagrams, acceleration table, and optimum scopes of chain for anchoring in various depths of water are typical of the items included. The bridge folder is a file of exact tactical data on the ship instantly available to the conning officer and his assistants for use in handling the ship.

One of the most valuable items in the bridge folder is the acceleration table. This specifies the time rate at which the shaft rpm shall be changed with increasing or decreasing speed. In following the table, the throttleman will gradually change the shaft rpm to complete the change in exactly the minutes and seconds specified. By the use of identical acceleration tables, ships can maintain precise station even while changing speed.

Unfortunately, there is no universal acceleration table. There is one for each major type, and a ship will ordinarily use the one for her type. In a mixed task force, the table to be used must be specified. The conning officer must know what acceleration table is in use, and must insure that this is the one that the engine room is employing.

The conning officer frequently wants to predict his "surge" (the distance gained or lost while changing speed) in a formation. When he approaches a new station at a speed greater than formation speed, he wishes to know when to slow to formation speed. When dropping back into a new station, he wishes to know at what distance ahead of station he should resume formation speed.

We can use an average value of surge as outlined in the previous chapters, and for a limited range it will be quite satisfactory. A surge of 65 *yards per knot* is a good average value which applies to a cruiser when operating at about 15 knots. Though this thumb rule applies to a number of cases, we should employ our acceleration data for a more accurate solution.

Actually, the concept of there being a constant surge of a certain number of yards for each knot of the speed change is quite incorrect. A moment's reflection will reveal that, if we decelerate at a constant rate, the amount we will surge varies as the *square* of the speed change, not by a constant amount per knot. For small changes within a limited range, a fixed surge per knot of change will work out, because the time lag (that is, the interval from the time the order is given on the bridge until the speed of the ship actually begins to change) is large and the throttleman actually executes the changes as rapidly as the engines will answer. If we always waited a fixed interval and then changed to the new speed instantaneously, the fixed number of yards per knot would be correct. On the other hand, if we effected all speed changes in exactly the same interval of time, the rule would also be correct. Since we neither make the changes instantaneously nor in a fixed interval of time, especially when following an acceleration curve, we should find a more accurate method of predicting surge.

If we plot our acceleration curve as indicated in Figure 12–3, it will be a useful addition to the bridge folder. A glance at the curve will reveal the change in slope between various sections of the curve, and will indicate the inaccuracy of assuming a constant surge at all speed ranges. At the lower end of the curve the acceleration is 5 knots per minute, but in the vicinity of 25 knots it takes a full minute to change one knot. Obviously the surge is much different in the two ranges.

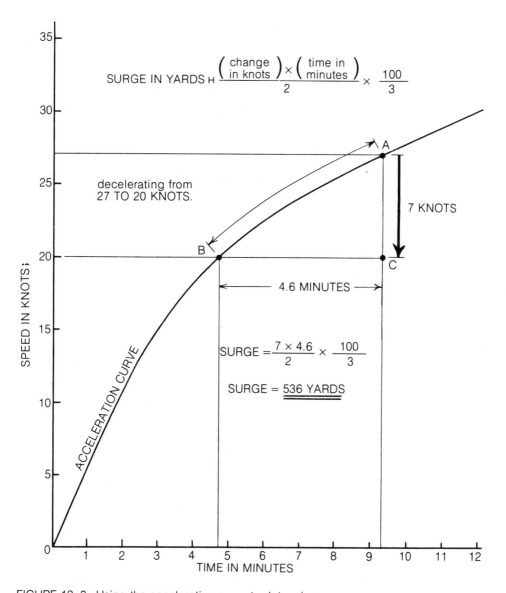

FIGURE 12–3. Using the acceleration curve to determine surge.

If, for a specific speed change, we note the elapsed time required to make the change, we can compute the surge by multiplying the speed change by the required time and then dividing by two. In approaching a station, our speed *advantage* over the formation *at the start of the change* is equal to the amount of the change; our speed advantage *at the end of the change* is zero. Therefore our *average speed advantage* throughout the change (assuming constant deceleration) is one half the amount of the change; hence we divide the speed-time product by two.

Referring to Figure 12–3, if we are making 27 knots and are joining a formation making 20 knots, we will decelerate along the curve from A to B. Our speed change is AC and the time required to accomplish this change is BC. Our surge, then, is equal to the *area* of triangle ABC. To convert this to yards we multiply this area by 100/3 (100 yards per minute is 3 knots). When operating at speeds above 15 knots or below 9 knots, this method is much more accurate than using the thumb-rule constant of 65 yards per knot. The only inaccuracy involved is the assumption that the ship decelerates along the chord AB instead of along the curve. The exact solution would include the small area between the curve and its chord, but the error involved in this method is inconsequential.

For handy use on the bridge it is useful to pre-compute the surge and to prepare a surge table (Table 12–1) covering the normally encountered speed changes. Note that no allowance has been made for time lag in the table. For use

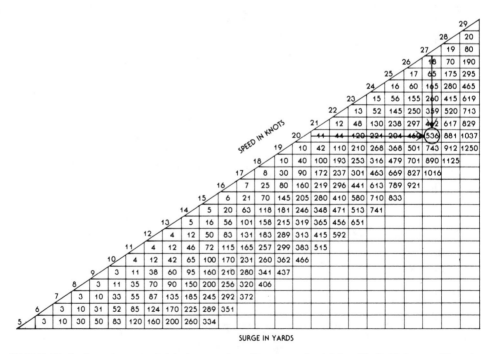

SURGE IN YARDS

TABLE 12–1. Sample surge table for a cruiser. To use, enter table with "initial speed," and read "surge" opposite "final speed." (Note: This table is for illustration purposes only; it does not apply to an actual ship.)

aboard ship, several entries should be determined by experiment and the table adjusted to include the actual lag.

With the facilities available on a cruiser and the number of officers available to assist in precise shiphandling, the cruiser should be handled to perfection. Habitual use of the turn diagram and the surge table should be made to take the guesswork out of the maneuver. The advanced maneuvering board solutions taking turning circle and surge into account should be used. Ranges and bearings should be exactly measured, and all maneuvers should be calculated to the limit of the information and time available. The excellence of shiphandling is often based on the care with which the situation is measured.

Handling alongside

The principles of handling a cruiser alongside a pier are, of course, the same as for handling a destroyer, but there is a temptation to approach too rapidly and overshoot the berth. The big ship glides so smoothly through the water that it seems inconceivable that she will be hard to stop, *but it takes a lot of backing to bring her to a halt*. For this reason we should always approach wide enough so that an overshoot won't get us into trouble.

On the other hand, should we approach to put the bow in position with a 15° inclination, the stern would be too far out to run the mooring lines. With a ship over 200 yards long we must make the final approach more nearly parallel to the pier so that both the forecastle and the fantail can reach with their heaving lines.

Wind causes less trouble in mooring the cruiser than it does a lighter ship. She will take longer to commence being blown downwind, and she will move more slowly when she does respond. Conversely, once the wind has taken hold and started the ship, greater momentum is involved and the damage which can be done is greater.

Where a fair approach is possible, a landing of the cruiser unassisted by tugs is perfectly feasible. Cruisers can—and frequently do—make landings without assistance. However, in comparison with a destroyer, this landing must be made at a lower speed and more cautiously. Should an error be made with such a heavy ship, severe damage could result. Where navigational hazards or adverse conditions make the evolution difficult, it is prudent to employ tugs.

When restricted maneuvering room dictates leaving the nest by going ahead, the conning officer may approach the situation with confidence. A cruiser can leave a nest by going out ahead just as easily as by backing. Her sides are free from annoying projections, and her slight tumble home assists in preventing fouling at the main deck level and above. The armor belt provides an ideal bearing surface for the fenders, and her long flat sides assure a clean, smooth getaway.

As in the case of the destroyer when going out ahead, the ship is first opened out laterally by slacking the forward lines and riding to number five as the bow moves out. When the bow has moved out enough, we cast off, kick the engines ahead, and swing the ship parallel to the nest with the rudder (and engines if necessary) to get the stern clear of the other ship. As the ship moves forward, we use the rudder to keep the stern out from the other ship's side, but we must do this cautiously until our ship's pivot point has come abreast the buoy (or anchor chain).

Anchoring

Even when fitted with sonar, a cruiser is not restricted from anchoring with head-way, so long as reasonable precautions are taken to prevent the chain from being snapped taut across the keel. The decision to anchor while moving ahead or astern should be based therefore on the heading on which the ship will lie when she finally rides to her anchor. In order to insure good holding, it is highly desirable that the chain be laid out from the anchor and not dropped upon it. In the latter case a bight of the chain might even foul a fluke and prevent the anchor from "digging in" in the proper manner. Since the ship will swing with the prevailing wind or current, she will ride downwind from the point where the anchor is dropped. Thus the ship should be moving (slowly) downwind when we order "Let go." This might require anchoring while moving ahead, while moving astern, or while being carried broadside by the prevailing wind or current. The manner in which the ship is anchored therefore depends upon the prevailing conditions of wind and current and the allowable approach.

In the case where the wind is from ahead as we approach our berth, we should pass through the anchorage slightly and let go as we back through the berth. If the prevailing conditions indicate that we will ride on a nearly opposite heading from our approach heading, we should anchor as we pass through the berth going ahead. In this case, however, it is wise to begin swinging the stern to the side opposite the anchor being used as soon as the anchor is released, in order to insure that the chain will not tend under the ship.

When the crosswind approach is used, the ship should be brought to a stop with the hawsepipe slightly to the windward of the "hole." As the wind moves the bow downwind, the anchor should be released as the hawsepipe passes over the center of the berth. The upwind anchor should be used to prevent the chain from riding under the ship or across the bow.

The crosswind approach is more difficult than an approach with or into the wind. As the ship loses headway, the leeward set becomes more noticeable. It takes a nice sense of judgment to determine the proper "lead" to place the bow in the desired spot. As the ship slows, the "crabbing" (sidewise motion) becomes more severe, and the final approach is usually a constant turn with full rudder to get the bow to windward of the berth with the little steerageway remaining.

The heavy ground tackle of a cruiser makes it even more desirable to "walk out" the chain so that the anchor is not dropped from too great a height. The momentum of the heavy chain can be difficult to arrest, and, if the anchor is falling rapidly, a certain amount of chain will pile up on top of the anchor before the chain can be stopped. As with a destroyer, the anchor should be walked out until it is within 10 fathoms of the bottom before it is dropped.

The rate at which an anchor chain can be hove in is limited by the speed of the anchor windlass, therefore an adequate time must be allowed by the officer of the deck to insure that the anchor can be brought to "short stay" and weighed on schedule. Time must be allowed not only for the designed maximum rate of the anchor windlass but also for delays caused when the wind or current puts excessive strains on the chain and slows the operation, or when a muddy bottom requires more time to clean the chain. On a windy day, with a long scope of chain, it may take a relatively long time to heave in the anchor.

Under severe conditions it may be advisable to assist the anchor windlass by turning over the screws slowly to ease the strain. The chain should only be *eased*, not *slacked*, in doing this. When there is danger of dragging, the chain can be eased in this manner also, but is important to keep a steady strain on the anchor. To slack the chain and then permit it to come taut with a jerk can initiate dragging.

The ship's bridge folder should have a table of optimum scopes of chain for various depths of water. The table is computed to insure maximum holding while employing the minimum chain required. This table can be made up from Chapter 9260 of the *Naval Ships Technical Manual*.

It is even more important in a cruiser than in a destroyer that the approach to the anchorage be carefully planned, since corrective action is more difficult to take. As was pointed out in Chapter 6, navigational fixes are always a step behind the ship's actual position, and the conning officer must be ready to bring the ship to her anchorage regardless of what the success of the navigator may be.

The easiest approach is one made on a constant bearing to a prominent object, with the "distance to go" to anchorage marked by predetermined bearings of objects near the beam.

Since her backing power is limited, a cruiser should be carefully calibrated to insure she can be stopped accurately when anchoring. Average data from eleven cruisers indicates that the following approach will put the hawsepipe over the center of the berth under no-wind, no-current conditions:

Yards To Berth	Action
1,000	Be making 10 knots through the water
800	STOP all engines
500	BACK ONE-THIRD

If there is appreciable wind or current, an adjustment will be necessary in the above procedure.

If the approach is being made on advice from CIC during reduced visibility, lower speed should be employed. The following is a good system when navigating by radar:

Yards To Berth	Action
2,000	Slow to 5 knots
800	STOP
200	BACK ONE-THIRD

Allowance must be made for the time lag between the order to "Let go" and the time the chain actually starts rattling out the hawsepipe.

Mooring

A cruiser can be moored by the same method as outlined for the destroyer; in fact, the "trolley method" of snatching a buoy was developed in a cruiser. A cruiser may take a bit longer to moor because of the weight of the gear involved, and is thus subject to the wind and current for a longer period before it can ride secured to the buoy. For this reason, in a heavy wind or strong current, it is desirable to have the assistance of a tug to control the bow.

Under normal conditions the cruiser can be moored to a buoy without assistance just as readily as a destroyer. As with the destroyer, placing the ship so that the buoy is abreast the bow instead of dead ahead will greatly facilitate the approach and initial connections. When ready to shackle the chain, however, the bow will have to be brought almost directly over the buoy by heaving in on the buoy line in order to permit the men on the buoy to handle the heavier chain.

We must bear in mind the large mass of the ship in proportion to the buoy and the men who are working the moor. A misjudged kick of the engines can work havoc. An imperceptible movement of the ship can result in the buoy being submerged by the strain. The ship must be handled delicately when her bow is at the buoy. Power should be applied with caution.

The men of the mooring party should spend the minimum time on the buoy and be taken off whenever there is danger of the buoy spinning or submerging. A ship can put a heavy strain on the buoy line, and the buoy may spin under this strain as turns in the buoy moorings are unwound.

When unmooring, the process can be expedited by running a "slip wire" and taking in the heavy chain ahead of time. The slip wire is run from the bow through the mooring ring on the buoy and back on deck. The bitter end is secured on deck with a pelican hook, and the ship rides to the bight of this wire. As soon as the slip wire is taking the strain, the chain can be unshackled and heaved in. The boat and buoy party, not needed for casting off the slip wire, can be hoisted on board. The ship can ride to the slip wire alone for the few minutes before casting off.

When ready to "slip" the buoy, the pelican hook is simply tripped (this can be done even under heavy strain). The end of the wire is then pulled through the buoy ring and the ship is completely clear of the buoy. In preparing for slipping, care should be taken when running the slip wire to prevent any twisting of the two parts of the bight. If there are any turns as a result of improper running of the wire or spinning of the buoy, these turns will run down to the buoy ring when the bitter end is tripped; the wire will tend to bind, preventing it from being pulled free from the buoy.

When making a Mediterranean moor, the ideal moor is made with the anchors well spread; but with a cruiser this is often impractical because of limited maneuvering and berthing space.

In lieu of spreading the anchors, it is customary to drop both anchors ahead, with the second anchor placed nearly underfoot. The first anchor, with its long scope, provides a good fore-and-aft restraint, and the second anchor quickly restrains any side component when the bow moves to one side in response to wind or current. Figure 12–4 illustrates this action.

If this method is used, a cruiser can usually make the moor unassisted. She should drop her first anchor at nearly maximum scope to allow ample margin for firmly digging in the anchor. The second anchor should be dropped when the stern is about 60 yards from the mole. Allowing 20 yards for digging in and 10 yards from the stern to the mole, this would leave the second anchor 30 yards ahead of the hawsepipe. At this short scope, the second anchor will begin to provide a side restraint when the bow has moved only a short distance to the side.

If a tug is available and the harbor permits, the anchors can be placed equidistant from the mole and spread by having the tug move the bow first to one side and then to the other while the anchors are being placed. This is not done when ships are moored close together, because if their anchors tend in a direction other than ahead, they can foul the chains of the vessels on either side. In most harbors where the Mediterranean moor is used, extra kedge anchors are provided by the harbor authorities to securely restrain the bows of large ships.

In making a Mediterranean moor with a cruiser, after the anchors are dropped and the first lines run to the mole, it is recommended that the captain shift aft to the fantail and supervise the completion of the moor from there. From the bridge the stern will appear several yards inland when the moor is completed; the true situation can only be seen from aft.

A danger of backing into the moles does, of course, exist and is met by controlling the sternward movement of the ship with the anchors. As the after lines are heaved in, the anchor chains are carefully eased, allowing the ship to inch

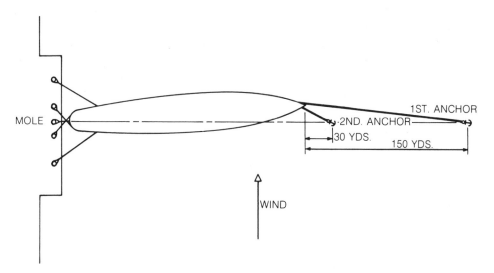

FIGURE 12–4. Mediterranean moor with a cruiser. (Note action of anchors with long and short scopes when bow is blown to the side.)

backwards toward the mole. Since this is rather an unfair tug-of-war, the engines must usually be used at low power to assist the deck winch aft.

The captain aft, controlling the maneuver, the OOD on the bridge controlling the engines, the first lieutenant on the forecastle controlling the anchors, and the gunnery officer on the fantail handling the after lines and judging the distance must work as a smooth team in placing the big ship in her berth.

When the ship is finally in place and the stern secured, a good strain is taken on the anchors to prevent the swells or wind from setting the ship against the mole. The chains are heaved in until they provide a nearly flat lead to the anchors. There is no room astern for taking up the slack of a normal catenary.

If heavy weather is expected and several ships are moored stern to the mole in adjacent berths, running normal mooring lines between the ships will add a good measure of security to the moor. The inter-ship mooring lines bind the ships into a nest and prevent them moving relative to one another. When we consider that this nest is secured by several anchors forward and multiple lines aft, we will recognize that this is one of the most secure methods of mooring.

Handling at sea

Intricate maneuvers in complex formations are not limited to destroyers. Our cruiser has its problems as well. While it is true that a reorientation of the screen has no effect on our cruiser, a change in formation axis often finds the heavier ships maneuvering while the escorts ride undisturbed in their circular screen.

Though destroyers are expected to maneuver so as not to embarrass the heavy ships, it would be foolhardy to depend on this when handling our cruiser in a large formation. Our only safe course is to presume that the converging destroyer will give us no special consideration. We must assume our share of the burden and be guided by the Rules of the Road as we maneuver in the proximity of others.

If bearings are being taken to insure that we are passing clear of another ship, we must take into account the size of our ship and the size of the other ship before concluding that we are passing safely. It is small consolation to have the bow bearing of *Enterprise drawing right* if the bearing on her stern is *drawing left*. Remember that one-third of our ship projects forward of the bridge and two-thirds projects astern. Just getting the bridge safely past the other ship is hardly enough. Take the bearings on the end of the other ship which is to be cleared and be sure to allow ample space to clear it.

A cruiser is a splendid sea vessel and does not suffer from wind and wave to the extent that a destroyer does. She will ride more comfortably on a course with the sea on the quarter or astern than on most other courses, but she rides well under almost any condition. This does not mean that a cruiser doesn't roll and pitch, but she can take almost any sea condition in her stride.

While a cruiser might be riding comfortably into the seas at, say, 18 knots, accompanying destroyers might be nearly submerging as they plow into the waves. A reduction of speed of a few knots could make all the difference to the destroyers without retarding the operation; it could even allow the bridge coffee to be drunk with sugar instead of salt. So our concern when the weather kicks up should be for the escorts. If we are carrying the OTC Officer in Tactical Command (OTC), we should see that he is informed when the destroyers are "taking it green."

A turn at the wheel by the conning officer will give him a better understanding of the problems of the helmsman and hence make a better shiphandler of him. It is equally worthwhile to take a turn at the throttle and to spend some time in the firerooms during maneuvers in order to become acquainted with the particular problems of your vessel's plant.

When maneuvering in formation we should anticipate as much as possible the next maneuver our ship will be called on to perform. Many times there is actual advance warning: the signalled night intentions of the OTC, a shift in the direction of the wind in a carrier task force, etc. We should plan our maneuver, even to the extent of having our maneuvering board solutions ready, so that when the time for execution arrives, the operation will be smooth and correct. In formation, foresight pays dividends.

Should a signal be executed for which we are not prepared, an experienced conning officer can roughly estimate an initial course and speed to head for the new station. We can start on this while a more accurate solution is being worked out. Such an estimate, however, should always be backed up quickly with an accurate maneuvering board solution. A ship equipped and manned as magnificently as a cruiser should be handled with precision at all times.

The use of the answer given by our maneuvering board should be tempered with judgment. The conning officer cannot follow the advice of his supporting team blindly at any time, and his experience and judgment will be most valuable in applying the simple vector solution.

The vector triangle of the maneuvering board makes no allowance for acceleration or deceleration, and it completely ignores the ship's turning circle. It assumes that the ship gains a new speed instantaneously, and that the turning circle can be neglected. In a cruiser, whose acceleration is slower and whose turning diameter is greater, these disadvantages are more pronounced than in a destroyer. The conning officer of a cruiser must be familiar with the advanced maneuvering board techniques described in Chapter 11.

The conning officer's excellence at station-keeping and maneuvering is most easily assessed in a column formation. In other formations it may take careful measuring and plotting to check the accuracy of his position, but in a column the success of his maneuver is obvious to the naked eye.

Changing course by "column movement" takes a nice sense of timing, for we must end up in column directly astern of the guide when our course change has been completed.

In this maneuver our best marker for determining when to put the rudder over is the swirl on the inboard side of the turn created when the rudder of the *ship ahead* is put over. As her rudder forces her stern to one side, a reaction current appears on the opposite side. The first surge of this reaction current is plainly visible on the surface of the water as a swirl in the white foam of the wake on the side to which the turn is being made. This swirl, or "rudder kick," plainly marks the spot where *our* rudder kick should appear.

To superimpose our rudder kick on that of the ship ahead (indicating that our turn started in exactly the same spot as his), we must allow for the time it takes our helmsman to put his wheel over and for our rudder to respond. On a cruiser, at 15 knots, the allowance will be about right if we order the rudder over as the other ship's rudder kick comes abreast our bridge. At other speeds we must use other reference points. The time lag between the order and the rudder response is constant at all speeds, so the distance from our rudder forward to the rudder kick of the ship ahead at the moment we should issue our order will be proportional to the speed. For example, at 20 knots the distance should be four-thirds the distance at 15 knots (indicating that the rudder should be ordered over when the swirl of the ship ahead is abreast turret one).

To be exactly in column we should follow directly in the water of the guide, regardless of what the other ships are doing. Thus we should initiate our turn on the rudder kick of the guide. This is usually impractical because the guide's "rudder kick" has usually been obliterated by the wakes of the other ships. Practically our only recourse is to turn in the wake of the ship ahead and trust that she has made her turn properly. Occasionally when the ship ahead makes a very poor turn, it is apparent and we can adjust accordingly.

Once we are in the turn we should check the progress of the turn by noting the position of our jackstaff (or bullnose) with respect to the outer edge of the wake of the ship ahead. This edge of the wake is clearly marked and from it we can make a very good evaluation of our turn. If the edge of the wake moves *down* our jackstaff, it indicates that ship is working toward the *outside* of the turn. Conversely, if the edge of the wake moves *up* the jackstaff, our ship is working toward the *inside* of the turn. If the edge of the wake is steady, our ship is *following the turn*.

If we are turning outside, tactical instructions and tradition dictate that we hold our rudder and steady up on the new course *out of column* until the ship astern has completed her turn. This rule prevents us tightening our turn and catching the ship astern in a dangerous position if she is turning inside.

Should we find ourselves turning inside, we can correct the situation by easing the rudder. We must be careful not to close the ship ahead when doing this, however, and should slow slightly if necessary. In addition to "cutting corners" when we ease the rudder in a turn, we are decreasing the drag of the rudder and thus increasing our ship's speed.

Should the method outlined above for gauging the time to turn not be working out because of sea conditions or the erratic action of the ships ahead in a long column, we can more accurately accomplish our turns by use of bearings to the guide and the turn diagram. The turn diagram gives us the range and bearing from the point of ordering rudder to the point where the required change of heading has been accomplished. We know what the distance in column to the guide should be, and we can measure it just as the column movement is started. By allowing (by visual estimate from the turn diagram) for the length of the curved path of the turn, we can lay out the maneuver on a maneuvering board (as indicated in Figure 12–5) and thus derive the bearing to the guide for the moment when our rudder should be ordered over.

Another method for making column movements that is especially useful at night is by stop watch. The conning officer of the guide can be depended upon to order his rudder just as the signal is executed; so if we measure the distance to the guide at "Execute," we can quickly calculate the time until our rudder should be ordered. We know our speed and we know the distance to the point where the rudder should be ordered, so it is a simple matter to compute the time when we

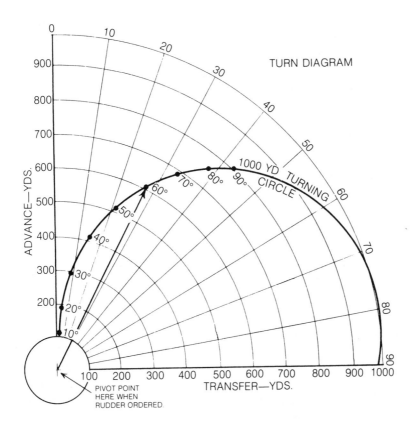

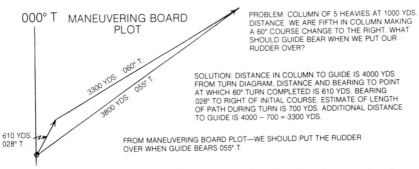

FIGURE 12–5. Turn diagram, showing method of turning in column on bearing to guide.

should order our rudder. For example, if the column speed is 15 knots (500 yards per minute) and the distance to guide's bridge at "Execute" is 1,625 yards, we should order our rudder over exactly 3 minutes and 15 seconds later.

Rules of thumb play their part in conning and, when properly employed, are sufficiently accurate for most situations. They are a valuable "assist" when the conning officer lacks the opportunity to use more exact methods. For example, let us assume that we are to join a column of ships, taking station astern the last ship presently in column. We are converging on the column from the quarter, and thanks to a correct maneuvering board solution, we are moving directly into our station. When do we put the rudder over to swing into column?

The most accurate solution for the turn would be obtained by referring to the Turn Diagram described in Chapter 11, but the following thumb rule has been found adequate when making such a turn of less than 70°:

To turn into the track of another ship, put the rudder over 250 + 5T yards before reaching the intersection of our initial course and our final course. ("T" is the amount of the turn in degrees.)

The derivation of this rule is shown in Figure 12–6.

This rule, of course, is equally applicable when arriving on any station or when swinging onto any new course.

Before leaving the subject of handling at sea, we should consider our ability to stop the ship in case of emergency. We have discussed the horsepower-per-ton ratio and we recognize that it takes a long time to stop our cruiser. When confronted with a dangerous situation, just how quickly *can* we stop?

From a moderate speed, if we order BACK EMERGENCY, we can expect to surge forward slightly less than our advance would be at FULL RUDDER, before we commence moving astern. This means that in an emergency we can stop our ship in about 800 yards. FULL RUDDER and BACK EMERGENCY will combine to produce an advance far less than either action will singly.

In an emergency we should remember that the rudder is also an aid to rapid deceleration. The giant rudder of our cruiser, when it is put over in either direction, has the same effect as dragging a sea anchor. The quickest way to decelerate the ship is to BACK EMERGENCY and use FULL RUDDER. If a particular line of advance must be maintained, the rudder can be "fishtailed" (i.e., shifted from side to side with as great an amplitude as possible).

Replenishment at sea

A cruiser is at her best during replenishment at sea. Thanks to her stable characteristics, she holds a steady course with ease. An experienced helmsman can steer her to the half degree. Seas which bounce a destroyer about merely cause a gentle lift to her bow.

The general method of going alongside is the same for the cruiser as for the destroyer, but the approach is made slightly wider, and, when alongside, the cruiser should ride slightly farther out. An initial distance of 100 feet between sides

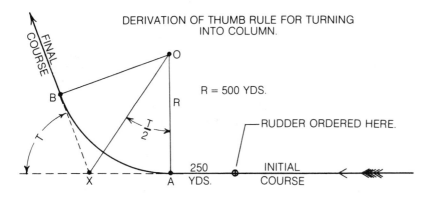

DERIVATION OF THUMB RULE FOR TURNING
INTO COLUMN.

R = 500 YDS.

RUDDER ORDERED HERE.

ASSUMPTIONS:
- (A). SHIP IS MAKING 15 KNOTS.
- (B). 1000 YARD TURNING CIRCLE IS USED.
- (C). ONCE TURNING, THE SHIP TURNS ON A TRUE CIRCLE.
- (D). 30 SECONDS ELAPSE FROM MOMENT ORDER IS GIVEN ON BRIDGE UNTIL SHIP COMMENCES TO SWING.

SOLUTION:
- (A). SHIP TRAVELS 250 YARDS BEFORE COMMENCING TO TURN:
$$\frac{30}{60} \times 500 = 250 \text{ YDS.}$$
- (B). $XA = R \tan \frac{T}{2}$, BUT FOR SMALL ANGLES WE CAN ASSUME $\tan \angle = \angle$ IF $\angle$ IS EXPRESSED IN RADIANS.
- (C). SO: $XA = R\frac{T}{2}$ (T IN RADIANS)

    OR $XA = R\frac{T}{2 \times 57.3}$ (T IN DEGREES)
- (D). SINCE R = 500 YDS., WE CAN EXPRESS XA IN YARDS BY:
$$xa = \frac{500 \ T}{2 \times 57.3} = 4.36 \ T \ (T \text{ IN DEGREES})$$
- (E). THEREFORE:
    ORDER THE RUDDER OVER 250 + 5T YARDS BEFORE REACHING THE INTERSECTION OF THE INITIAL COURSE AND THE FINAL COURSE. (T IN DEGREES.)

FIGURE 12–6. Rule for turning into column.

is good while handling lines; and after the ship is "connected up," riding at 120 feet will be found to fit the tanker's rig nicely.

The "back down" approach for going alongside another ship works beautifully in cruisers, especially because of their slow deceleration and long surge (65 yards per knot) when no backing power is used. With a 25-knot approach on *Mississinewa* making 12 knots, *Springfield* should be backed TWO-THIRDS when her jackstaff is abreast the oiler's stack—about 150 yards short of her final position. It is quite useful to have the forecastle give a hand signal as the jackstaff comes abreast the stern of the other ship.

It is better to overshoot slightly than to undershoot the required position. This allows the lines to be passed more quickly and the ship will be settled back into her correct position by the time the gear is ready. An approach that is too short delays the chance to get the shot lines over until the ship is finally brought up to position.

Though there has been more discussion concerning the tendency for ships to pull towards one another when close aboard, cruisers may come as close as 40 feet to ships alongside without experiencing difficulty in opening safely. The good shiphandler, when he finds himself too close, comes out very gradually, using a course not more than two degrees from that which has held him in position. A cruiser is a long ship, and when we open out, the stern swings toward the other vessel. We must come out slowly to prevent the stern from swinging in too far toward the other ship. There is also a tendency to over-correct when we get in too close; this tendency should be guarded against to keep from parting our lines. Correcting in small increments may avoid a series of over-corrections that magnify in amplitude as they compound.

In like manner, if the ship opens to the point where the transfer gear is in danger, only a small course change should be made to close the distance; a larger change might throw the stern out and thus part the after lines.

When handling alongside, it is worthwhile to remember that we can see what the ship is doing more quickly by observing the position and movement of the stern than by watching the bow. Two-thirds of the length of the ship is abaft the pivot point. This means that the stern moves two yards for every yard of bow motion. When the side is used as a reference for parallelism, remember that the "flat of the side" is abaft the bridge.

Changing in small increments applies to speed as well as to course. Add and take off turns sparingly. Allow time for the change to take effect before adding another change. An impatient conning officer will fail to obtain accurate control of speed because he changes his speed order before the throttleman has had a chance to smooth out the adjustment made for the last command. Changing speed only a few turns is a delicate adjustment at the throttle, and it takes a minute or two to actually obtain the new rpm.

If we are fueling from an oiler and a ship comes alongside her opposite side, the oiler will usually slow down slightly. Likewise when a ship clears her opposite side, we can expect the oiler to increase speed a little. We should note when ships approach and clear the opposite side of the replenishment ship, and be ready to compensate for the change.

When clearing the side, the length of our ship must again be considered. The turn-away must be made gradually in order that the stern will not swing into the other ship. A considerate conning officer makes sure that his maneuver will not interfere with the other ship as he clears her side. If he must cross her bow in heading for his new station, he makes sure he is far enough ahead so that he does not embarrass her.

BATTLESHIPS

From the turn of the century until Pearl Harbor, battleships were the main strength of the fleet. The Navy had nearly two dozen battleships at the end of World War II, but carriers replaced them so effectively that twenty years later there was not one battleship in commission in the U. S. Navy.

As a matter of historical interest, and because some of the problems involved in handling a battleship will also be met in handling such large ships as the new AO and AOE types, portions of the original text on battleship handling are included here.

This discussion is based on the battleship USS *Missouri* (BB 63) (Figure 12–7), which had the following characteristics:

Length	887 ft.
Beam	108 ft.
Draft	38 ft.
Displacement	
Standard	45,000 tons
Full load	57,000 tons
Total shaft horsepower	212,000
Maximum speed	32 knots
Crew	115 officers
	2,200 enlisted

A battleship had only 3.7 horsepower per ton at full load. Such power was adequate for steaming steadily at a speed nearly equal to that of any other type, but it dictated slow acceleration. The battleship built up to speed gradually, and it took a long time to bring her to a stop. A battleship had the greatest inertia of any type, except the super-carriers, with the least proportional power.

Figures 12–8 and 12–9 show the unusual propeller and rudder arrangement of this class of battleship. The twin rudder arrangement with twin skegs improved the flow in the vicinity of the inboard screws and the rudders. This gave them nearly the same diameter as most destroyers.

Shallow water

At sea the battleship was as easy to handle as the destroyer; sometimes easier, because the wind and sea conditions are seldom severe enough to disturb the heading of so large a ship. It was in port that serious difficulties were experienced in handling such a ship.

Shallow water had a major effect on the maneuverability of the battleship; she handled sluggishly, accelerated slowly and did not respond to her rudder.

The shallow-water effect on ships was of special importance to the battleship conning officer because most of the principal channels of the world were dredged with major warships in mind. In New York or Norfolk the battleship's keel might be within one fathom of the bottom. When alongside a pier, the margin could be so small that mud often entered the main condenser intakes. For this reason battleships usually secured their condensers as much as possible when alongside.

In deep water, the flow about the hull of a ship is three dimensional, and much of the water displaced from ahead of the ship flows down underneath the ship. The

FIGURE 12-7. USS *Missouri*.

streamlines from such flow are clearly shown in Figure 12-10. If we remember that a ship is turned by inclining it (by use of the rudder) to the direction of motion through the water, and that it is the hydrodynamic reaction on the hull that forces the ship around in the turn, we will realize that it is the displacement of water to the sides (indicated by the horizontal streamlines) which governs the steering of a ship. Thus, in deep water the hull is a very inefficient hydrofoil in the horizontal plane and the rudder can easily produce an inclination to the motion through the water, and so initiate a turn.

In shallow water, on the other hand, the proximity of the bottom prevents the normal flow under the ship, and the water from ahead is displaced to the sides, as indicated in Figure 12-11. The flow about the hull becomes nearly two-dimensional, and the displacement of the streamlines in the horizontal plane becomes more pronounced. The hull becomes much more efficient as a hydrofoil, and the forces produced are larger.

FIGURE 12–8. Stern view of a battleship's rudders and propellers (model).

When a ship is inclined to its direction of motion, not only is the side force mentioned above produced, but, since the resultant force does not pass through the center of gravity, a turning moment is also produced. In a normal, well-designed ship this moment is such that it tends to reduce the angle of inclination and thus return the ship to a straight course. To hold a ship in a steady turn, the rudder must produce a moment which will just balance this reaction moment and thus maintain the ship at a constant inclination to the relative water flow.

FIGURE 12–9. Side view of a battleship's rudders and propellers (model).

In shallow water, as the flow becomes more two-dimensional, the reaction moment for a given inclination becomes larger and larger until it is several times that experienced in deep water. Whether in deep or shallow water, the flow about the rudder is essentially two-dimensional (displacement caused by the body of the rudder is in the horizontal plane), so there is little difference in the turning moment produced by the rudder as the depth decreases. Consequently a given rudder angle at a given speed in shallow water is balanced by a smaller inclination of the hull, and less turning effect is achieved. Thus, a battleship with only a fathom of water under her keel responded very sluggishly to her rudder. It was almost always necessary to augment the rudder with the engines when turning in very shallow water.

In addition to its effect on turning characteristics, shallow water makes the speed unpredictable. Accompanying the increase in side forces as the flow becomes two-dimensional in shallow water, the hydrodynamic drag increases. The shallower the water, the greater the drag. This meant that the battleship accelerated more slowly and slowed more rapidly. In a narrow channel, or at high speed, the more complex shallow-water effects discussed in Chapter 10 also came into play, but the simple shallow-water effect of increased drag significantly affects shiphandling.

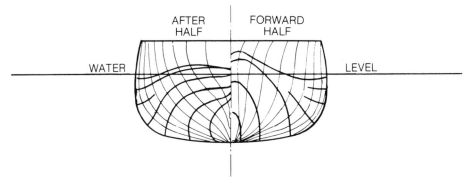

FIGURE 12–10. Streamlines about hull as ship moves ahead in deep water. Observe how streamlines go down and under the hull. (Drawn from Figure 28 in *Speed and Power of Ships*, by Rear Admiral David W. Taylor (CC), USN (Ret.).)

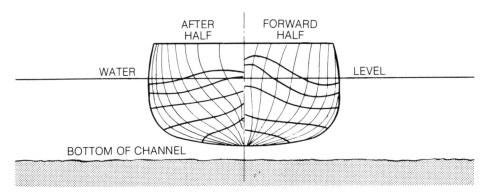

FIGURE 12–11. Streamlines about hull as ship moves ahead in very shallow water. Observe how streamlines spread to the side. (Figure 12–11 is an application of the Shallow Water Effect to Figure 12–10.)

For a more complete discussion of the shallow-water effects on a ship, the following references will be found interesting: (a) "Maneuvering of Ships in Deep Water, in Shallow Water, and in Canals," by Captain R. Brard (CC, French Navy), printed in the *Transactions of the Society of Naval Architects and Marine Engineers*, Volume 59, 1951; (b) *Speed and Power of Ships*, by David W. Taylor, Rear Admiral, (CC), USN (Ret.), Chapter 15.2.

At sea

In maneuvers at sea, the rules developed for cruisers were applicable to battle-ships.

One significant difference in a battleship was the amount she slowed during a turn. The increased drag, caused by the rudder angle and the inclination of the ship relative to the water flow, rapidly overpowered the thrust of her screws. Even though the engine rpm were maintained, a battleship initially making 25 knots would slow to 16 or 17 knots during a 180° turn.

A battleship moved a considerable amount of water aside as she plowed through the ocean, and the effect reached well out; the bow wave was greater, and the following hollow deeper. The hollow forward of the screws was also deeper as the water rushed to fill in behind the broad counter.

A battleship going alongside another ship had to allow more distance than with other types. Distances acceptable with a destroyer would seriously disturb the steering of the other ship as the bow wave and the successive crests and hollows of the wake affected the other ship.

When going alongside a service type for replenishment, it was good practice to come up parallel about 150 feet out, and then ride at from 120 to 150 feet distance while alongside.

Smaller ships going alongside a battleship had to consider the big ship's wake. The stern waves and the hollow near the screws made coming alongside her quarter difficult. While this position had the advantage of leaving the destroyer's stern free to swing, it subjected the destroyer to the full force of the battleship's stern wake. Since this increased with speed, a destroyer went alongside abreast the big ship's bridge rather than her quarter, when operating at speeds greater than 12 knots.

In port

In the confines of the harbor, and in making a berth, the great size of the ship, combined with shallow-water effects, made the use of tugs necessary. Though battleships did make landings at piers without assistance, this was the exception and not the rule. Under severe current and wind conditions, as many as eight tugs were sometimes required to handle the great mass of such a ship. Fewer tugs could be used, depending on the conditions, but if the maneuvering room was restricted, it was recommended that at least four tugs be available.

Two tugs, if available, were used when making a buoy. It took a long time to shackle the heavy chain to the buoy, and without assistance the bow would most probably be carried away from the buoy before the chain could be secured. Because of the battleship's long forecastle and high, flared bow, it was impossible to see a mooring buoy from the bridge once it was close aboard. The buoy was kept to one side during the initial operations so that the conning officer could see it, but when the bow moved close to the buoy to secure the chain, the buoy invariably disappeared from sight from the bridge. It was customary to handle the conning of the ship and the direction of the tugs from the eyes of the ship. Anchoring was about the only evolution in the harbor that a battleship normally performed unassisted.

Different ships, but same principles

Whether our ship is a cruiser, battleship, or one of the several variations that range from 6,000 tons to 60,000 tons, handling one of these major ships of the fleet requires the application of the same principles we explored in discussing the destroyer. Though the time constants are different, the fundamentals are the same. Once accustomed to the new dimensions of the larger ship, we find that the rules we discovered in destroyers apply to her just as well. The mass of the big ship is greater, she occupies greater space, and she often requires more sea room. But the same alert application of the principles of good shiphandling that serve so well in smaller ships will serve equally well on the big ships.

13
carriers

In essence the aircraft carrier (Figures 13–1 and 13–2) is a seagoing air base. She is a ship in which every detail of design is pointed toward accomplishing the prime functions of launching, controlling, recovering, servicing, and stowing combatant aircraft. She must be prepared to operate a maximum number of aircraft of the highest possible performance in playing her part in modern naval warfare.

Like the aircraft which are her reason for being, her body is of low density. The hangar, which provides a protected stowage and servicing area, contributes most to this characteristic.

She is long, because there must be sufficient space on the flight deck for landing and arresting and launching aircraft, since it is most desirable that the ship be able to launch and recover aircraft simultaneously. Even when the launch is by steam catapult and recovering is on the angled deck, this requires a long flight deck.

Since it is extremely difficult to operate aircraft from the deck of a ship which is rolling heavily, the carrier must be designed for a minimum roll. This, combined with the desirability of a wide deck for operating and parking aircraft, calls for a ship of wide beam.

Thus the length and beam requirements dictate that the aircraft carrier be a large ship.

The flight deck must have an unobstructed runway with the largest possible area for handling planes, so all interfering structure must be eliminated from the flight-deck area. Control stations, directors, guns, missiles and all other topside equipment are moved to the sides and ends of the ship, and, where possible, they are lowered below the level of the flight deck. The carrier thus acquires a pronounced overhang at the bow and stern, and has many projections from her sides.

The one structure allowed to project above the flight deck is the "island." This structure normally contains the navigating bridge and conning station and whatever other control and signal stations require all-around vision. These components are usually integrated with the funnel and are surmounted with a maze of radar and radio antennae. To afford maximum clearance for the flight operations, the island is placed as far to the side (the starboard side, by convention) as the ship's structure

FIGURE 13–1. USS *Enterprise* (CVAN 65) refuels *The Sullivans* (DD 537).

will permit. The island is as narrow as possible because it must present minimum interference to air traffic; and it must cause minimum turbulence of the air flowing over the after portion of the flight deck and astern of the ship.

In the eyes of the shiphandler, then, the aircraft carrier is a large ship of low density. She has an outward flare of the hull at the bow and stern to support a maximum area of flight deck, and her sides are festooned with numerous projections such as gun sponsons, elevators, and flight deck galleries. The navigating bridge is small, and is offset to the starboard edge of the flight deck. On those ships in which the smokepipes are included in the island structure, there is an unavoidable obstruction to vision aft. These factors give the conning station a degree of awkwardness which the shiphandler must recognize and include in his calculations.

All is not bad, however, in the eccentric conning station of the carrier. The ship control instruments are close at hand, and a good view of the starboard side of the ship is afforded. When it can be arranged to go alongside a pier starboard side to, or to take station to port of the supply ship during an underway replenishment, the situation is excellent. Since the peculiarity is obvious and well known at sea and in port, provision is normally made for the carrier to do all of her precise shiphandling to starboard.

Shadow diagram

The extensive obstruction to vision which is caused ahead, to port, and astern by the flight deck may be turned to the advantage of the shiphandler if he constructs a "shadow diagram" for handy reference on the bridge. The shadow diagram is outlined by points where one's line of sight from the normal conning positions on the bridge intersects the surface of the water as the eye sweeps along the edges of the flight deck. A small floating object cannot be seen when it is within the shadow, and, conversely, *can* be seen when it is outside of the shadow. Such a diagram, constructed by reference to the ship's plans, will not only delineate the blind spots from the conn, but also provide a means for estimating distance.

The shadow diagram is useful in estimating the range to objects close aboard. For instance, if one sees that the waterline of a buoy ahead appears tangent to the forward ramp of the flight deck on a certain relative bearing, reference to the shadow diagram will tell the shiphandler that the buoy is a precise number of yards—for example, 220 yards—from the stem. Thus the flight deck and other obstructions can be used as a sort of built-in stadimeter, an aid to seaman's eye. Large changes in draft, trim, or list, or motion in a seaway will, of course, affect the accuracy of the shadow diagram.

Offset conning

The conning officer needs always to bear in mind that he is offset to starboard from the centerline about half the beam of the ship. It is useful to post at each pelorus a sign which states, "At this pelorus you are——feet to starboard of the centerline." Knowing the distance of our pelorus from the centerline, we realize that our line of sight "dead ahead" (000° relative) marks a line parallel to the keel of the ship but always displaced to starboard by this distance.

Suppose our carrier is steaming in column astern of a cruiser. A fleet review is in process, and we wish to be exactly in column. Looking ahead, we admire the symmetry of the cruiser and know that the conning officer on her bridge can stand on the centerline and keep perfect station by keeping the center of the ship ahead on a bearing equal to the formation course. Though we can't stand on the centerline of our carrier when conning, we can achieve the same results by understanding and compensating for our offset.

Suppose our offset is 60 feet and the beam of the cruiser ahead is 80 feet. We can select a point in the water 60 feet to starboard of the centerline of the cruiser by using her beam as a measuring stick. She is 80 feet wide, so a point in the water one-quarter of her beam width to the right of her *starboard side* will be 60 feet to the right of her keel. If we maneuver our carrier to bring the bearing of this point in the water to exactly equal the formation course, we will be perfectly in column.

We can solve many of the problems created by our offset conning position by applying an equal offset "at the target." Having compensated for the offset at the target, we can use our bearings in the normal way.

Since we are not on the centerline of the ship, we cannot use the normal centerline objects such as the jackstaff for determining the ship's "head." Though we can establish the ship's heading by sighting through an alidade set on 000° relative, we should provide a quicker reference for use in emergency when time does not permit attention to the alignment of an alidade. Most carriers are equipped with a "steering staff" mounted vertically from the outboard side of the walkway at the forward end of the flight deck. If one stands directly behind the helmsman and looks forward over the steering staff, he is looking "dead ahead." If the ship is steaming steady on course, with no arthwartship set, this is also the direction of motion of the ship. This reference, unfortunately, is not always available at sea, because it must be unrigged at flight quarters. One should, therefore, establish

FIGURE 13–2. Aerial view of USS *America* (CV 66) showing angled deck and catapults.

other points of reference. The conning officer should locate objects well forward of the bridge which will be on the fore-and-aft line from his normal conning positions. Such points may be stanchions, points on gun sponsons, or distinctive points on the antenna outriggers. But one such mark should be selected for each conning position.

Looking aft, we may find that the plating of the outside of the stack is exactly in a fore-and-aft plane. Thus, sighting along this plane establishes the direction astern which parallels the keel. When situations arise that require immediate action, it is very valuable to have established fore-and-aft "bench marks" beforehand. In such cases the seconds wasted in focusing the eye for careful setting of the bearing circle, and then in refocusing on the situation ahead or astern, cannot be spared.

Wind effect on the carrier

As one would expect, a ship of large volume and low density such as a carrier is more sensitive to the wind than is the normal warship. This is more noticeable in the shallower draft carriers like those of the *Essex* class than in the deeper-draft carriers of the *Forrestal* or *Midway* classes. But regardless of class, the large, bulky hull and superstructure of the carrier act as a sail, and the force of the wind on the ship is large.

As a typical instance, if the wind is blowing the ship against the face of a pier when getting under way, the effect of the "sail area" of the carrier will be unpleasantly noticeable, for the wind will tend to hold the ship firmly against the face of the pier. Winds of 25 knots or greater can make it very difficult to clear the berth.

Hence, when clearing a pier with a strong wind blowing us on, we must have tugs of sufficient aggregate power to hold the ship broadside in the wind. If we did not have such assistance, the ship would rub and scrape against the pier as she cleared, which might cause serious damage. If we do not have enough tugs to hold the entire ship against the wind, then we should place whatever tugs we do have forward to hold the bow off the pier. Under most circumstances we can hold the stern away from the pier with our own engines.

If it becomes necessary to get under way from a pier with a wind setting us on, and there are no tugs available, we can clear under our own power alone if the conditions are not severe. In this case we twist the stern out from the pier and then back out quickly, just as with smaller ships. In doing this we use a camel or float forward as a pivot. With this as a pivot, the stern can be walked out slowly with the engines. But care should be taken to insure that the pressure against this pivot float is steady during the twisting operation. When ready, with all lines clear, the ship should be backed away from her berth with as much power as the circumstances allow, so that the ship will gather way quickly. This minimizes the time the wind has to work on the bow, and gives us the speed necessary for control in a minimum time. Once we are moving at a safe distance out from the face of the pier we can reduce the backing power as may be desirable.

With winds of appreciable velocity, the carrier must be kept a safe distance upwind of obstructions. We should always maintain sufficient way to be able to keep our bow from being set to leeward. Lying to, broadside to the wind, with an obstruction to leeward, is a situation to be avoided.

Because of her large freeboard and unusual superstructure, the carrier yaws markedly with the wind when at anchor. Her motion is similar to that described in Figure 5–5 for a destroyer, but the effects are more noticeable. When the carrier brings the chain taut as she reaches the extremity of her swing, she may do so with a jerk. If this becomes too severe, it can start the anchor from the bottom and cause her to drag.

We can ease the situation by veering chain. The more chain, the heavier the catenary—and the greater the tension before the chain is "straightened out." The tension is, of course, a measure of the force being applied to the ship by the anchor chain, and if we can obtain enough tension to stop the motion of the ship before the chain is straightened out, there will be no jerk. As link after link is picked up from the bottom, weight is added to the catenary. With enough chain, the ship will usually be brought about from one tack to the other steadily, without any jerk.

A large scope of chain also exerts a damping effect on the yawing by its resistance to being dragged sideways across the bottom. This adds to the catenary effect of the weight of the chain, but is more effective in pulling the bow through the wind because it causes the chain to lead more to the side as the ship sails across the wind. If the yaw becomes serious, the situation can be relieved by dropping a second anchor "under foot." This second anchor will be very effective in reducing the sidewise excursions.

Winds on the beam have a marked effect on steering a carrier at sea. The stronger the wind, the more *downwind* rudder must be carried to hold a course. If the helmsman is having difficulty steering the desired course, reminding him of this effect of wind may assist his steering. To obtain smooth control, he should seek an average of downwind rudder, and then apply corrections of a few degrees on either side of this average.

Problems caused by the overhang

A characteristic of the carrier which must be considered in handling close aboard is the overhang. Projections from the side of the ship always complicate handling alongside (Figure 13–3) and no type has a greater array of projections than the carrier, especially the *Forrestal* class.

The many projections from the sides, and the outward flare near the bow and stern give the carrier a degree of awkwardness from the point of view of the tug master. In working close to the carrier's side, the masts or other top hamper of the tug all too frequently foul on some overhanging appurtenance of the carrier. This can, of course, cause expensive damage to the tug. For this reason a tug may be expected to approach gingerly and to work with her stern as far out from the carrier's side as possible. If, because of current or ship's motion, the tug is swept in parallel

FIGURE 13–3. USS *Forrestal* (CVA 59) approaching a pier at Norfolk. (Note large barge alongside pier to the left to hold her off.)

to the side, she will often have to cast off and clear the side to keep from suffering damage from the carrier's projecting structure.

A tug master prefers to pull on a hawser rather than push against the side, when working against the flared part of a carrier's hull. When pulling on a line the tug is well clear of the side and safe from the threatening projections. Also, when the tug comes alongside, she will probably ask for one of our lines instead of using her own, for operational as well as economic reasons. Not only does it save the wear and tear on the tug's gear, but the tug master *knows* that *he* can cast off as rapidly as required—and he is not sure that we will cast him off as quickly as he might desire. By using our line the tug master is sure that he will be carrying all of his own gear with him should he be required to cast off suddenly.

In sending him a line we should remember that, though a line can be cast off from the tug's quick-releasing hook regardless of the strain, a line must be slacked before the "eye" can be cast off from a normal set of bitts or a cleat. Because of the inability to slack a line quickly enough under certain circumstances, an eye over a bitt occasionally must be cut with an axe in order for the tug to get free. For this reason, unless we are certain that the line is going to the tug's towing hook with its quick-release feature, we should send the tug the whipped end of the hawser instead of the eye end.

When it is desirable to place a tug parallel to the ship, as when being moved in a navy yard, with no power on the ship, a camel should be placed between the tug and the ship's side to hold the tug clear of the overhang. The tug should make sure that the camel is secured in place (usually by lines to the tug) before the move is begun. Otherwise the camel may become dislodged as way is gotten on the aircraft carrier.

Overhang is also a consideration when mooring alongside a pier. A camel between the pier face and the ship's side is essential to prevent contact between projections from the ship's side and the pier. The camel must hold the ship far enough off not only to prevent contact at the time of mooring but also to guard against projections being brought down on top of the pier as the tide ebbs. Sufficient clearance must be provided for the full range of the tide.

Since the camels are so important for safe mooring, it must be determined that there are sufficient camels of the required size and strength at the berth before going alongside. A U. S. naval facility will usually have adequate provisions of camels and floats, because such a facility is accustomed to handling carriers; but at commercial or foreign facilities, this may not be the case. An otherwise magnificent approach can be completely blighted if the screw wash sweeps away improperly secured camels when backing the engines the final time upon arriving in the berth. If a poorly designed camel upends and allows the ship to come in against the camel's narrowest dimension, or if a camel crushes through structural weakness, the ship may be hard against the pier with a damaged side.

Handling alongside

The shiphandler will find other oddities when handling the carrier alongside. When starboard-side-to the view from the bridge is excellent, but the great length of the ship and the many projections from her side make it very difficult to see the condition of the mooring lines from the bridge. The conning officer cannot observe either the forecastle or the fantail crews as they work the lines, so he must depend upon verbal reports to determine their progress. To keep all stations informed of the situation, it is essential that dependable and accurate communications be maintained between the bridge and the line-handling stations.

A large carrier is normally moored to a pier with many mooring lines as indicated in Figure 13–4. For handling these mooring lines there are winches of adequate power only on the forecastle and fantail. Line-handling stations elsewhere are usually in cramped spaces and devoid of any adequate winches. Any heavy hauling required should be done with the forward or after lines, because not only are the midship lines not adjacent to winches, but they must be handled from narrow galleries.

The great bulk of the aircraft carrier, and the effect of the wind on that bulk, increases the need to have each mooring line carry its share of the load. If a beam wind drives the carrier directly away from the face of a pier, all of the breast lines should come taut at the same time. Thus each contributes its full strength to

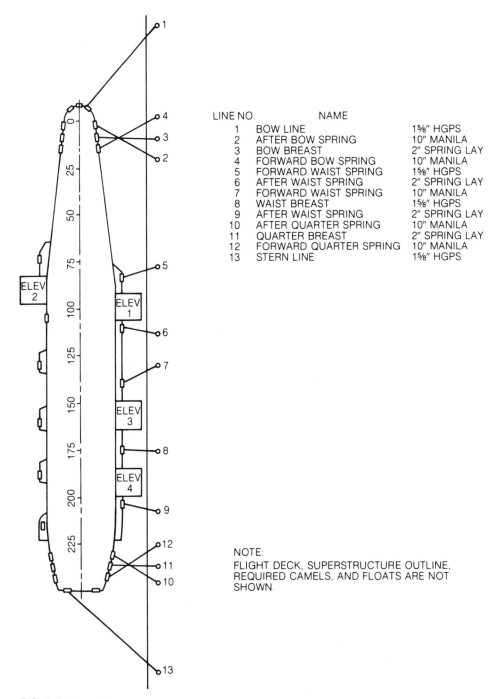

LINE NO.	NAME	
1	BOW LINE	1⅝″ HGPS
2	AFTER BOW SPRING	10″ MANILA
3	BOW BREAST	2″ SPRING LAY
4	FORWARD BOW SPRING	10″ MANILA
5	FORWARD WAIST SPRING	1⅝″ HGPS
6	AFTER WAIST SPRING	2″ SPRING LAY
7	FORWARD WAIST SPRING	10″ MANILA
8	WAIST BREAST	1⅝″ HGPS
9	AFTER WAIST SPRING	2″ SPRING LAY
10	AFTER QUARTER SPRING	10″ MANILA
11	QUARTER BREAST	2″ SPRING LAY
12	FORWARD QUARTER SPRING	10″ MANILA
13	STERN LINE	1⅝″ HGPS

NOTE:
FLIGHT DECK, SUPERSTRUCTURE OUTLINE,
REQUIRED CAMELS, AND FLOATS ARE NOT
SHOWN.

FIGURE 13–4. Standard mooring plan for a large carrier.

holding the moor. But if one comes taut while the others are slack, the load on that
one line may exceed its breaking strength and it may part before the other lines
have begun to work. Thus the lines may snap in succession, each as its breaking

load is exceeded. The whole moor may carry away under conditions which would not have caused failure had each breast line been laid out and tensioned to share the load with the other breast lines. Similarly, if wind or current causes the carrier to surge forward, all after-leading springs should come taut together. If the ship surges aft, all forward-leading springs should come taut together. These principles apply in the mooring of any ship, of course, but they are of particular importance in carriers, where a larger number of mooring lines are used.

Because of the high freeboard of the carrier, the chocks through which mooring lines are led are high up on the side of the ship and frequently are on projecting sponsons. If one tries to lead a breast line out through such chocks, a very steep angle in the mooring line will result. This is obviously inefficient, for, resolving the tension force of the line into the horizontal and vertical directions, one finds that only a small component is applied to holding the ship to the pier, and the most of the force is applied *downward*. Further, such steep, short leads are troublesome as the ship rises and falls with the tide. It is better, therefore, to use such chocks for spring lines, thus obtaining greater force components in the directions desired. Breast lines can be run at locations on the ship farther forward and farther aft where the contours of the ship have carried the chocks to a greater distance from the pier. Leading the lines to the opposite side of the pier can provide a greater horizontal component, but this is often not desirable because it interferes with traffic on the pier. Many of the larger carriers have mooring bitts recessed into the side just above the waterline. If very strong breasting forces are desired, these bitts are available for flat leads from pier to ship's side.

Handling in restricted waters

Because of the small size of the bridge on a carrier, the number of instruments and assisting activities immediately accessible from the bridge is reduced to the minimum. Many stations vital to good ship control are remote from the bridge, and the conning officer should endeavor to keep these closely in touch with the progress of the ship. Frequent questions from the bridge, and the supplying of coordinating information, will maintain the interest and teamwork of the remote stations.

First and foremost of these stations is the Combat Information Center. No matter how good the visibility, nor how simple the problem, it is worthwhile to have a complete navigational plot of the ship's track kept in CIC, and to have continual advice from the CIC officer arriving by telephone on the bridge. This should not be a one-way flow: the bridge should cross-check with CIC. When the ship arrives in the open sea, it is well to have the CIC officer bring his track chart to the bridge for a check. All points of divergence should be discussed with the navigator, and the acknowledgement of a job well done is appropriate. Only by continual practice and support can the CIC be developed into an aid upon which we can depend when the visibility is reduced to the point where the CIC facilities are the only means of entering or leaving port safely.

Steering the ship is obviously so important a function that extra precautions should be taken against a possible steering casualty occurring at the worst possible time. It is well, for instance, to have not only an expert helmsman on the bridge, but also a competent and alert crew below in the steering-gear room itself. The alertness of this crew will be enhanced if it is kept generally posted on what is happening topside. In traversing a long, narrow, or tortuous channel, it may even be prudent to have a qualified deck watch officer in the emergency steering station. If he had a chart and is notified when significant navigational points are passed, he will be in a position to know when periods of particular vigilance are required. The latest order to the helm should be a matter of record in the emergency steering station. The stand-by helmsman should follow continuously what his counterpart on the bridge is doing so that he will know what rudder angles are being used and what is their effect in holding the ship's course.

If the crew in the emergency steering station is both alert and ready, they can take control smoothly and efficiently in the event of a casualty. Steering casualties usually occur through failure of the long electrical control circuit from the bridge. False alarms are often caused by failure of the transmission lines to the rudder indicator on the bridge. In the rare event that the failure is actually in the steering machinery itself, so that the rudder is immobilized, the bridge should be informed immediately so that the conning officer may use the engines to minimize the hazard to the ship.

Other remote stations of particular interest as we maneuver in restricted waters are the control engine room and the forecastle—the former for accurate and speedy control of the engines; the latter because there must be an anchor ready for letting go so long as the restrictions of maneuvering room require it and the depth of the water permits. Neither station should be slighted in the development of the shiphandling team.

Handling at sea

When we reach the open sea, the aircraft carrier will devote the major part of her time to the operation of aircraft. This preoccupation requires certain considerations not entirely strange to other types of ship, but differing in degree of emphasis.

In order to understand the basic requirements of the carrier's operation, let us look first at the aircraft which fly from it. The airplane flies because of the flow of air over its wings and control surfaces. This flow is generated by the forward speed of the aircraft through the air. There is a minimum airspeed below which this flow of air becomes inadequate for lift and control. At this minimum, the aircraft "stalls" and begins falling out of control. When an aircraft is taking off or landing, the airspeed can closely approximate the stalling speed, but there must always remain a small but safe margin above the stalling speed if the aircraft is to remain airborne. When a plane is in the air, it is its motion relative to the mass of air in which it is flying that keeps it up. This motion differs from the motion of the aircraft relative to the earth's surface in every case except in a flat calm.

An aircraft at rest on the ground, but headed into the wind, will already have an airspeed equal to the velocity of the wind. Taking advantage of this fact, a take-off run into the wind affords the shortest run, in distance and time, required for the aircraft to become airborne. Likewise, in landing, a direction into the wind is chosen, since the wind thus reduces the velocity of "touchdown" and shortens the landing run. A crosswind land or take-off not only loses the advantages explained above, but also throws objectionable side loads on the landing gear, since the aircraft, when airborne, takes on the sidewise motion of the air mass itself.

The foregoing basic considerations enter into the operations of launching and recovering aircraft on any aircraft carrier. The conning officer, by combining the ship's speed with the true wind, can create a relative wind down the flight deck—a "wind-over-the-deck"—for maximum effect during the operation.

In launching or recovering aircraft, a relative wind is needed of sufficient intensity to keep within reasonable bounds the energy required of catapults to impart flying velocity to aircraft, or the energy required of the arresting gear to decelerate aircraft in alighting. At the same time the intensity of the relative wind should not be so great as to make overly difficult the towing or taxiing of aircraft as they are moved about the flight deck. Compromising between these considerations, it is usual to employ a relative wind of from 25 to 35 knots.

Ideally, the direction of the relative wind would be that which would permit aircraft to head directly into it when landing or taking off. It is necessary, however, to keep the downwind eddies of the island and the turbulence of the flue gases clear of the landing area; hence, one finds the best direction of the relative wind usually to be from dead ahead to slightly on the port bow.

Modern attack carriers are fitted with an angled deck, inclined 10° to port of the centerline of the ship. This feature provides an unobstructed deck for recovering aircraft regardless of the congestion on the forward part of the axial deck. Launching can be conducted from both the axial and the angled decks simultaneously if desired, and aircraft can be recovered on the angled deck while others are being launched from the axial deck (Figure 13–5). When only one deck is being used, the relative wind should be along the axis of that deck, i.e., dead ahead for the axial deck and 10° to port for the angled deck. When both decks are being used for launching, the relative wind should be kept between them, i.e., 5° to port. When launching from the axial deck and recovering on the angled deck, the wind should be adjusted to favor the recovery operation and be kept 10° to port.

With modern aircraft and the powerful catapults installed in our carriers today, relative wind is not so critical as before. If the catapult is sufficiently powerful for the aircraft under consideration, crosswind—or even downwind—launches may be made. It is the resulting *airspeed* of the aircraft at the end of the catapult that determines the safety of the getaway, and a satisfactory airspeed may be achieved with a sufficiently light aircraft even though no component of wind relative to the carrier was favorable during the catapulting. With modern equipment, if other operational requirements dictate, launching and recovery can be conducted safely with relative winds up to 20° to either side of the optimum direction.

FIGURE 13–5. Flight operations aboard USS *Enterprise* (CVAN 65), showing axial deck and angled deck.

From the above discussion it can be seen that the conning officer of the aircraft carrier must have an appreciation for the true wind, the ship's motion, and the vector combination which generates relative wind. A flight of aircraft returning to the ship low on fuel will require an expeditious turn into the wind by the carrier, so it is basic that the conning officer of the carrier know at all times the direction and velocity of the true wind. This will permit him to turn to a heading and set a speed which will combine to provide the correct direction and velocity of relative wind for the recovery operation.

By keeping cognizant of the present and forecast true wind velocity, the conning officer can estimate the boiler power he will require to obtain the desired wind over the deck. If a breeze of 15 to 20 knots is predicted, only moderate boiler power will be required, for a ship's speed of 15 knots can generate the 30 to 35 knots required for flight operations. In light airs or in a flat calm, full boiler power will be required since the ship must generate by her own speed nearly all, or all, of the required relative wind for her flight operations.

In modern naval ships, the power available depends not only upon the number of boilers in use, but also upon the temperature of the superheated steam. Furthermore, when a ship is using her superheaters, she cannot change her steaming condition very rapidly because of thermal expansion and contraction problems. Finally, speed ranges and limits vary with different combinations of boilers and superheat.

The conning officer of the carrier must plan ahead, basing his plans on the present and forecast wind velocities, the aircraft to be flown, and the speed-boiler combinations of the ships in company. He should assume the responsibility of advising the escort vessels of expected speed requirements, and do this sufficiently in advance to allow them time to make the necessary adjustments in an orderly and efficient manner. Especially should he remember that after the speed range for the operations has been selected, any change may require considerable time for the escort ships to adjust their own boiler arrangements.

Another matter of concern to the conning officer of the carrier is when, where, and how to turn into the wind for the air operations. Restrictions in sea room or the desire to make good a general advance downwind, may require that the time in which the carrier is headed into the wind be held to the shortest duration possible. In that case the conning officer will wish to be sure that all is ready for the launch or recovery before he turns into the wind. Further, if high speed is required, he will wish to build up to high speed while still running downwind, thus conserving precious distance to windward. Some speed will be lost during the turn—as much as 5 to 7 knots at high speeds. Therefore, if the conning officer wishes to start recovery or launching immediately upon completing the turn, he must have a margin of speed above that required for flight operations when he begins his turn. In this way he will make allowance for the loss of speed in the turn, and, as he comes out of the turn, he will have adequate relative wind over the deck to begin air operations at once. The engine rpm can be reduced after the turn has been completed to hold the desired speed.

Carriers list outboard in a turn, because of their extensive above-water structure. The degree of list will depend, of course, on the speed and radius of the turn. If the turn is made through the trough of the sea, a roll may be superimposed on top of the list. Aircraft unsecured or being moved about the deck when such a list occurs, may skid or roll out of control. Obviously the conning officer must be aware of this possibility, and must give adequate warning throughout the ship before executing a sharp turn.

Just as the mariner in a sailing ship abhors a lee shore, so does the carrier captain regard with distrust an obstruction to windward. If the obstruction is a shore line or shoal water, it may not allow sufficient room to windward to permit the planned launch or recovery. A fog patch to windward carries a double threat: it will advance *toward the ship* with the wind as the ship moves *toward it* against the wind. Whatever the restriction, the conning officer must measure the situation and insure that he has sufficient clearance to remain on the launching or recovery course for the required time.

FIGURE 13–6. Deck layout of USS *Forrestal* (CVA 59).

Plane crash

Air operations include the possibility of aircraft accidents for which the conning officer should have well-thought-out procedures. One of the most urgent situations is that in which a plane's engine fails on take-off and the plane lands in the water dead ahead. A careful study of the turning characteristics of the carrier will show that for a certain distance ahead (depending on the speed), putting the rudder over either way will tend to force the survivors into the side of the ship and possibly under the keel. When the ship responds to the rudder, her bow moves one way and her stern moves the other about her pivot point. It is the side force developed by the water against the inclined side of the ship that forces the ship around in her turn, and, for a certain distance, the ship proceeds forward in this inclined orientation before she leaves her initial path. In this process, tremendous currents are spilling under the keel, and these might draw the survivors under the ship. In a turn, the ship sweeps a broader path through the water than when on a steady course, because of the characteristic inclination of the ship's keel to her actual direction of motion. Thus, if we turn, we increase our chances of hitting the survivors because of our wider path, and we increase the possibility of injuring them, should we strike them, because of our direction of motion and the current spoken of above.

One would think that by putting the rudder over one way, and then, after a change in heading of a few degrees, reversing it, the ship could be displaced far enough to the side to clear the men in the water. This can indeed be done, depending upon the speed of the ship and the distance to the men in the water; however, a careful study of the specific maneuvering characteristics of the ship will show that a very *considerable* distance ahead is needed for this maneuver. The conning officer should remember that using the rudder will induce large currents under the stern, and its injudicious use could mean the death of the men in the water.

On the other hand, if the rudder is held amidships and if the aviators have cleared the plane and are floating in their life jackets, their chance of being struck directly by the stem is very small, and in any other position the bow wave will tend to push them aside. They will most probably be in good shape if they are not drawn into the screws. Our problem then is to stop the great indraft of water to the propellers. The conning officer should order STOP SHAFTS as soon as it becomes apparent that the men in the water are going to pass close aboard. Even if the throttlemen are not able to completely stop the shafts in time, the indraft will cease as soon as the propellers stop driving.

When the survivors are actually alongside the ship and there is no doubt at all as to which side they will pass on, the rudder can be ordered over to move the stern *away* from the men in the water. But any confused or unreliable information should be a signal to the conning officer to keep his rudder amidships. Though there is some advantage to the men in the water if the stern is moved away from them, it will be very dangerous to them should a mistake be made and the stern be thrown *into* them.

If a plane is seen to go over the side anywhere else than at the bow, the situation is clear and the rudder may be put over immediately toward the side to which the plane was seen to go over.

A more difficult situation that occasionally arises is that in which an airplane goes over the side and remains caught in the bight of the arresting wire. When this happens, the steady pull on this wire causes it to be pulled out to its extreme length.

This often means that the plane is already in the water, and if the arresting crew doesn't cut the wire immediately, the plane may be towed through the water backwards. The only indication of the situation visible from the bridge will usually be the two parts of the arresting wire leading over the side. Stopping all shafts and putting the rudder over a small amount toward the plane will help the situation. Backing the engines to kill headway is not acceptable, because the plane is usually in the vicinity of the screws, and the swirling turbulence caused by backing might augment an already bad situation. On the other hand, turning with a small rudder angle will tend to move the stern away from the plane and prevent damage from the ship's structure. A large rudder angle might cause the plane to tow too far out from the side for access in rescue operations from the ship.

When a plane goes into the water during a recovery or launching, the conning officer of the carrier must keep in mind the safety of the fliers in the other planes aloft. If the downed plane will pass clear of the ship, and if the ship has been handled in such a way as to minimize the hazards which she herself creates, then it is usually best to turn the rescue operations over to the rescue destroyers and complete the air operations. If planes, low on fuel, are not recovered promptly, they may be forced to ditch. The distraction of having a plane in the water must not lead the conning officer to forget the general situation.

Operating with a task force

A carrier is seldom at sea unless she is in company with other ships. With a task force, the conning officer will wish to know the general capabilities and characteristics of the other types in the formation. Fuel capacity, maximum speed for the boiler combination in use, time required to change this condition, etc., are all items of interest to the conning officer of the carrier. Though all ships are expected to use fleet standards for speed changes and turns, it behooves the conning officer to check the speed and turning characteristics of the other ships in the formation. The shift of the formation guide from a carrier to a cruiser might be the occasion for us to get off station during the next subsequent maneuver until we are familiar with that type of guide. Perhaps the cruiser loses less speed in a turn or regains her speed more promptly, and thus causes us to lose our position, even though all ships are using fleet standards with the engines and rudder. We must learn and remember the peculiarities of each of the ships of our formation in order to be ready to conform to them should that ship be designated guide. To have a bit of difficulty keeping station on a new guide can be forgiven for a few maneuvers, but the conning officer who plods ahead blindly, dogmatic in the accuracy of his own ship's calibration, and so repeatedly arrives off station—well, such a shiphandler does anything but gain the admiration of the other ship shiphandlers of the force.

In war or in peace, a carrier will almost invariably be at sea with destroyers doing her screening and plane guarding. It is appropriate, then, that the conning officer of the carrier be thoroughly acquainted with all destroyer types. Characteristically, destroyers need fuel, and there will be frequent fuelings from the carrier.

During combat operations it is customary to keep destroyers fueled to above 65 percent capacity as long as the operational demands permit. It is necessary that these ships have ample fuel for the high speed steaming that air action requires. To accomplish this, the carriers are kept rigged for fueling destroyers at all times, and the destroyers are called alongside with little warning as soon as a lull develops. The alert carrier conning officer will insure that his crew, as well as his rigging, is ready on a moment's notice for this vital service to the destroyer.

Courtesy among seamen requires, also, that the assigned destroyers be queried about other logistics requirements; many things which are plentiful on the carrier might be badly needed on the destroyer. Passengers, light freight, and mail must also be passed under most circumstances. The "high line" is a busy rig when a destroyer is alongside.

If a destroyer is alongside for other purposes than fueling, it is advisable to take her at one of the after transfer stations. When alongside at these stations, only the bow of the destroyer overlaps the carrier, and her stern is free to swing without danger of fouling the carrier's side. Transfer stations on each side of the fantail afford an area for working the lines and landing passengers and freight, and the underside of the flight deck provides an elevated point for attaching the rig.

Because of the working area and relative size of her crew, it is best to use the carrier's rig when using the high line. When a transfer is ordered, the destroyer will appreciate a prompt message designating the transfer point and stating that the carrier's gear will be used. This will obviate the requirement for the destroyer to rig her own gear on her wet forecastle as she makes her approach.

With a destroyer alongside for fuel, or at the quarter for personnel, mail, or stores, the conning officer's job is simple, since the carrier has only to steer a very steady course at a steady speed. He should be careful, however, about his own ship's actual course and speed. He must quickly detect and remedy any casualty. The engine rooms and steering station aft should be kept informed as the destroyer makes her approach, rides alongside, and finally clears. The personnel in these stations must be aware that special vigilance is in order. The conning officer should also keep an eye on the destroyer so that he can take assisting action should a casualty occur aboard her.

If a course or speed change is ordered with a destroyer alongside, it can be made safely if made slowly, with complete information going to the destroyer at all times. It is usually best to make the change in moderate increments instead of one steady change. The carrier should make the course change with a small rudder angle, notifying the destroyer continuously of the carrier's heading to the half degree. The carrier should steady up for a couple of minutes about every 30° in order to allow the destroyer to settle down. Speed changes can be made in a single increment if desired, however, because the carrier accelerates or decelerates so slowly that the destroyer has little trouble keeping pace with the change. Further, the destroyer can surge farther off station fore and aft than she can to the side, and there is little danger of a collision inherent in a speed change when alongside.

When a carrier goes alongside an oiler or a storeship at sea, we have some of our most interesting shiphandling opportunities. The carrier may go alongside as many as four other ships during a day of replenishment because of the requirement to take aboard aviation fuel and ammunition in addition to the usual ship requirements. She is usually placed to port of the supply vessel in consideration of her offset conning station. The techniques of bringing a carrier alongside are the same as for the other large warships described in Chapter 12, so they will not be explored here; but it is worthwhile to note that carriers can be handled alongside as effectively as any of the other fleet types.

14
submarines

Of all the types of seagoing vessels now in operation, the submarine is one of the most unusual. During a century of development, the submarine has progressed from a small, cranky craft which operated on the surface except for brief, shallow dives to an oceangoing, nuclear-powered ship with practically unlimited propulsion endurance, so designed that it normally operates submerged for long periods of time. Submarines have propellers and rudders, but there most resemblance to surface ships ends.

Most of the submarines in the U. S. Navy are now nuclear-powered and equipped with single screws, so this chapter will be devoted to discussing the handling characteristics of this type.

Construction characteristics of the submarine

As indicated in Figure 14–1, a modern submarine is a slim, cylindrical ship with a minimum of superstructure. The manned compartments of the submarine with all propelling and auxiliary machinery, weapons, control equipment, and living accommodations are contained within the pressure hull delineated by the heavy line. The air and watertight pressure hull is welded of heavy steel plating and designed to withstand the pressure of the sea, which increases approximately 50 psi for each 100-foot increase in depth.

Outside the pressure hull, the superstructure built of lighter plating forms a streamlined, free-flooding covering over piping systems and around various mechanical devices in the fairwater that extend retractable periscopes and electronic antennas above the surface of the water while the submarine is at a shallow, submerged depth. Access from the superstructure to the inside of the pressure hull is through heavy, hand-operated watertight hatches. Also outside the pressure hull and between it and the exterior shell plating at certain sections of the ship are the main ballast tanks. These tanks contain air for positive buoyancy to keep the ship afloat while surfaced. A submarine submerges by opening large vent valves in the main ballast tanks, thus allowing the air to escape at the top while seawater floods the tanks through openings at the bottom. To surface, the vent valves are checked

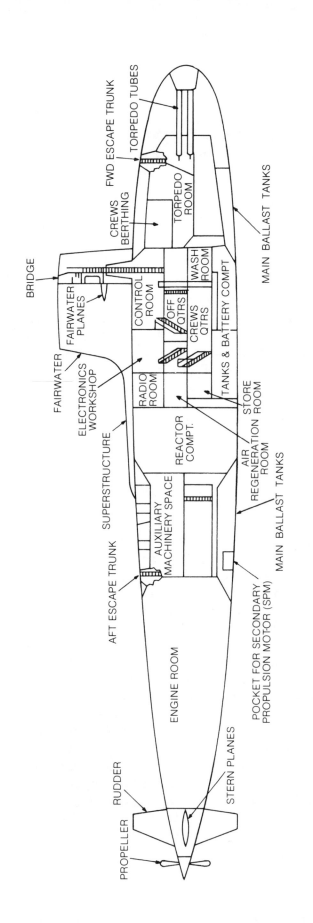

FIGURE 14–1. Inboard profile of an attack submarine.

shut and the water is expelled through the bottom openings by the force of high- or low-pressure air directed to the tanks.

The control surfaces, consisting of fairwater planes, stern planes, and rudder, are located as shown in Figure 14–1, and are operated to change depth and course.

During submerged operations, ship control functions are carried out in the control room. Engine orders are transmitted from the control room to a control station in the engine room, where they are carried out. When the submarine surfaces, personnel proceed from the control room to the bridge at the top of the fairwater, where they maintain a lookout and control movement of the ship by communicating orders to control room personnel. When maneuvering alongside a pier, the officer conning the ship also directs topside personnel in the handling of mooring lines.

As a result of the streamlining required to give the desired underwater capability, most of the normal deck and navigating equipment has been eliminated or made retractable or portable (Figure 14–2). In some submarines the topside is the curved surface or the exterior pressure hull or superstructure plating. In other classes it may consist of a narrow, flat surface built up above the pressure hull and enclosing equipment and lockers for mooring lines.

A submarine's anchor is located at the bow or stern, depending on the class and where space that is not occupied by other equipment is available.

FIGURE 14–2. For streamlining, deck and navigating equipment on submarines is now portable or retractable. Here, USS Benjamin Franklin (SSBN 640) is shown at dockside with cleats and mooring lines in use.

Tanks in addition to the main ballast tanks are located throughout the submarine for such purposes as storing potable water, fuel oil for the emergency diesel generator, lubricating and hydraulic oil, and trim water for adjusting weights to achieve a neutral buoyancy when the submarine is submerged.

Characteristics which affect surface handling

To assist in maneuvering the submarine alongside a pier, a secondary propulsion motor or SPM is provided. This consists of a submersible electric motor directly driving a small propeller and attached to a vertical shaft which extends the unit below the keel or retracts it up into a pocket in a main ballast tank located aft. The motor is turned on and off from the control room; direction of the thrust is changed by rotating the shaft attached to the motor. The SPM is trained in azimuth in this manner to apply its limited force in the direction desired.

The submarine's main screw is submerged several feet under all conditions of loading. Most of the upper section of the rudder is out of water when the ship is surfaced and this part makes a convenient auxiliary rudder angle indicator for bridge personnel. The bridge cockpit is only large enough for three or four people, and it is cramped at that. Communication between the officer of the deck on the bridge to the helmsman (who also operates the engine order annunciator) and other watch personnel in the control room and throughout the ship is by telephone or announcing system. Bridge personnel are powerless to control the ship if these communications fail, so casualty control procedures and backup systems are important.

Other equipment on the bridge which is either portable and brought up after surfacing or contained in pressure-proof casings and permanently mounted includes a gyrocompass repeater, rudder angle indicator, collision and diving alarm contact makers, and a whistle operating lever or lanyard.

Bearings can be taken using the bridge gyro repeater, but it is more accurate and convenient to have bearings taken by periscope in the control room. The navigating station is in the control room, where charts can be laid out and data obtained from periscope bearings, the radar, and the echo sounder. When in restricted waters, it is important for the officer of the deck to have duplicate charts on the bridge to check information with the navigator. All-around visibility from the top of the sail is excellent and the whole length of the ship can be seen.

A submarine's topside is close to the water and the absence of lifelines and lack of flat surface make placing personnel out on deck hazardous outside of sheltered waters. A submarine's topside is usually swept continuously by the sea when outside harbor and making any speed. In heavy seas even the bridge can take green water over it and if the submarine has to remain surfaced under these conditions, it may be necessary to bring personnel below, secure the bridge, shut the access hatch, and conn the ship from the control room, keeping a continuous visual watch through the periscopes. The streamlined hull shape, designed for optimum submerged characteristics, is generally circular in cross section and tapered at the ends. It therefore lacks flare and rise at the bow. This causes the forward end to dig in at speed on the surface and the apparent bow moves aft from the actual bow sometimes even to the base of the fairwater. The cockpit at the top of the fairwater is then only a few feet aft and above the sea so it does not take much wave action to seriously hazard bridge personnel. It is usual practice to obtain the captain's permission to send personnel out on deck at sea and then they must be equipped with lifejackets and safety harnesses which attach them to the ship by means of a line and fitting that slides along a track.

Both extremities of a submarine are vulnerable to damage. It is important in the final stage of making a landing that the ship's side make contact with deep-draft separators along the pier and that the extremities not bump. At the bow are located torpedo tube moving parts and sonar system components, while the planes at the stern are tender as well.

Since the rudder is located forward of the propeller, rudder effect is not obtained from propeller wash when the propeller is turning in the ahead direction. This, of course, is a significant difference from single-screw surface ships of comparable displacement, where an ahead bell with the rudder over can create considerable turning moment even before the ship gains significant headway.

On the other hand, with the propeller turning astern, the wash moving forward against the deflected rudder does not produce much usable turning moment and the stern tends to move uncertainly. With stern way on, the rudder may or may not be effective in controlling the stern depending on the class of submarine, so the conning officer must be prepared for the unexpected.

The secondary propulsion motor or SPM can be an aid when preparing to get under way or when easing the ship alongside while mooring. The SPM is located aft of the pivot point so that when it is trained on either beam and turned on, it can be used to move the stern away from or towards the pier. If the SPM is trained ahead or astern, it can be used to move the submarine along the pier with low power. Since the SPM can only be used when it is extended out of its pocket and below the keel, it is important that the resulting increased ship draft be considered. Operating the SPM close to the bottom can sometimes clog it with mud or sand.

A submarine displaces upwards of 4,000 tons surfaced and most of the ship is below the surface, resulting in a draft of 26 feet or more. The deep draft and limited superstructure combine to cause more effects from currents and less effects from winds on the ship.

The low silhouette can also be misleading to other ships and it is difficult to determine a submarine's course and speed from visual observations. At night the side lights are low; there is a masthead light but no range light, and the stern light is close to the water. A submarine identification signal consisting of flashing all-around amber light is displayed by U. S. submarines, but it is not provided for in international rules of the road. A submarine is also a small radar target and this, combined with the visible characteristics, frequently results in mistaken identification as a fishing vessel or other small ship of size and maneuverability greatly different from a submarine.

These characteristics and the strong likelihood that a submarine will sink if a collision ruptures ballast tanks and the pressure hull make submarine officers particularly alert to the necessity for taking early and sufficient action to prevent a collision situation from developing.

Characteristics which affect submerged handling

The effects of a submarine's characteristics on its submerged handling can be complex and only some of the more basic conditions will be described here.

The submerged submarine moves in response to the three-dimensional resultant of various forces on it. Underwater, it is a body with six degrees of freedom. The fairwater planes and the stern hydrofoil planes are mounted horizontally athwartships and can be rotated about their horizontal axes. Up or down forces on the planes' axes, and therefore on the ship, result from inclining the planes relative to the flow of water over them. The right and left halves of the fairwater or stern planes operate together. The fairwater and the stern planes are each controlled by a separate operator in the control room.

The fairwater planes are located back from the bow and towards the vertical pivot point of the ship. Therefore, the deflection of these planes relative to the water flow tends to move the whole ship up or down as well as moving the bow up or down.

On the other hand, the stern planes are located at the after end of the ship and the deflection of these control surfaces moves the stern up or down, rotating the ship about its vertical pivot point.

Inclination of the complete hull envelope in the flow of water causes another major force on the ship to move it up or down. If the hull assumes an angle of attack with respect to the relative water flow as the result of a rapidly applied plane angle or unbalanced buoyancy forces, the vertical force can be large.

The remaining control surface, the rudder, operates in the normal fashion except that the upper half which was out of water on the surface now contributes to maneuverability when submerged. Helmsman duties are handled by one of the two planesmen.

Since the control surfaces are hydrofoils and depend on water flow over them to produce maneuvering forces, the speed of the submarine directly affects the control forces available. At low speed large deflection angles on control surfaces are required to obtain the desired effects while at high speeds only small angles are needed. In fact, at high speed a large stern plane's angle will quickly change the angle of the ship and the combination of high forward speed and tremendous forces on the ship because of the angle of the hull relative to the water flow will cause rapid depth changes and possibly a casualty situation.

If the ship is pointed down relative to the horizontal, it is said to have a down angle or "down bubble" from the inclinometer which is used to measure the angle. With a down bubble, the ship moves to an increased depth. The opposite effect takes place if the hull has an "up bubble."

When submerged, a submarine's main ballast tanks are full of water. This eliminates the positive buoyancy which maintained it on the surface and produces approximately neutral buoyancy. When submerging, a down angle is put on the ship with the stern planes to drive it under, and as the fairwater planes submerge they can be used to help reach and maintain the desired depth. Adjustments in the weight of the submarine to compensate for loading and expending consumables to maintain neutral buoyancy and an even fore-and-aft trim are made by flooding seawater into or pumping seawater out of variable ballast tanks located inside the pressure hull at the ends and near the center of the ship.

The control surfaces can be used also as temporary or emergency compensation for out-of-neutral buoyancy conditions. For example, if a compartment has flooded with thousands of pounds of sea water as the result of a casualty, this weight increase or negative buoyancy tending to make the submarine sink can be offset by angle on the planes and the ship, if enough speed can be maintained to produce the necessary forces.

Depth control submerged is achieved by using the fairwater and stern planes together to produce the right combination of dynamic forces on the planes and the hull to change depth or to maintain an ordered depth. Some examples will help to explain how this works. At periscope depth, which is a shallow submerged depth to permit periscopes and antennas to be raised above the surface, the submarine will be running at slow speed. Close attention to depth control is important to prevent either exposing too much of what is raised above the surface, which invites detection, or submerging what is raised, which defeats its use. The fairwater planes operator is given the ordered depth and the stern planes operator is given an ordered angle or bubble to maintain on the ship. But like driving a car, continual adjustments to both planes angles must be made to achieve the ordered conditions on an average. Most of the time the ordered conditions are being passed through as the operators sense changes and take corrective actions. If conditions change so that the ship varies significantly from the ordered condition, then both operators interact with each other to correct the situation. If the stern planes operator was ordered to maintain a one-degree down angle on the ship and the ship was several feet below the ordered depth with the fairwater planes operator having difficulty regaining depth, then the stern planes operator would take off the down angle and put on a zero or slight up angle to use the water flow forces on the hull to help regain the ordered depth.

As another example, at high speed and deeply submerged, depth is maintained usually within several feet by use of small stern planes' angles only, which change the angle of the ship, and the resultant water flow forces on the hull cause depth to change. Under these conditions, the fairwater planes are left at a zero angle of tilt and are available to use if an emergency or casualty occurs.

In addition to changing the course of a submarine, the rudder has some interesting effects when operating submerged. Since the metacenter and center of buoyancy of the circular cross-section hull coincide when submerged, and also since the center of gravity is below the center of buoyancy because of the location of heavy equipment and lead ballast low in the ship, a course change causes a heel or bank toward the direction of the turn. The flow of water at an angle against the fairwater during the turn produces a force above the center of buoyancy, also tending to bank the ship toward the direction of the turn. A turn at high speed with large rudder angle in some classes of submarines can cause a large snap roll and possibly loss of control. Another interesting effect of the snap roll is that the rudder axis at the cruciform stern which was vertical at the start of the turn now has rolled away from the true vertical and produces a force component in the vertical plane, which can put a serious down angle on the ship.

Lines and deck equipment

Although there is not much deck space, a submarine must be equipped to meet the mooring requirements of other ship types while not degrading submerged performance. The bull nose, capstan heads, cleats, and lifelines are all retractable or removable for streamlining and must be rigged and unrigged for entering or leaving port.

Manila mooring lines have been used in the past, but now the various synthetic fiber lines have come into common use. Lines are normally rigged as shown in Figure 14–3 for the smaller attack submarines or as in Figure 14–4 for the larger ballistic missile submarines. Lines are handled by a hydraulically powered capstan at the bow and stern. It is important for a submarine to lie against deep draft separators when moored at a pier to prevent tender parts from bumping.

Depending on the class, ground tackle consists of a mushroom or four-fluke anchor and 135 to 180 fathoms of three-quarter inch or one inch chain. The anchor is located at the bow or stern, depending on the class, and the hawse is below the surface waterline. The anchor is housed in a recess so that a smooth hull exterior is maintained to cut down water resistance and flow noise. Operating controls for the hydraulically powered anchor windlass are in the bow or stern compartment and orders are transmitted there from the bridge. Since the chain and anchor cannot be observed, the tend and strain on the chain and the clear or foul condition of the anchor cannot be determined. The amount of chain out and the housed position of the anchor are determined by remote indicators at the operating station.

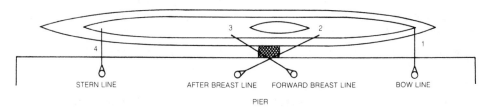

FIGURE 14–3. Mooring lines for a small attack submarine.

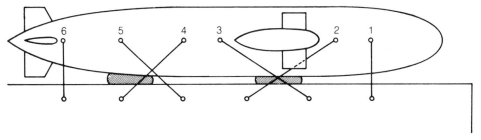

FIGURE 14–4. Mooring lines for a large ballistic missile submarine.

Towing and alongside operations

Submarines cannot reasonably be used for towing because of the limited deck space for rigging gear, the generally unsafe conditions topside at sea, and the great hazard of damaging the rudder, stern planes, and propeller.

Submarines do not conduct alongside operations. With nuclear propulsion and sufficient stores and provisions stowage capacity for long unsupported periods at sea, there is no need for this evolution.

Shiphandling considerations

Three characteristics of the single-screw, deep-draft submarine that play an important part in shiphandling are that it is unable to twist while dead in the water; when backing it is difficult to predict in which direction the stern will go; and when making slow speed ahead, from one to two knots, the ship's head is difficult to control.

Even with these limitations many landings can be made unassisted, particularly where small turns are required in order to get lined up. Often, however, it is prudent to use tugs to assist the ship during the landing or underway evolution, or to have them standing by to assist if necessary.

If a pilot comes with the tug, it is important to discuss the plan for maneuvering with him. Of course, it is essential for all concerned to know who will have the conn for the evolution. If the submarine will keep the conn, then it is important to discuss and agree on the location and makeup of the tug and how it will be directed. In some cases the most practical procedure after making up is to tell the tug master or pilot how the conning officer wants the tug assistance applied and let him handle rudder and power orders to the tug.

The techniques that will be discussed are by no means all-inclusive. No two situations are the same, nor is any one situation limited to a single solution. It should also be stated that no amount of written material can ever substitute for the benefits of actual shipboard experience. Shiphandling experiences are relatively infrequent, considering the long endurance and deep water operations of present submarines. Therefore, each opportunity to handle the ship must be exploited to obtain the maximum in training for ship's personnel.

Getting under way

Getting under way from a berth in slack or near slack water offers an excellent opportunity for an unassisted maneuver.

As an example, in Figure 14–5, line 4 is slacked and a strain is put on line 1 by heaving with the capstan in order to get the stern away from the pier. The SPM trained on the beam can also be used to move out the stern. When a satisfactory angle with the pier is attained, check line 4 so that the stern will be not be swinging. Take in lines 1, 3 and 4 and BACK ONE-THIRD, putting the rudder over in the direction you desire the stern to go. We will go LEFT FULL in order to move the stern upriver. When the ship has sternway, take in line 2. Watch the stern carefully; when it starts to swing to port, BACK TWO-THIRDS for a short period of time. This will increase the rate of turn as the wash hits the rudder. Slow to ONE-THIRD, and when the ship's head is within 30 degrees of channel course, order ALL STOP, RUDDER AMIDSHIPS. Now it is only a matter of ordering an ahead bell and maneuvering to conform to the channel course. The same procedures can be used for a starboard side moor. One word of

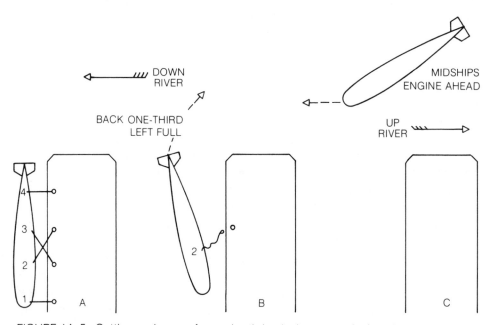

FIGURE 14–5. Getting under way from a berth in slack or near-slack water.

caution: the movement of the stern with sternway is unpredictable, so watch it closely.

An unassisted backing maneuver should not be attempted under conditions where current or wind tends to set the ship against the pier, and in any case, it is prudent to have a tug standing by for assistance if needed to turn the ship.

Making a landing

Next, let us look at Figure 14–6 for an unassisted landing where there is no set from wind or current. As a rule for both port and starboard landings the final approach to the pier should be planned so that the ship stops parallel to and 20 to 30 feet off the assigned berth. The last few feet are taken care of by heaving around on lines 1 and 4, using the SPM or using lines 2 and 3 to spring in on.

The ship makes the approach at an angle of 10 to 15 degrees with the pier at a speed of two to three knots. As the bow approaches a point abreast of the end of the pier, commence backing. Ensure that ship's head is steady in the final approach

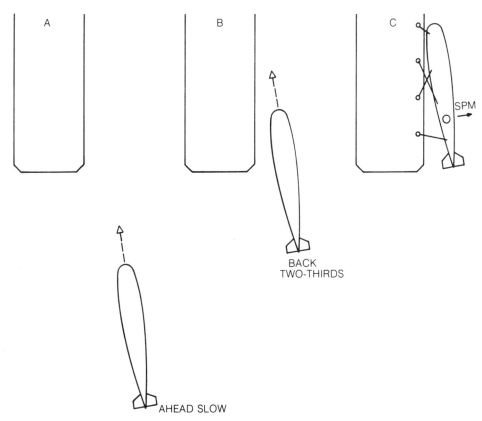

FIGURE 14–6. An unassisted landing with no set from wind or current.

phase. This is important since if there is turning momentum on the ship, it may tend to sheer when the backing bell is put on. A two-thirds backing bell should be used and the effect watched carefully. Continue backing until most of the headway is killed. At the same time put over all lines. Lines 1 and 4 should be put on the capstans. Use line 2 to spring in on and kill the rest of the headway. When the ship is dead in the water, heave around easy on lines 1 and 4 to settle the ship into the berth. The SPM trained on the beam may also be used to bring the submarine alongside.

Unassisted landings should not be attempted when a moderate current is running. Unless the timing is letter perfect, the landing could result in damage to the bow or stern because of improper line-up or the current working on one end of the ship.

Good seamanship is the exercise of good judgment. With a modern submarine when damaging the bow or stern is likely, the decision not to attempt an unassisted maneuver is good judgment. The ability to use a tug to complete the maneuver is good seamanship.

The use of tugs

There is nothing tricky or particularly difficult about handling tugs to help maneuver a submarine (Figure 14–7). It is a matter of being aware of all of the forces available or that must be contended with and then using these forces in whatever combination is necessary to do the job. A general discussion of pilots and tugs is given in Chapter 18 and the handling of single-screw ships is covered in Chapter 7, but following are a few points which apply particularly to submarines:

Be alert to prevent damage that may be caused by tug contact, particularly in the tender bow area, and ensure that tugs keep clear of the rudder, screw, and stern planes. Tugs specially equipped to handle submarines have bow fenders extending to the forefoot, but tugs in non-submarine ports may not be so equipped.

There are three basic methods of communicating with the tug—walkie-talkie, bull-horn, and hand signals. All commands, no matter how they are given, are acknowledged by an appropriate signal on the tug's whistle.

Standard hand signals are used for Navy tug control. If necessary, a few practice sessions will demonstrate the simplicity of the technique and develop confidence in its use.

When hand signals are used, the conning officer, who normally conns from the top of the fairwater, can usually give the signal himself. If necessary, he may have someone else relay for him. The person doing the signaling should station himself in such a position that he can clearly see, and be seen by, the tug master. This will help to prevent any misunderstanding.

At this point a word of caution should be mentioned. Conning a ship is a one-man job. This is particularly true when tugs are being employed. The *responsi-*

FIGURE 14–7. USS *Lafayette* (SSBN 616) returns to port with tug assistance, as seen through the eye of a periscope.

bility for the conn cannot be divided between two people. It makes no difference how capable either individual might be by himself. Having one person control the ship's propeller and rudder while someone else controls the movement of the tug, with each operating independently of the other, is a sure way of getting into trouble. Sooner or later one person will misinterpret the intentions of the other.

Submerged operations

The principles and techniques of submerging and operating under the surface are quite foreign to the surface sailor. A discussion of the basics and systems involved follows.

A submarine is submerged by completely flooding its main ballast tanks with seawater to eliminate the positive reserve buoyancy and then driving the ship beneath the surface. Once submerged, the weight of water contained in its variable ballast tanks is adjusted until the weight of the submarine and all it contains is equal to the weight of the seawater displaced by the submarine. In accordance with the principle of Archimedes, this will result in a balance of forces, and neutral buoyancy is attained.

Though in perfect neutral buoyancy, the fore-and-aft distribution of weight may be such that the ship will tend to be bow or stern heavy. In order to compensate for this condition, two of the variable ballast tanks, forward trim and after trim, are located in the bow and stern, respectively. By adjusting the amount of water in these trim tanks, the submarine can be balanced with a neutral pitching moment in addition to having neutral buoyancy.

Factors affecting buoyancy

The buoyant condition of the submarine, whether positive, negative, or neutral, is continually subject to change, both from external and internal effects. The weight of the submarine changes as seawater is distilled and stored in the tanks and is used from these tanks, as bilges accumulate drains, and as wastes are discharged overboard. Also the weight of water displaced by the submarine changes with variations in depth, temperature, and salinity content of the surrounding seawater. As density increases, the weight and consequently the buoyant force of a given volume of water increases. Water density increases slightly with increased depth and salinity content, and more significantly with decreasing temperature. Additionally, as the surrounding pressure increases with depth the submarine is compressed slightly, thus decreasing the volume of displaced seawater and decreasing the positive buoyant force. Adjustments must be made to the submarine's trim as these factors change.

Preparing to dive and submerging

Immediately after leaving port the submarine is rigged for dive. This entails a thorough check of all fittings and systems, such as hatches and doors; hydraulic, compressed air, seawater, ventilation, and electrical systems which are critical for submerged operations. Valves and switches are positioned or checked in position separately by two individuals. This double check is typical of the redundancy of systems and supervision utilized in submarines to increase safety and operational reliability. Once the ship is rigged for dive the captain's permission is required to modify this condition. The officer of the deck keeps track of all exceptions to the rig for dive and is responsible for correcting deficiencies which violate the rig for dive. When surfaced, a diving trim is maintained and other exceptions to the rig for dive are minimized so that the ship can be submerged expeditiously. A minimum

FIGURE 14–8. The nuclear-powered ballistic missile submarine USS *James Monroe* (SSBN 622) under way.

number of men are permitted on the bridge so less time is needed to get them below.

When directed by the captain or other designated officer in the control room, the officer of the deck passes the appropriate tactical information to the officer who is relieving the officer of the deck and orders that officer to rig the bridge for dive and lay below. The former officer of the deck then clears the bridge of all portable equipment and personnel, shuts the bridge cockpit fairing cover, shuts the upper and lower bridge hatches, and proceeds to the diving station to assume the duties of diving officer. When satisfied that all personnel are down from the bridge and that all hatches and ventilation hull closures are shut, the officer of the deck orders the diving officer to submerge the ship to a specified depth, normally to periscope depth. On diving, the officer of the deck relinquishes speed control to the diving officer until a satisfactory submerged trim has been obtained. Normally, the submarine dives at two-thirds speed with the rudder amidships and masts and periscopes housed. Moderate down angles are used to avoid broaching the screw and stern planes. The main ballast tank vents are opened to allow these tanks to fill with seawater and cause the ship to settle. The stern planes are placed on dive to cause the desired down angle and the ship is driven under the surface. As the ship approaches periscope depth it is leveled off and the diving officer slows to one-third as soon as he feels the trim is close enough to allow him to control depth at reduced speed. He directs the shifting of water to achieve a satisfactory trim, as described earlier. When able to maintain ordered depth at a neutral bubble (0-1 degree down) with only a few degrees of stern and fairwater planes angle, he reports satisfactory trim to the officer of the deck, who then regains speed control.

Experienced submariners prefer to dive heading away from or across the seas rather than heading into them. Depth control at periscope depth in a heavy sea is more difficult when heading into or away from the seas than when running the trough. Though there is no increase in the buoyant force as a wave temporarily covers the submarine to a greater depth, there is an upward surge of the water and a reduced pressure area on top of the submarine as the wave passes over. This is troublesome to the diving officer and can cause the submarine to broach. To counter this effect in a rough sea, it is normal to trim the ship heavy overall and maintain an up bubble to stay at periscope depth so that an increase in depth can be made more quickly if the submarine starts to broach or break the surface. To prevent broaching, it is often advisable to increase speed to get better planes control.

Coming to periscope depth and surfacing

The transition from a safe submerged depth, that is, one at which the highest portion of the submarine structure is safely below the deepest draft surface ship, to periscope depth, where the officer of the deck can visually sight hazards, is a period of potential danger. Until an all-around periscope observation can be made, the officer of the deck may not know of the presence and location of surface ships. This is particularly true for certain sonar conditions when the detection range against surface contacts is limited, for contacts closing the submarine from astern where the submarine's sonar is baffled, or for large, deep-draft surface ships approaching with a small bow aspect where the hull blocks most of the machinery noise.

The normal procedure for coming to periscope depth is to slow at safe depth, make a careful sonar search for contacts while maneuvering to search astern, and if clear, come smartly up to periscope depth. There a rapid visual search is made to confirm the absence of threatening contacts.

Except in emergencies, surfacing is commenced from periscope depth so that conditions on the surface can be known in advance.

The surfacing evolution is the reverse of diving. The main ballast tanks are blown dry of water to regain the positive buoyancy which gives the submarine its surface trim.

When the submarine is holding at a steady depth near normal surface draft, personnel proceed to the bridge, rig and check out equipment, and take over ship control.

Man overboard

The methods used in submarines for picking up a man overboard are similar to those used in surface ships, but here again there are limitations. The danger of placing a rescue party on the rounded main deck, the lack of lifeboats, and the limited lookout and searchlight facilities all hamper the submarine in this evolution. With decks awash in moderate seas, the submarine may utilize the horizontal surface of the fairwater planes as a staging area for launching a swimmer and recovering personnel. The difficulties in recovering a man overboard make it very important that precautionary measures be taken to prevent losing a man overboard.

Conclusion

This chapter is not intended to make the reader competent in handling a submarine, but merely to acquaint him with the submarine as a type, to explain the technical principles of submarine operation, and to discuss elementary submarine shiphandling.

15
large amphibious and service ships

The ships which make up the Navy's mobile attack and support forces—the amphibious and the service ships—are the most varied and often the most interesting ships that challenge the shiphandler. Varying in size from seagoing tugs to mammoth "one stop" replenishment ships, they have nothing in common except their diversity. As a rule, they are large, moderate to low-powered ships, usually ill-equipped to maneuver unassisted, but there are important exceptions. In this chapter, they will be discussed by groups, touching only upon a few of the most significant characteristics of each type.

Amphibious and service ships now in service are vastly different from their predecessors of 20 years ago. Instead of a motley collection of underpowered, usually single-screw, merchant ships converted to naval use, the Navy now has specially designed ships, each created for a specific task. The 20-knot amphibious force is a reality—Marine combat teams, complete with all their equipment, can now be deployed at the rate of 500 miles a day. The service ships are as fast or faster, and can be depended on to support the deployed fleets in the most distant seas and to move in support of the strike fleets as operations require. The ships live—year in, year out wherever they may be—on the never-ending chain of replenishment ships which connect them to the United States. Though ships of the Sixth and Seventh Fleets visit ports for recreation and support from the service ships, it is literally true that they operate without the need for permanent advance bases. They receive all of their supplies and obtain all of their repairs and technical assistance from the mobile support base that moves with the fleet. Fueling, rearming, replenishing stores, transfer of personnel and all of the logistic activities required in the operation and support of a fleet are now *underway* evolutions. Day and night, in fair weather and in foul, the logistic replenishment of the fleet goes on. For every example of splendid shiphandling executed as the strike fleet replenishes its stores, there is a complementary piece of good seamanship on the service ship with which it is operating. To move the troops and their equipment, to keep the fleet operating and supplied as it moves about the world, requires dependable and skillful shiphandling on the part of all.

The least maneuverable yet very numerous group of amphibious and service ships is the large, single-screw, single-rudder ship of which the following three classes are typical:

Class	Iwo Jima LPH 2	Samuel Gompers AD 37	Mars AFS 1
Length	602	645	581
Beam	84	85	79
Draft	29	23	24
Displacement	18,000	20,700	16,260
Horsepower	22,000	20,000	22,000
Speed	24	18	20
Crew, Officers	44	135	34
Enlisted	512	671	441
Troops	1,800	—	—

These ships are designed to carry their payloads—helicopters and troops, repair shops and material, and general stores—efficiently across the oceans and to provide adequate space and accommodations for handling them at their point of origin and at the destination. They were not intended to be able to maneuver smartly unassisted. It was planned from the beginning that they would require tug assistance in port and anchor in a broad roadstead at an advance base. At sea they spend most of their time steaming steadily on a set course and if there are transfers to or from other ships, the other ship does the maneuvering. But, of course, there are exceptions, and it is to meet these exceptions that the conning officer of the large single-screw ship must study all of the maneuvers required in fleet operations and be ready to make the most of his ship and her equipment.

Before examining the maneuvers which will be required of a large single-screw vessel, it is necessary to know her characteristics. Such a ship is bulky, with enormous sail area. When loaded, the draft is equal to a carrier. Engine power is only about one horsepower per ton—about one-twentieth that of a destroyer. Backing power is much less than her ahead power, so the engine must be backed early and long to take effect. The ship will back to port very noticeably, will veer to port a bit when starting ahead, and has all of the maneuvering limitations of any single-screw ship and proportionally much less power to counteract them. Once under way, however, at speeds well above steerageway, she will be as steady and controllable as any other type ship.

Getting under way from an anchorage

Because of her rather limited maneuverability at low speed and relatively slow acceleration, it is particularly desirable with a large single-screw ship to get more than 5 knots way on as soon as possible. For this reason it is frequently desirable to "cast" (twist about the anchor) to the direction desired for clearing the anchorage prior to getting under way, and then, immediately on getting under way, to build up speed which will permit more ready handling.

Although the ship is rather limited in maneuverability, as compared to a multiple-screw warship or the twin-screw service type, she can be turned smartly and handled nicely, under light wind conditions, by judicious use of her large rudder, coupled with her relatively slow acceleration rate. For example, a rapid change of course can be effected while at slow speed or even without steerageway by "kicking" the engine ahead while holding full rudder in the direction of the desired course change. A kick, consisting of ringing up TWO-THIRDS or even STAN-DARD SPEED for a short interval, will produce a maximum turning effect for a short time but will not be of sufficient duration for the ship to gain much headway. To swing to the right (stern moving to port) kick the engines astern and the stern will move smartly to port. Unfortunately we cannot move the stern to starboard by kicking the engine astern, but, except for this, we can swing nicely by using short bursts of power.

Getting under way from a pier

Because of her characteristics, a large service-type ship requires a little more preparation for getting under way than most other naval types. It is essential that her loading and cargo stowage be carefully checked prior to getting under way. Abnormal draft or trim can materially complicate shiphandling, and shifting cargo may lead to disaster. Because of her low power and relatively poor backing characteristics, it is advisable to call for tug assistance under all but ideal conditions—particularly until her characteristics are thoroughly learned by per-sonal experience. The use of pilots and tugs will be discussed in Chapter 18; however, since there will certainly be times when tug assistance will not be available, let's consider handling the ship without the luxury of tugs.

Before taking in the gangway, it is advisable to walk to the end of the pier and study the situation—noting the general construction of the pier, any obstructions, the locations of pilings and buoys, etc. This "look-see" is particularly advisable when clearing from between two solid piers (as opposed to open or pile-supported piers), since the ship will be clearing relatively slowly and may en-counter a situation where her bow is in relatively still water, while her stern is being acted on by the current in the channel. This situation can produce both a rapid drift and a radical turning moment which must be encountered until the ship is clear of the piers. In the absence of tugs, the ship's boats may prove useful in countering this effect.

In conning from a pier, it is almost mandatory to take a station on the open bridge above the pilothouse because of the restricted visibility from the covered bridge. If there is any appreciable wind or current, it may be desirable to use an anchor and the ship's boats as described later under the section "Poor man's tugboat." Under any circumstances, make sure there are plenty of well-tended fenders available.

The first consideration in maneuvering the ship from the pier should be to keep her stern well clear. This can usually be accomplished by holding number two line and kicking AHEAD TWO-THIRDS, with the rudder toward the dock. When the stern has moved out a sufficient distance we can clear with BACK TWO-THIRDS and by adjusting the rudder to keep her backing fair with her stern well cleared. If moored port-side-to a long pier, we may have to kick ahead briefly to counter her natural tendency to back to port (into the pier). Once sufficiently clear of the pier face, it is desirable to use more engine power in order to clear the pier head as rapidly as possible.

Handling at sea

While a single-screw ship may have some limitations in "close-in" handling, there are no material differences in her maneuverability from that of a cruiser or carrier at speeds about 12 knots. Under normal conditions of wind and sea, condition of loading has no noticeable effect on maneuverability; the ship can maintain station in formation with any Navy type within her speed range, and can perform all the common maneuvers handily. The pivot point is about under the bridge structure, and coincidentally, a good rule for column movements is to apply rudder when the rudder kick of the ship ahead is just forward of the bridge structure.

Although other ships normally come along her side during replenishment exercises, she is on occasion required to go alongside other ships for transfer of cargo. Going alongside under way presents no particular problems, but it is prudent to make a wide approach and to maintain a distance of at least 100 feet from the other ship. An average value for surge when going alongside is about 50 yards per knot, but this will vary with loading.

For man-overboard, because of limited backing power it is usually preferable to put a large single-screw ship in a 360° turn to return to the man rather than to attempt to back and lower boats. In case the location of the man is not known, the Williamson turn should be used.

In connection with her backing characteristics, though we know that she will back to port, one might wonder what would happen should we back the engines while moving ahead. It has been determined experimentally that backing while moving ahead is like applying FULL RIGHT RUDDER (stern moves smartly to port). Thus if we back in an emergency while going ahead, we must expect the ship to veer to starboard, and, as heading is lost, even the use of FULL LEFT RUDDER will not prevent her from swinging to starboard.

Though the ship maneuvers handily at sea, do not overlook the heavy-weather problems caused by her combat cargo and complex rigging. At the first sign of heavy weather, all hands must be called to double check the stowage, lower and secure the cargo booms, and check the gripes on the boats. Much topside gear can break loose and many things below decks can be damaged by heavy rolling. It is significant to note that her merchant sisters normally rig for heavy weather *prior to sailing* on any voyage.

Anchoring

Coming to anchor in a designated berth requires careful attention to piloting with any ship, but a large single-screw ship requires extra care. She is sensitive to the wind and to the current, and restricted as to power and maneuverability at the low speeds required in the approach. If possible, the approach should be made from such a direction that the effect of the wind and the current is minimized, and this requires making the final approach directly into the wind. This is most desirable, but unfortunately the limitations of the harbor and the presence of other ships often make this impossible.

In the cases where it is not feasible to approach directly into the wind, the tendency to be set downwind should be countered by *large* course corrections *early* in the approach. It is much better to overcorrect than to undercorrect, because the drift effect increases as the ship slows. The penalty of "too little and too late" is to have the bow pass to leeward of the "let go" point, and either have to anchor incorrectly and then correct later, or make another time-consuming pass at the anchorage. It is much more pleasant to arrive slightly to the windward of the berth and make the necessary correction by simply waiting a few moments before letting go. (The wind will carry the ship down into the center of the berth after she has stopped.)

For making a normal straight approach to an anchorage, the following procedure has been found useful (but each ship should be calibrated individually at her normal load):

Distance to Go	Action
1,000 yards	Be making 5 knots
750 yards	STOP
Zero yards	LET GO and BACK FULL

This will cause the anchor to be dropped while making slight headway, which is quite acceptable in this type, and the chain can be laid out and the anchor "dug in" as desired by continued backing.

Once riding to the anchor, the large ship yaws considerably in the wind. It may be necessary to drop a second anchor underfoot to reduce the yaw; also, turning the screw over slowly ahead will ease the strain on the chain and moderate the yawing.

The ship's boats will also be found to affect her yawing. With several large boats riding to the booms, she will yaw more severely than with her sides clear. The boats do not ride well as she moves to a strong breeze; they ship water and veer into the side of the ship as the ship yaws. If the breeze is troublesome, it may be advisable to secure the boats to a long sea painter astern of the ship rather than to keep them at the booms; or, even better, to get them out of danger by hoisting them aboard or by sending them into a protected cove.

Going alongside a pier

Though it is usually prudent to have tug assistance when handling a large single-screw ship alongside a pier, we should be prepared to take her alongside a pier without assistance. Before attempting such an evolution, however, review her handling characteristics at low speeds and as she is being brought to a stop. Although she handles reasonably well in either direction with the screw going ahead, she *always* backs to port. If we back the screw while going ahead, she will veer to the right, no matter what we do with her rudder. We must *allow* for at least a small turn to the right as she is brought to a halt, but it is nearly *impossible to produce* a turn to the left during the last moments before she stops.

If we remember that it is convenient to approach a pier at a small inclination (perhaps 10°) and then swing parallel to the face of the pier as we arrive at our berth, we will see that it is much easier to bring the ship alongside port-side-to than starboard-side-to the pier. Port-side-to, the stern will swing in alongside the pier nicely as the ship comes to rest; and if she is too far out, the stern can be worked in with a couple of alternate kicks ahead and astern. Starboard-side-to, on the other hand, the inclination is *increased* if the engines back to bring the ship to rest. Once stopped, if the stern is too far out, we may not be able to work it in by alternate kicks as when port-side-to, because each time the engine is backed, the stern moves to port. To work the stern in when alongside starboard-side-to, the usual practice is to run number two line to the pier and work against it with the engines ahead and with the rudder LEFT FULL.

The poor man's tugboat

In handling this large low-powered, single-screw ship, we find her at her worst in the confines of the harbor where precise handling at minimum speed is required. In the well-developed ports of the world, such a ship is met at the harbor entrance by a pilot and the necessary tugs to place her in her berth. The ship's engines, if used at all, are merely secondary in importance, and the big ship is babied into her berth as though she were completely helpless by herself.

Though tugs and pilots are comforting when available, there are many times, even in ports like Norfolk or San Diego, when neither is available, and the ship must either move unassisted or delay until such services become available. In other ports, they are just not available and the ship must move alone. What can be done to achieve the precise control that is not designed into this ship?

Analysis of the problem will present a solution which has long been known to merchant mariners. The trouble lies in the susceptibility of the ship to the wind and current and in her inability to turn without at the same time gaining speed ahead or astern. We cannot *twist* the ship in place. Her rudder is effective enough to give a large force at the stern if the engines are turning over rapidly enough, but this also produces headway. Going astern, the ship must be moving through the water with considerable speed before the rudder effectiveness is sufficient to control the direction of motion. How can we hold the ship against the wind or current? How can we eliminate the undesired headway coupled with turning?

The anchor, of course, is the solution. This "poor man's tugboat" offers the means of restraining the ship while working the engines and rudder. This allows excellent control, even in very tight situations, and gives a flexibility otherwise unavailable except through the use of tugs.

If we drop an anchor under the ship's forefoot and work against it, it will restrain forward motion but will have no effect on the sidewise swinging of the stern. We can therefore work the engines ahead at relatively high power and obtain good rudder forces from the resulting screw current without any forward movement. The ship can twist to the right or left and turn completely around the anchor if desired. The anchor under the ship's forefoot makes it possible to twist in place without any forward motion.

When we have twisted to the desired heading and wish to move ahead, we can apply more power and drag the anchor. The anchor is normally held at a short scope of chain so that it will not dig in and will begin to drag when the screw is turning over for a moderate speed. The amount of fore-and-aft restraint provided will depend on the scope of chain in use and the character of the bottom, so we can adjust the scope of chain to provide the desired restraint. In a typical situation, in 7 fathoms of water, with a mud bottom, and with 20 fathoms of chain at the hawse, a large service-type ship would make about 2 knots over the ground when turning her screw for 8 knots ahead. Under these conditions she would be under excellent control—turning quickly to the desired heading in response to her rudder, and stopping nearly instantaneously when the power is reduced.

When working against the anchor, the ship will handle differently than when steaming unrestrained. The turning and fore-and-aft movements are made nearly independent, and, depending upon the scope of chain in use, the pivot point will shift. If the anchor is snubbed at short stay, the pivot point will move forward to the bow. If a long scope of chain is used, a strong side force will be produced by the chain (as indicated in Figure 15–1) when the ship "over-rides" the chain, and the ship will swing rapidly in an unaccustomed manner. It is worthwhile to experiment with a ship to determine the motion to be expected at different scopes of chain.

In addition to providing greater flexibility of control, the use of an anchor will hold the ship against a troublesome beam wind or current. When making a landing at a pier with the wind blowing onto the face of the pier, it is useful, even when being assisted by tugs, to drop an anchor to restrain the bow as it moves in against the pier. Though using the windward anchor is normal to insure a clear lead, when the situation is tight, it is often advisable to use the leeward or pier-side anchor and let the chain ride under the keel. This will allow the bow to be snubbed up by the anchor in a much shorter distance than is required when using the windward anchor. When alongside, the chain can be slacked to the bottom, and it will prove useful later when clearing.

Another type of "poor man's tugboat" available to the conning officer of an amphibious ship is the landing craft (Figure 15–2). Powered for landing through the surf with a heavy combat cargo, these boats are very effective aides in moving

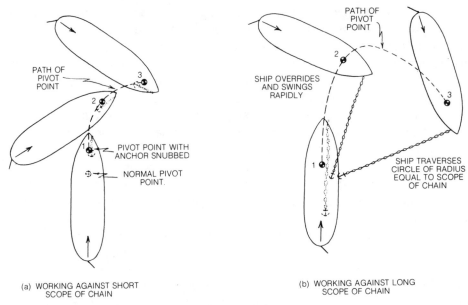

PATH OF
PIVOT
POINT

PATH OF
PIVOT
POINT

2

PATH OF
PIVOT
POINT

3

SHIP OVERRIDES
AND SWINGS
RAPIDLY

2

3

PIVOT POINT WITH
ANCHOR SNUBBED

NORMAL PIVOT
POINT.

1

SHIP TRAVERSES
CIRCLE OF RADIUS
EQUAL TO SCOPE
OF CHAIN

(a) WORKING AGAINST SHORT
SCOPE OF CHAIN

(b) WORKING AGAINST LONG
SCOPE OF CHAIN

FIGURE 15–1. Turning by working against an anchor.

about the harbor. Several of these boats can handle her easily, and they can substitute for a harbor tug.

Because of their construction and bluff bows, these craft are well designed for pushing, and most ships equip one or two of their boats with large fenders on their bow ramps so they will not mar the side of the ship when so used. When used in conjunction with the ship's engines, the landing craft must be kept well clear of the propeller, but except for this, they can be placed anywhere along the side of the ship as desired. The boats, having no convenient tow point and handling poorly when towing to a cleat on the quarter, are not as well designed for pulling, therefore the conning officer should plan the employment of these boats so that they are pushing instead of pulling.

In order to employ the ship's landing craft effectively in moving the ship, it is mandatory that a reliable system of communications be set up between the conning officer and the coxswains of the boats. As will be outlined later in Chapter 18, it is usually best to rely on voice communications entirely and to make sure beforehand that the necessary telephone or loudspeaker system is set up and working. Though a system of hand and whistle signals can be set up, no code but the English language is needed if verbal commands are used exclusively.

Handling mooring lines

These very large ships with their great freeboard present a special problem when handling mooring lines, especially to a low pier or to a nest of ships alongside (Figure 15–3). With the main deck high above the level of the pier's bollards or the

284   NAVAL SHIPHANDLING

FIGURE 15–2. Using ship's boats to "cast."

level of mooring bitts of a destroyer type, it is difficult to get a proper horizontal lead for a breast line. When a tender or a stores ship is in port, smaller ships must moor alongside, and using the main deck chocks results in a very loose and unsatisfactory moor.

To provide mooring points at a reasonable height above the water the AD-37 class ship, for example, is provided with special "mooring stations," five along each side, located on the tender's third and fourth decks at a height just about even with a destroyer's deck edge. These mooring stations are enclosed compartments containing a mooring winch and capstan and two sets of bitts with a single closed chock set in the ship's side convenient to the bitts. Access to the outside of the hull for heaving lines, communications, etc., is through a small "mooring station port" about three feet square. Though this arrangement solves the problem of providing a mooring point of suitable height for a tight moor, it is nearly impossible to handle a heaving line through such a small port and alternative methods must be used to get the lines to or from the mooring stations.

In the AD-37 class, with the bow anchors and windlasses on the second deck, a stern anchor and gear on the third deck, and five isolated mooring stations along either side, communications during mooring operations are a problem. A single 1JV circuit tends to become overcrowded and some ships have found it desirable to split the telephone circuits into sectors or to use "walkie-talkies" between the bridge, bow and stern stations, leaving the 1JV for the five mooring stations. To ensure a secure moor with a ship of this size, as many as a dozen mooring lines may be used and all of them must be effectively controlled by the bridge if the ship is to be positioned and the moor tightened properly.

FIGURE 15–3. Low "mooring stations" in huge slab-sided ships such as the AD 37 class are a definite advantage when "nesting" with smaller ships.

The advantage of the lower mooring points in huge slab-sided ships such as these should not be passed over lightly. It takes a great deal of force to hold a large ship against a pier when a boisterous wind is trying to blow her off and that force can only be supplied by her mooring lines. The fraction of the strength of a mooring line which can be applied to holding the ship against the pier can be determined by the ratio of the horizontal distance between the vertical fore-and-aft planes of the points of attachment to the distance between them. For example, if the fore-and-aft planes containing the chocks of a destroyer and a tender are only 5 feet apart athwartships, but diagonally the chocks through which the mooring line runs are 50 feet apart, the maximum force to hold the two ships together which can be exerted by the connecting line can be only one-tenth of the line's breaking strength. The necessity of having breast lines lead as nearly abeam as possible has already been discussed. Also, they should lead as nearly horizontal as possible. A single line leading horizontally abeam from a suitable lower mooring point might well provide more holding power than several parts of a line run from the main deck.

Handling boats alongside

Though not exclusively a shiphandling problem, the conning officer of a large amphib must realize the part he can play in the employment of her "main battery"—that is, her boats. Hoisting and lowering these heavy landing craft is a herculean task which is made many times more difficult if the ship is rolling even slightly. Loading or unloading the boats alongside is greatly complicated by a running sea. The conning officer must be alert to improve the boathandling conditions by timely employment of the ship's engines and rudder.

If the ship is rolling at anchor to such an extent that it interferes with the boats, the roll can often be eliminated by twisting the ship (by working against the anchor) to another heading. If the boats alongside are having trouble with the waves, the situation can be eased by creating a lee by the same method. If the ship's roll is interfering with hooking on and hoisting, the situation can often be improved by weighing anchor and steaming slowly in the wind.

The conning officer should never sit idle while the boats are having a difficult time alongside. He should analyze his problem and take corrective action with the tools at his command. If his first attempt is not successful, he should try another solution; and he should keep working on the problem until he is sure that he has found the best solution possible under the circumstances.

OILERS AND COMBAT SUPPORT SHIPS

Two terms in general use to designate ships built for the transportation of fuel cargoes are *tanker* and *oiler*. Tanker is the name for the general class of ships and, specifically, for ships designed for transporting liquid fuels from port to port. Oiler is a naval term used to specify a ship designed and equipped to refuel naval ships at sea. Though tanker is widely used throughout the fleet to indicate all ships of this type, oiler is a more specific term and will be used throughout this chapter. It is only the true oiler that is adequately equipped to meet all the demands of fleet replenishment at sea.

The older fleet oilers are basically a Navy conversion of a twin-screw merchant tanker of the Maritime Commission T-3 hull design with slight modifcations.

The newer fleet replenishment oilers (Figure 15–4) and the fast combat support ships (Figure 15–5), which carry a full line of ammunition in addition to liquid cargo, are truly enormous ships with the following characteristics:

Class	*Neosho* (AO 143)	*Sacramento* (AOE 1)
Length	655 feet	795 feet
Beam	86	107
Full load		
Displacement	38,750 tons	52,483 tons
Draft	35 feet	41 feet
Light load		
Displacement	11,600 tons	19,821 tons
Draft fwd	2 feet	7 feet
Draft aft	27 feet	28 feet
Shaft horsepower	28,000	100,000
Propellers	2	2
Rudders	1	2
Speed (full load)	22 knots	27 knots
Crew: Officers	13	23
Enlisted	220	553

FIGURE 15–4. Fleet Oiler, USS *Neosho* (AO 143).

The fleet oiler might be referred to as a "seagoing service station" since its primary function is to provide fuel to the ships of the fleet while at sea. This fuel consists of "black oil," diesel oil, aviation gasoline, and jet fuels, and it is carried in the cargo tanks of the oiler and pumped to the receiving ship through the fuel transfer hoses. In addition to the bulk fuels, the oiler carries lubricating oils, bottled gases, ammunition, stores, provisions, and other consumable supplies needed by the ships of the fleet; these latter are transferred to the receiving ships by "high line" while the ship is alongside fueling. As a matter of fact, it is because oilers have been modified to carry so many re-supply items that some have been redesignated as "replenishment oilers."

In converting a ship designed as a commercial tanker for use as a fleet oiler, certain modifications must be made. Since she will be required to carry and handle several different kinds of fuels, the various fuel systems must be separated, and special pumping and protection equipment provided. In addition, guns, ammunition, radio, radar, and many other types of special Navy equipment must be installed. The weight added to the basic ship is appreciable, so the

FIGURE 15–5. USS *Sacramento* (AOE 1), a "seagoing service station," refuels USS *Walke* (bottom) and USS *Mars*.

amount of cargo which can be carried must be reduced by an equal amount. This must be borne in mind when loading cargo, because, though there may be sufficient tank capacity available in the ship, her designed strength limit might be exceeded.

Effect of load in an oiler

The oiler, under any circumstances, is a heavy ship with limited power by Navy standards. With a full load she rides deep in the water and her inertia is tremendous. She is slow to accelerate, and once up to speed she wants to maintain her way. It takes a lot of backing to bring her to a halt. When empty, on the other hand, though she is more responsive to her engines, she is also very much more at the mercy of the winds.

   The rudder of the oiler, though adequate for maintaining a steady course and for entering and leaving port, is relatively small and the ship has a large turning circle under all conditions. The effectiveness of the rudder, however, varies markedly with the degree of loading. Since the loading of the ship affects not only the total effective keel area but also the fore-and-aft distribution of the keel area, it produces both a change in rudder effectiveness and a shift of the pivot point. At full load the keel of the ship is nearly horizontal and the pivot point is in its normal location, about 30 percent of the ship's length abaft the stem. At light load, with the bow high, the center of the effective keel area moves aft, and the pivot point moves aft correspondingly. Generally speaking, at full load the ship is slow to respond to her rudder, while at light load she responds more quickly.

When her tanks are empty, the bow of an oiler may rise until the forefoot of the ship is actually at the surface of the water and the draft forward is *zero*. This means that the area of exposed hull and superstructure forward has been greatly increased while the counterbalancing keel area forward has been almost eliminated. To say that an oiler is sensitive to the wind when lightly loaded is a gross understatement; she is nearly at the mercy of the wind when empty.

Normally, when loaded and trimmed for an equal draft fore-and-aft, an oiler tends to head into the wind. As indicated in Figure 15–4 there is a preponderance of superstructure aft, and the wind, acting on this, tends to carry the stern downwind more rapidly than the bow. At light loads, as indicated above, this situation might be completely reversed. There have been occasions when an oiler, forced to slow down when lightly loaded and with her bow high out of the water, has been swung completely around by the wind despite her engines and rudder.

Though greatly affected by the wind at light loads, we normally find the oiler at sea with a full cargo of oil, and in this condition she is one of the most stable of ships. The effect of the waves on a fully loaded oiler at sea is slight; in general she plows steadily through even heavy seas with little pitch and a slow, steady roll. Though her decks may be swept by combers in heavy weather, she can maintain her course very accurately, and she is admirably suited for her role as reference ship in the evolution of refueling at sea.

Loading for sea

Fleet oilers as a class are very seaworthy, provided they are properly loaded and ballasted. Since an oiler's hull is essentially a long series of tanks whose walls form the structure of the hull, the stresses on the hull will vary, depending upon which tanks are in use. A full tank adjacent to an empty tank will apply a shear stress to that section of the hull. Full tanks at the ends of the ship, with empty ones in the middle, will cause the ship to "hog"; full center tanks, with empty end tanks, will cause the ship to "sag."

To assist the shiphandler in insuring that no undue stresses are placed on his ship, a draft and stress computer, popularly called the "Ouija Board," has been provided for determining the load condition of the ship. Because of the tremendous cargo tonnages being handled, great care must be taken in the distribution of the cargo at all times. Essentially, the cargo should be distributed evenly throughout the length of the ship so that the ship rides with an even fore-and-aft trim. Should the cargo become depleted, seawater ballast should be taken on as necessary to insure the proper load distribution and stability. Under no circumstances should the ship be permitted to become so light forward that her bow comes clear of the water and can pound into the oncoming seas. The hull of a tanker is not as strong as the hull of a high-speed warship, and severe structural damage can result from pounding.

Problems of deep draft

When heavily loaded, the oiler draws more water than any other craft except the largest battleships and carriers. In the case of the oiler, with her limited horsepower and her great draft, the shallow water effect discussed in Chapter 12 and the bank effect discussed in Chapter 10 become major problems.

The keel of an oiler is often only a few feet from the bottom of the channel as she moves about the harbor, and with her relatively small rudder, the shallow water effect makes her very sluggish. Large rudder angles must be used in shallow water, and the ship responds slowly. The conning officer must not expect to be able to turn in a short radius with the rudder alone when in a shallow harbor.

In a narrow channel with steep banks, the bank effect will be quite noticeable. The ship will tend to veer as she comes close to the edge of the channel or passes close to a shoal. The conning officer must anticipate this and must caution the helmsman to compensate promptly for the effect. A relatively large rudder angle may be required to overcome the tendency of the ship to veer when she is close to a bank.

Fueling operations

It might be said with accuracy that the "main weapon" of the oiler is her fuel hose. It symbolizes her reason for being, and the operation of our modern fleet depends on the fuel that flows through the hoses of our fleet oilers. We then should examine carefully the handling of an oiler during the evolution of fueling at sea.

The task of the oiler's conning officer during fueling is to maintain a steady course and speed throughout the operation (Figure 15–5). This is not as simple as it sounds, because he might also keep station on the guide at the same time. He must adjust his position as necessary to maintain his station, but he must minimize all changes in course or speed. The conning officer of the oiler should maintain station with infrequent small alterations of course or speed rather than with the continual adjustment usual in normal station keeping. Each incremental change should be announced to the ships alongside so that they can compensate for the change as necessary.

The key to a safe and efficient fueling operation is excellent steering. The best helmsman in the ship should be used during fueling, and he should be backed up by a competent helmsman in the after steering station to take over in case of emergency. The stand-by helmsman in steering aft should keep abreast of all orders to the helm in order to be completely ready to take over in case of casualty.

If there is little wind or sea, replenishment may be accomplished on any course. However, if the wind and sea are appreciable, fueling is usually carried out on a course into the wind. Heading directly into the wind usually allows the best course keeping, but, if the seas are rather large, severe pitching may be experienced. A major disadvantage of heading into the wind (the wind and waves are normally from the same direction at sea) is that the decks of the fueling ships are frequently swept by seas endangering the line handlers and the fueling rig. The wet decks and frequent interference by the waves cause the operation to be slowed down seriously.

Downwind fueling is often preferable in rough weather because the ships ride more easily and the decks are not swept by the onrushing seas. If a course and speed can be selected which will minimize the yaw, downwind fueling can be quite safe and comfortable. The fueling speed should be relatively high to insure good rudder control as the wave crests pass the stern. The limiting factor in rough weather fueling of a task force is usually the destroyer's ability to keep station close alongside the oiler. Though a destroyer may roll steadily on a downwind course, she can usually maintain fueling station more easily than when beating into the seas. If there is any doubt about the destroyer's ability to keep station alongside safely, a trial run at double distance should be made to see how she rides. If all goes well on the trial, she can move into normal distance and commence refueling.

Fueling operations should be conducted with the refueling ship between 80 and 180 feet from the oiler (Figure 15–6). Distances greater than 180 feet will part some fuel rigs, and a ship riding closer than 80 feet will have an appreciable effect

FIGURE 15–6. The refueling ships should be between 80 and 180 feet from the oiler, depending on their size. Here, USS *William R. Rush* (DD 714) (left) and the aircraft carrier *John F. Kennedy* (CVA 67) refuel from the oiler USS *Canisteo* (AO 99).

on the steering of the oiler. The magnitude of the effect of a ship alongside on the steering of the oiler will depend on the size of the other ship and its distance from the oiler's side. Any ship in fueling station will affect the steering of the oiler, but with large ships the effect becomes severe. A large carrier at normal fueling distance (120 feet) will require the oiler to use as much as 15° rudder to compensate for her presence. As ships approach or leave from alongside, the oiler's helmsman must alter his rudder angle accordingly, and it is advisable to warn the helmsman when ships are approaching or departing from alongside.

A large ship coming alongside will also affect the speed of the oiler; usually the result is to decrease her speed, thus requiring her to increase her rpm to keep on station. The reason for this effect on the oiler's speed is that the wave systems created by the two ships interact. Depending on the relative positions and sizes of the two ships, this interaction might tend to oppose the motion of one ship while assisting the progress of the other. This will result in real and apparent speed changes, and the conning officers of both ships must be alert to correct for the effect. It is because of this interaction that the conning officers of ships coming alongside seldom believe that the oiler is actually making the speed that she should be making (they find they must use a different shaft rpm than they expected to keep station alongside for the formation fueling). It can be proved that the oiler is maintaining the proper speed because she is remaining on station with respect to the formation guide, so the difference must lie in the fact that the fueling ship requires a different rpm to maintain a given speed when steaming in the wave pattern of the oiler than she requires when steaming in open water well clear of other ships.

An additional factor which may affect the speed of some oilers when operating at near maximum speed is the large amount of steam required to drive the cargo transfer pumps. This steam must be supplied from the main boilers and therefore during fueling operations is not available for driving the main engines. If we try to fuel at near the maximum speed of the oiler, we may experience fluctuations in her speed as the steam demand of the pumps and winches varies. For this reason it is best to fuel at a speed several knots slower than the maximum speed of the oiler.

Going alongside another ship

Though the oiler is the reference ship during a normal fueling operation and though the other ship maintains station on her, an oiler is frequently required to go alongside another oiler at sea to transfer cargo ("consolidate cargoes"). The approach is similar to that described for other types, but the correct surge to use will vary with the loading of the oiler. A value of 70 yards per knot for surge has been found useful as an average value, but considerable variation will be found at different load conditions. When large quantities of fuel are being transferred, the change in draft and trim will affect the speed of the ship; but since these changes occur gradually, the conning officer can compensate for them by adjusting the ship's rpm.

The Landing Ship, Dock (LSD) was developed during World War II to provide a ship suitable for launching heavily loaded landing craft in a seaway and to provide a mobile landing craft repair base (Figure 15–7). Since that time these ships have

FIGURE 15–7. The versatile LSD (Landing Ship, Dock) was developed during World War II for launching landing craft in a seaway.

proved to be such useful additions to the fleet that the Landing Platform, Dock (LPD) was developed with greater capacity, cargo flexibility, and helicopter facilities. The LHA (Amphibious Assault Ship), soon to join the fleet, will combine the attributes of the LSD, the LKA, and the Attack Transport with excellent helicopter facilities.

These ships are among the most versatile in the fleet. Built around a dock or well in which they carry their landing craft or amphibious tanks, upon arrival at their destination, they "ballast down" by flooding certain ballast tanks, then flood the well, open the tail gate, and let the cargo craft proceed out from the protection of the ship's hull under their own power (Figure 15–8). At anchor, with the well flooded, they become a floating small craft harbor. They can launch and retrieve large landing craft without the difficulties and hazards associated with the use of booms and davits.

The dimensions and characteristics of the LPD and LHA are as follows:

Class	LPD	LHA
Length	569 feet	820 feet
Beam	105 feet	106 feet
Draft:		
Full load	22 feet	27 feet
Ballasted down	34 feet	40 feet
Displacement	16,913 tons	39,262 tons
Shaft horsepower	24,000	70,000
Propellers	2	2
Rudders	2	2
Speed	21	24
Bow thruster	No	Yes
Accommodations:		
Officer	101	262
Enlisted	1335	2533
Well dimensions:		
Length	164 feet	280 feet
Breadth	50 feet	76 feet

Because of the presence of the large well in the center of the ship, the twin screws and rudders are mounted under the "wing walls" at the extreme edges of the ship. The rudders are relatively large and are mounted directly abaft the propellers. The combination of large twin rudders and the unusual distance between the screws gives these ships exceptional turning characteristics.

The superstructure of the LPD and the LSD is concentrated forward, making the ship sensitive to the wind. The wind will tend to blow the bow to leeward—to such an extent that she will often pivot rapidly when exposed to the wind with little way on.

The concentrated superstructure forward also causes the ship to yaw badly at anchor. With high winds this becomes troublesome and may cause the anchor to drag. The use of an anchor underfoot is recommended under such conditions,

FIGURE 15–8. A Utility Landing Craft (LCU) prepares to enter the open tail gate of LSD 30.

and some shiphandlers have found it useful to turn the engines over slowly to ease the strain on the chain. The ship will ride much better at anchor if she is ballasted down, but the shiphandler must weigh this advantage against the possibility of having to get under way during a storm.

The hull shape of the LSD must be taken into account by the conning officer when handling his ship alongside a pier or another ship. The sides of the older LSDs are unusual in that they have an outward flare for the first few feet above the waterline, after which they rise vertically to the top of the wing walls. As the ship moves in against a pier, the structure of the pier will often bear against the flared portion, making it difficult to place fenders; so it is advisable to use camels or floats between the ship and a pier if they can be obtained. If there is any swell running, the height of the vertical sides of the ship will be of concern to the shiphandler. It takes a very small angle of heel to bring the deck edge of an LSD against the side of an adjacent ship, even though their waterlines are separated by a sturdy fender.

Except for the characteristics mentioned above, these ships handle similarly to other large twin-screw types of similar power and tonnage. Probably the only characteristic which is different is the vulnerability of the stern in a severe storm. Because of the stern gate and the danger of flooding the well during a storm, they should head into the seas in heavy weather. If one were "pooped" by a large following wave, severe consequences might result. This is not a severe limitation, however, since they ride well head-on into the seas, but it is a characteristic which should be borne in mind when operating with these interesting types.

16
landing ships and small combatants

The progress of modern warfare has brought about a requirement that runs contrary to all that the mariner has learned and practiced. To gain flexibility in the movement of the masses of men and equipment it became necessary to develop the ability to land great quantities of cargo without the protection and facilities afforded by the normal port. Ships were to deliver their cargoes directly upon unprotected beaches. The mariner, who from the beginning of civilization has struggled to keep his craft clear of the treacherous shore, had to learn to run his ship aground deliberately. He had to learn the art of beaching his ship, of holding her firm while the cargo was handled, and of retracting her in the teeth of the pounding surf.

Boats have been landed through the surf since historic times, but such operations have always been accompanied by a distinct element of risk. Only the most skillful seamen were entrusted with the steering oar, and once the craft had touched the shore she was quickly withdrawn or dragged up on the beach beyond the reach of the surf. Double-ended boats were often provided for such operations to more easily cope with the waves from astern. The threat and danger of broaching (in a surface ship, falling off to a position broadside to the seas) was always present, and many a seaman was lost when boats capsized in the rolling surf.

If a conventional ship of any considerable size were to attempt to "beach" on an exposed shore, the first disadvantage would immediately become apparent: her forefoot would ground while the bow was still in water much too deep for cargo-handling. She would probably be hard aground while still beyond the breaker line, and she might as well still be at sea from the point of view of unloading her.

Next, even in cases where her bow was relatively close to the beach, unloading over the bow of a conventional ship would be about the most awkward way that could be devised. We *could* let her broach and try to unload while parallel to the beach, but we would find her sides no closer to the water's edge than was her bow, and after the waves had nudged her firmly aground, we would probably never be able to get her off. She would be hard aground from stem to stern, and any force we could exert with her own propellers would tend to move her along the beach, not away from the grip of the sand.

Even if we were satisfied with the position of the bow relative to the beach and had made suitable arrangements to discharge the cargo, it would still be difficult to hold the conventional ship perpendicular to the shoreline. She would tend to pivot on her pointed bow, since her propellers and rudder are not well suited for moving the stern in opposition to the waves. Furthermore, her screws are not protected from damage when she is aground. Lastly, we should have an anchor to seaward to keep from broaching—and few normal ships are equipped with stern anchors. Obviously, the conventional cargo ship is not suited to loading and discharging her cargo on an open, unprotected beach.

To meet the requirement of landing cargoes on unprotected beaches, a new type of ship had to be developed. World War II with its extensive amphibious campaigns saw the introduction of the Landing Ship. These ships were developed to meet a number of different requirements, and several different sizes were built. All of them, however, had to meet the primary requirement of landing on an unprotected beach.

THE LST

The largest and best known of the ships capable of direct discharge onto a beach is the Landing Ship, Tank, or LST. These ships are of about the same size and cargo capacity as an ocean-going freighter; in fact, two of the new LSTs can be considered equivalent to an APA and an AKA combined, from the point of view of troop and cargo capacity.

To allow the ship to ground securely on a sloping beach, the LST is designed with a flat bottom and a sloping keel. Fully loaded at sea she might draw 11 feet forward and 21 feet aft, but in "landing condition" (10 percent fuel and 500 tons of cargo) she draws only 6 feet forward and 16 feet aft (between 4 to 6 feet forward and 10 to 13 feet aft in the older classes). In all cases, LSTs are designed to ground evenly on a beach with a slope of about one foot in every 50.

The LST was designed to unload while lying with her bow to the beach. Fitted with large bow doors and a steel bow ramp located in a protected position inside the doors, the ship can swing the doors open as she beaches, drop the inclined ramp, and discharge her cargo of troops and vehicles through a 15-foot-wide passage in the bow of the ship. The bow ramp extends about 20 feet forward of the grounding point and thus allows discharge in even shallower water than indicated by the forward draft.

To hold her stern to seaward and keep her from broaching, the LST is equipped with a stern anchor and anchor winch. This winch is similar to the towing engine on a large tug, and allows a steady strain to be taken on the stern anchor wire.

The propellers of the LST are well protected from damage while grounded by being set up clear of the base line and well inboard from the sides of the ship. Each propeller is protected by a skeg which extends forward from it and provides a sturdy "runner" beneath its blades. The twin rudders are mounted directly behind the screws, and thus achieve maximum effectiveness as a result of the propeller discharge.

A very interesting feature of the LST is the provision and use of her ballast tanks. She is equipped with an extensive ballast system which is very useful both during cruising and when beaching. The combined capacity of the "clean ballast" (water) tanks and the "dirty ballast" (fuel and/or water) tanks give the ship a ballasting capacity of nearly 4,000 tons.

In a normal beaching to discharge cargo, it is desirable to place the bow as close to the water's edge as possible. In preparation for beaching we discharge ballast forward and take on ballast aft to obtain the desired trim. Once the ship has grounded and has been driven as far up the beach slope as she will go by use of the ship's engines, it is desirable to take steps to insure that the ship will remain in place. Consequently, once the ship is aground, the ballast tanks are refilled to hold the ship on the beach more firmly. This also prevents the ship from working up the beach farther as the cargo is discharged and she becomes lighter. When ready to retract from the beach, the forward ballast is pumped out, lightening the bow and letting it come free from the sand more easily.

When beaching to load cargo, if the ship came in light, beached high up on the slope, and *then* loaded a heavy cargo, she would probably not be able to retract. For this reason, when beaching to load, we ballast the ship *down* forward before coming in. After the cargo has been loaded, the ballast can be pumped out and thus compensate for any equal weight of new cargo taken on board.

At beaches where an extensive rise and fall of tide is experienced, an LST may be left high and dry at low tide. If it were not for foresighted designers, this could be uncomfortable, for one forgets how much a ship depends on the water in which she rides for various secondary services. Normally, a ship is continually taking in sea water for various purposes such as cooling machinery, supplying

FIGURE 16–1. USS *Lorain County* (LST 1177).

evaporators, supplying the fire main, providing flushing water, etc. If special provisions were not made, the routine ship services such as electric power and fire protection would cease when she is left on the beach by a receding tide.

An LST solves this problem by utilizing the water in her "clean ballast" tanks to replace the water normally drawn from the sea. She can circulate her ballast water through her machinery as necessary, and can thus maintain her normal services regardless of the tide.

To summarize the dimensions and characteristics of the largest of the family of landing ships, the four classes of LSTs currently in service have the following characteristics:

Class	542	1156	1171	1179
Length	328 feet	384 feet	442 feet	563 feet
Beam	50 feet	55 ½ feet	62 feet	70 feet
Full load	4,080 tons	6,225 tons	8,650 tons	8,400 tons
Draft forward	8 feet	10 feet	12 feet	11 feet
Draft aft	14 feet	16 feet	17 feet	21 feet
Landing condition	2,400 tons	3,300 tons	4,600 tons	5,624 tons
Draft forward	3.9 feet	3.8 feet	4 feet	6 feet
Draft aft	9.8 feet	11.0 feet	13 feet	16 feet
Total shaft horsepower	2,600	6,000	14,000	16,000
Maximum speed	11 knots	14 knots	18 knots	23 + knots
Crew: Officers	7	9	9	10
Enlisted	110	150	160	160
Troop capacity	160	400	600	430
Cargo (dry & liquid)	1,695 tons	2,300 tons	3,000 tons	2,800 tons

The discussion which follows immediately deals with the three older classes of LSTs as a group—the 542, 1156, and 1171. The extraordinary LST 1179 class is listed in the table above for comparison only. These unusual ships are discussed farther on in this chapter.

Beaching

Beaching is an art which demands all the skill, judgment, and seamanship which the LST conning officer has to offer. Although his ship has been designed specifically for this job, the effects of the surf, wind, bottom character and "long-shore" current can be important in determining the success of the evolution. Poor judgment can turn a routine beaching operation into a salvage problem with disturbing rapidity.

The first requirement for successful beaching is that the ship be moving *directly perpendicular* to the waves as she grounds. This is normally perpendicular to the shoreline also, but, if there is a difference, make sure that the ship comes to rest with the breakers dead astern. The conning officer must weigh the direction of the prevailing wind, the character of the shoreline, and the direction and magnitude of the ground swell in estimating the final direction of motion of the breakers. If we end up with the surf on one quarter, we will have a continual fight to keep from broaching.

A next important step is to insure that the stern anchor is correctly placed and securely dug in. It takes careful calculation beforehand to estimate the point at which the ship will ground. If we place the stern anchor too far to seaward, we will lose the anchor and its wire. If we don't place the anchor far enough from the shore, and to windward of our beaching spot, it will be of little use in holding the stern into the oncoming surf.

If we know the gradient of the beach, we can quickly calculate the distance our forefoot will be from the beach when it first touches bottom. Assuming that our ship is trimmed in accordance with her design, if the beach gradient is steeper than 1 to 50, the first point which will ground will be the forefoot. We can measure the ship's draft forward just before making our approach, and by multiplying this draft by the beach gradient we can determine the distance from this point to the water's edge at the moment of grounding. For example, if the beach gradient is 1 in 40, and if we are drawing 6 feet forward, our *forefoot* will be 240 feet (6 × 40) from the water's edge at the moment of grounding. Should the beach gradient be less steep than 1 in 50, the *stern* will ground first, an undesirable condition resulting in our coming to a halt much farther from the water's edge than would have occurred had we trimmed down by the bow and thus raised the stern.

Having calculated the first point of grounding, we must now estimate how much farther up the beach we will move before the ship is brought to a stop. This will depend upon the speed of approach, the surf, the wind, and the manner in which the propellers and stern anchor are being used. For purposes of illustration, let's assume that the ship will slide forward until the point of grounding has been raised 1 foot. This means that we must allow for the ship sliding forward a number of feet equal to the numerical value of the denominator of the beach gradient. If the gradient is 1 in 50, we must allow for the ship to move forward 50 feet after touching bottom.

Our ship is equipped with 900 feet of wire on the stern anchor. If we come to rest on the beach riding to 600 feet of wire, we will have ample scope to the anchor and will have allowed ourselves a 300-foot margin for error. Consequently it is good practice to try to drop the stern anchor when the ship is 200 yards from her projected beached position. On a beach of 1 in 40 gradient, when we are drawing 6 feet forward we must drop the anchor when our forefoot is 800 feet (600 + 240 - 40) from the water's edge.

For a precise approach, "drop bearings" should be determined. These can be checked by seaman's eye if we know where the line of sight from the conning station to points on the surface of the water 600, 800, and 1,000 feet ahead of the bow intersect the ship's forward structure. As we approach our "drop bearing," the water's edge should come into line with these points at the appropriate time.

When we beach, we wish to beach firmly in order to minimize the chance of broaching. We do not, however, wish to go aground so firmly that we cannot retract when we desire. Proper use of the stern anchor and ballast, however, will almost eliminate the likelihood of being unable to retract, so as we come in our thoughts should be concentrating on getting the ship firmly *on* the beach.

When an LST beaches on normal bottom, there is no sudden, jarring shock. It is more like a toboggan coming to the end of its run. The ship just stops. There is little chance of damage to the ship resulting from beaching at too high a speed if the beach is smooth and free from rocks, coral heads, and other obstacles.

To insure firm beaching and good control during the approach, come in at TWO THIRDS speed or even STANDARD speed. To reduce the stress at the bearing point, it is desirable to have at least 30 percent of the bottom area aground, and this requires that the bow be forced well beyond its point of contact (Figure 16–2).

Even after the forward part of the ship is grounded, the ship can usually be kept at the desired inclination to the beach by use of the engines and rudders. With the screws driving ahead slowly, the rudders can be utilized to swing the stern from side to side as required. The conning officer can give the helmsman a course to steer, and the helmsman can steer in the normal manner. Should the helmsman be having trouble keeping the ship on the desired heading, more ahead power can be used and the effectiveness of the rudders will be increased.

If the ship has a tendency to broach, and, even with a good strain on the properly placed stern anchor and liberal use of the engines and rudders, the stern still tends to move to one side, it is time to retract to avoid broaching.

The state of the tide and the range of succeeding tides should be carefully considered in beaching an LST. If we beach "light" at high tide and then load, we are inviting difficulty in retracting. To *beach* on an *ebb* tide and to *retract* on the next succeeding *flood* makes an ideal operation which insures the ship firmly holding her position during unloading and promises the best chance of a dry ramp during the intervening period. However, during an amphibious operation, the timing of scheduled events is such that we can seldom choose ideal situations. If we do beach on the ebb tide and remain beached for an appreciable period of time, we must be prepared to accept the fact that we may not be *able* to retract until the level of the water rises on the flood.

It should be apparent that the characteristics of the beach are of vital interest to the LST conning officer and also to the amphibious planner. All available information should be gathered during the planning period, for the remarkable flexibility of the LST can only be utilized if the beach characteristics are *known*. Once the operation has been started, the Underwater Demolition Teams (UDT) can provide a vital service to the LST. Their charts of the underwater obstacles, depth of water, surf and current conditions can make the difference between a successful

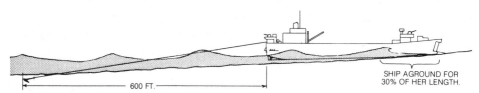

600 FT.

SHIP AGROUND FOR 30% OF HER LENGTH.

FIGURE 16–2. Sketch of an LST correctly beached.

beaching and utter chaos, for nothing is more useless than an LST solidly aground and unable to land her cargo. During assault landings, the information provided by the UDT may be all that is available at first, but as each LST makes her approach and beaches, the pool of information grows and should be passed on to ships that follow, for the LST officers themselves are the ones best qualified to advise their sister ships. For the normal non-combat beaching on an unfamiliar beach, reconnaissance by boat before beaching the ship should always be carried out.

The danger that the ship may broach is always at hand. Should she get out of control and be swept broadside to the surf, severe damage and even the loss of the ship could occur. The time to prevent broaching is just as the ship *begins* to move from her heading perpendicular to the waves, and not *after* she has already assumed a severe angle and is being swept nearer the beach by each succeeding wave. Vigorous action should be taken *as soon as* the change of heading is noticed. Engine speed up to FULL should be used to increase the rudder effectiveness. If the stern anchor is not properly placed, we should retrieve it with one of our LCVPs and place it in a better position to windward. If the surf conditions are not too severe, we can use our boats, or available LCMs, to help pull the stern around. The results of broaching are too severe to take a chance with a poor beaching. If we are having trouble, it is usually wise to retract and try again.

When beaching to land amphibian vehicles, the depth of water at the end of the ramp is not a problem, since the LVT and the DUKW type vehicles are quite at home in deep or shallow water, nor do we have any particular trouble with steep gradient beaches where the slope is about 1 foot in 40 or greater. When handling amphibians we normally do not use the stern anchor, since the evolution can be completed in a matter of a few minutes and there is little chance of broaching.

The pontoon causeway

Shallow gradient beaches with slopes of less than 1 in 50 present a difficult problem. On these beaches, we often find offshore sand bars and these may cause us to ground at the stern in 13 or 14 feet of water while still several hundred yards from the water's edge. On the other hand, if we ballast down forward to raise the stern to clear these obstacles, we may still come to a halt well short of fordable waters with 7 or 8 feet of water at the end of the bow ramp. Close-in sand bars often exist with deep water on the inshore side, and here again, we require some method of bridging the gap between our bow and dry land. The pontoon causeway has been developed to solve such problems.

A pontoon causeway is made up of specially designed sectional floats which are carried to the objective area on the sides of the LST. Floating piers extending several hundred feet from the beach can be constructed by assembling a number of causeway sections, and through the use of such a causeway an LST can be loaded with far more than the designer's 500-ton beaching load (Figure 16–3).

FIGURE 16–3. Tanks ride the causeway into the "mouth" of the USS *York County* (LST 1175).

The problem of "marrying" the bow of the LST to the seaward end of the pontoon causeway is a delicate one requiring expert shiphandling and the very closest liaison between the bridge, where the conning officer is trying to make an eggshell landing on a mooring he can't see, and the bow, where the first lieutenant is coaching the ship in. An LCM to tend the causeway is most helpful in completing the marriage. The stern anchor is a *must* to assist the LST in maintaining her position married to the seaward end of such a semiflexible floating pier, and the conning officer should insure that he has 600 feet of wire out and that the anchor is dropped upwind or upcurrent from the causeway.

Retracting

When the time comes to retract from the beach, the normal procedure is to pump out the ballast forward, take a strain on the wire to the stern anchor, and back both engines. As the ship comes free, care must be taken not to overrun the stern wire or we may foul a screw. By keeping close contact with the crew handling the stern anchor, we can gauge our backward motion well enough to keep the wire out from under the stern. Constant information on the amount of wire still out and the direction toward which it tends must be sent to the conning officer as the ship moves away from the beach.

Though it is best to back directly out into deep water, as the ship comes free the wind and current may cause her bow to swing to one side. Normally we can let her swing and just use the engines to keep the stern wire taut and leading astern. If the beach is congested we may wish to drag a bow anchor underfoot to hold her more perpendicular to the beach until the stern anchor is aweigh.

The above procedure describes how the ship *should* come free, but unfortunately it is not always as easy as this. As the ship's weight is taken by the sand of the bottom, the thin film of water that separated the ship from the bottom is gradually squeezed out. The longer the ship stays in position, the more the water is squeezed and the more the ship's bottom comes into contact with the particles of sand. This increases the friction tremendously, and the force required to slide the ship toward deep water goes up with the friction.

To enable the ship to slide easily over the surface of the bottom, we must replace this lubricating film of water. This is not easily done, especially since the action of the waves may have built up shoulders along the edges of the bottom. The so-called "bottom suction" (the reaction to the ship rising and allowing the water to sweep in under her bottom) can be very great. To break this suction, some means of introducing water between the ship's bottom and the sand must be found.

When the screws are backing, the discharge will tend to force water forward under the ship's bottom. See-sawing the stern with the engines and rudders will help break the suction. Further, the sidewise motion moves the stern out over areas from which the water film has not been squeezed. Also, as the stern moves to the side, any unevenness of the bottom will tend to open channels through which water can seep and restore the lubrication.

Turning the screws alternately ahead and astern at high power will at times help the situation. When turning ahead, they tend to draw out the sand from under the ship's stern; when going astern, they tend to move the ship astern and to force water under the ship. Using the ballast tanks in an effort to put a list on the ship may also help.

If continued work with the stern anchor, the engines, the rudders and the ballast system produces no result, patience, in the form of waiting for a higher tide, may be the best answer. If during the wait a low tide permits such action, fire hoses can be used to good effect to wash away the sand banked around the edges of the hull and to open channels under the bottom to break the bottom suction. Once the suction has been broken and the water film restored, the ship will come free with ease. One moment she seems cemented in place; the next, she is gliding effortlessly toward open water.

Handling characteristics of the LST

The first difference apparent to an officer trained in other ship types is the location of the conning station on an LST. Her bridge is nearly at her stern. From his conning position, the conning officer can see four-fifths of his ship stretching out before him, instead of only the forecastle. He need not change his position to see all of his mooring lines. Far from being a disadvantage, this unusual conning location gives an excellent vantage point for observing the position of the ship relative to other objects. Conning "from the fantail" gives the LST skipper the same viewpoint for controlling his ship as that enjoyed by the coxswain of a motor launch; he can see the entire situation at a glance.

The bridge of the 1156 and 1171 classes of LST is similar to the bridge of a destroyer in both size and equipment; the older classes of LST are not nearly as well equipped. The 1156 class has, in addition, a main engine console on the bridge, from which the engines are controlled. This class, equipped with reversible pitch propellers, has most unusual shiphandling characteristics and the officer privileged to handle one has enjoyed a unique experience. The characteristics of ships with reversible pitch propellers will be discussed under minesweepers.

The bridge is not the only thing that has moved aft: the pivot point has come after with it. Because of the very shallow draft forward, the deep draft aft, and the twin skegs, screws, and rudders at the extreme after end of the ship, the pivot point of an LST has moved aft almost as far as the bridge. An LST literally "spins on her heel."

Wind affects the LST to a marked degree. She has high freeboard fore and aft, and she draws relatively little water. With little power available to combat it, the ship is very susceptible to the wind. Because of her shallow draft forward, her bow is unusually prone to be carried downwind; so much so that in all but the lightest airs an LST will invariably back into the wind regardless of her rudder.

Though not designed for high speeds, those equipped with diesel engines can almost instantly bring their full horsepower to bear either ahead or astern when maneuvering. The rudders, being directly in line with the propellers, are very effective when the engines are turning over ahead, and though the propellers are tucked in under the sides, the lever arm between them is sufficient to insure some twisting moment when the screws are opposed.

Except when opposed by the wind, an LST turns in a remarkably small space. Because of her shallow draft forward and her flat bottom, she has much less effective keel area than other warships of comparable length. Once in her turn, however, she has a tendency to keep on swinging, especially when twisting in place. Once the angular momentum has been acquired, vigorous efforts must be employed to oppose it because keel area forward is not enough to quickly slow down the swing. When twisting to a heading, the engines must be placed in opposition to the swing well in advance of reaching the desired bearing, if the ship is to be stopped before swinging past the course.

The combination of relatively low power and excellent twisting characteristics is strikingly demonstrated when "backing and filling" to get out of a small turning basin. If, when the ship is moving slowly astern, both engines are ordered AHEAD at high power and the rudders put over FULL to one side, the LST, instead of gathering headway and commencing a normal turn, will seem to "squat" in place and spin rapidly in the direction dictated by the rudders. Though the side force produced by such a combination is ample to begin spinning the ship rapidly, the fore-and-aft component of propeller thrust is insufficient to kill the sternway and start the ship moving ahead within the same time interval.

One should remember that much of the side force available from the rudders is lost when the engines are backing. When the propellers are turning astern, the discharge current is not being directed on the rudders. They are subject only to the much less concentrated suction current. Consequently the ship, when backing, is much less sensitive to the rudders. To twist rapidly, the propellers must be turning ahead.

Handling alongside

Approach slowly when bringing an LST alongside. She is slow to respond to a backing bell, and if we are not careful we will overshoot. An easy approach, using the rudders and engines as necessary to maintain her heading, is the best solution. Coming in wide and slow will avoid embarrassment.

The long, flat sides of the LST are an asset when handling alongside. Free from projections, they provide an excellent bearing surface. The LST can slide forward or aft alongside a pier, as necessary, with little chance of damage to either the ship or the pier.

The wind is the greatest problem when handling the LST alongside. As the ship slows, it becomes more and more difficult to hold her bow up into the wind. The "poor man's tugboat," as described in Chapter 15, is most helpful when we are faced with a cross wind in an approach to a pier. We also have a stern anchor and powerful winches on the forecastle and the fantail, as well as the LCVP's "tugs." But perhaps our most unusual asset, when required to back and fill awaiting a berth, is the beaching ability; we need only to shove the bow gently onto a mud bank and stand-by until the situation clears.

In going out, an LST can leave a berth alongside a pier even with a strong wind setting her against the face of the pier if she is handled properly. By opposing her engines and using FULL RUDDER, the stern of the ship can be walked out from the pier even in the face of a 20-knot breeze. Her bluff bow makes an excellent pivot, so her stern should be walked out from the pier until the ship is inclined as much as 45° to the pier face. Using FULL ASTERN, the ship should be backed smartly out of her berth and into the stream. If sea room permits, we should take advantage of her tendency to back into the wind instead of fighting it. These LSTs have a mind of their own when it comes to turning against the wind, particularly when they have little or no way on. It is often wiser to turn through the greater angle *with* the wind than to attempt a smaller turn *against* it! The angular momentum built up during the turn to leeward works to the advantage of the conning officer and helps achieve a heading into the wind that he might not have been able to make had he insisted on turning against the wind. This may not be a "pretty" maneuver, but when one sees an LST, in a heavy wind, squatting on her heel and turning through 270° or even 330°, one can be sure that there is an experienced LST shiphandler at the conn.

When anchoring, the LST enjoys a flexibility unknown to more conventional ships. She can use her bow or stern anchor, or both. It is often convenient to anchor with the stern anchor and ride with the bow to leeward; the bow doors can be opened, the ramp lowered, and the ship has a ready boat landing.

In addition to her duties as a primary carrier, an LST is frequently called upon to perform a task usually left to the smaller craft, that of unloading the transports. The transport usually rides at anchor and, if conditions dictate, drops a second anchor "under foot" to cut down the yaw. The LST approaches from astern, parallel and well out. She drops her off-side anchor about 125 yards off and slightly forward of the bow of the ship to be unloaded, then turns and maneuvers alongside the other ship, walking out her anchor chain as she approaches. Bow lines are passed and secured and the anchor is snubbed. The stern is twisted in until the two ships are parallel and about 10 feet apart; then the remaining mooring lines are passed and secured. While her bow is held firmly between her anchor chain and her forward mooring lines, her stern is held clear of the larger ship by opposed engines and *in* rudder. With this combination, the LST is moored securely alongside but held safely clear while the larger ship passes troops, vehicles and cargo. If we have calm waters, there is no need to use this "stand-off" mooring and the ship can be brought against the transport for a conventional alongside mooring. In rough weather, however, the use of an anchor by the LST is recommended to insure a safe separation between the rolling ships and it will be found the transfer can be made in weather too rough for smaller landing craft. After completion of the transfer, the anchor will be useful in hauling the LST's bow clear of the transport.

The LST has proved herself a seaworthy and sturdy ship. None were lost at sea as a result of weather during World War II, and they were at sea during the worst of it. Though seaworthy, the unusual hull structure gives the LST certain characteristics at sea not found in other types.

The sloping bottom and bluff bow of the LST cause her to slap and pound in a rough sea. The shallow draft at the bow allows the forefoot to come clear of the water even when pitching only moderately, and, once clear, the flat bottom produces a resounding slap as it comes down against the surface again.

When heading into the seas, a distinct pounding is felt when a wave crashes against the bluff bow. In a rough sea such a wave causes the ship to lose headway momentarily and to "shimmy" as though stunned. The hull structure of the LST, though strong enough to stand the stresses of beaching, is quite limber. One can actually observe the bending in the main deck as the force of the wave travels through the ship. If shimmying starts, we must do something to reduce it; continued flexure of the hull can cause failures.

To reduce the slapping and pounding, we can ballast down forward, change speed, or change course. Filling the forward ballast tanks will increase the draft forward and increase the moment-of-inertia opposing the tendency to pitch. Changing course or speed can change the frequency of the waves hitting the bow to one to which the ship responds less readily. Choosing a course upon which the ship rolls may ease the pounding because of the differing inclinations of the bow as the waves strike.

Except for her unusual motion in rough weather, the LST is quite conventional at sea. Her motion will change greatly as her displacement varies. She is a different ship at light displacement from what she is at full load. When "light," she bobs about like a cork. When heavily loaded, she is less responsive to the waves and tends to plow through them. To improve her sea-keeping qualities, it is usual to take on ballast when carrying no cargo.

Special problems of the LST

The LST is often handled differently from other types because of her special features, and it is interesting to examine how she meets many of the ordinary problems which confront all ships. Her versatile bow access is a great asset in loading and unloading, but the shiphandler must be ready to depart from the conventional to position the ship so that this asset can be utilized.

Instead of the Mediterranean moor, the LST is frequently called upon to moor bow to the quay to allow loading through her bow doors. Since there is no necessity for the facilities of a pier for such an operation, LSTs are often handled at a sea wall or mole where they take up less berthing space and a larger number of them can be loading at the same time. When moored in this manner, the ship is secured so that the ramp can be lowered just to the edge of the mole. This allows vehicles to be driven in and out of the ship if desired in addition to the normal foot traffic.

When mooring bow to a sea wall, the ship makes her approach perpendicular to the sea wall and drops her stern anchor as far out from the face of the sea wall as practical. The bow doors may have to be opened before arriving at the mooring, because, if there is an obstruction at their height just in front of the bow, they cannot be swung open. This presents a problem: although the doors are quite sturdy in their closed position, should the ship ride against one of them in the open position, it might be sprung so that it could not be closed again. If available, a camel placed between the bow and the sea wall will usually provide enough clearance to allow opening the doors after mooring.

Doors open or closed, the approach should be made quite slowly, and it is advisable to use the ship's LCVPs as tugs to control the bow during the last stages of the approach. The wire to the stern anchor is eased gingerly as the bow nears the quay. Lines are sent over from each bow to the quay, and they are heaved in as the stern wire is eased out, until the ship is in position for using the bow ramp to the quay. In final position the ship is held in a taut moor between the bow lines and the stern anchor, with her bow just the right distance from the face of the quay so that the ramp will span the intervening space to the quay.

An LST is actually a large ship, but because she is designed for a specific task, she has many characteristics unusual in the normal ship. To handle her effectively, one must study her peculiarities and make use of her advantages while avoiding situations where her limitations will be restrictive. By employing her good characteristics and avoiding her bad ones, the shiphandler can meet almost any situation.

The LST 1179, Newport class LST, is as different from her sisters of previous classes as the original LST was from the conventional freighter (Figure 16–4). She is not a "jerry built" solution to an almost non-naval problem, but is the refined product of years of experience and, finally, sufficient investment on the part of the Navy. She is the result of an evolutionary process that has taken a quarter of a century, and is probably the most versatile and maneuverable ship ever built. The LST is fascinating to the shiphandler, for with her he can undertake without assistance many evolutions impossible for most other ships.

The LST 1179 was designed to embark or debark tanks, amphibious vehicles, combat vehicles and other heavy equipment over both her bow ramp and through her stern gate. The design further specified a capability of discharging her 2,000-ton, combat-loaded assault troops over a causeway and the capability to beach on a 1:50 gradient (2 percent) with 500 tons of cargo. Her characteristics called for a ship 500 feet in length, with displacement of 8,000 tons and a sustained speed of 20 knots. To achieve the design speed, the designers had to

FIGURE 16–4. The tank landing ship USS *Newport* (LST 1179) under way.

throw away any thought of the blunt bow so familiar in the LST since they were first developed in 1941. Although there are many other unique features of this class LST, the most radical change from previous LST design is the sharp "clipper" bow and refined hull lines necessary to attain the design speed with a reasonably sized propulsion plant.

Her refined lines also necessitated development of a new "over-the-bow" concept for operation of the bow ramp. Other improvements in these ships as compared with their predecessors are the stern gate, which is new to LSTs; the between-deck ramp; the bow thruster; the quick-acting cargo hatch; the pontoon causeway handling and stowage system; the helicopter handling facilities; and the single lever remote control for the propulsion system.

With the over-the-bow design for the bow ramp, the ramp acts as a bridge from the main deck level to the causeway (or beach) to load of offload vehicles weighing up to 75 tons. The ramp rides out from its stowed position above the main deck, and in its extended position it is supported by wires from the "derrick" arms built into the bow. These wires lower the ramp to the causeway or beach where it is then ready for vehicular traffic (Figure 16–5). The length of the ramp (109 feet) is such that, when the ship is beached on a 2 percent gradient with a forward draft of 6 feet, there will be 4 feet of water at the end of the ramp, or less. In this condition the ramp has an incline of only 21 degrees. When required, the ramp can be

FIGURE 16–5. A Marine jeep offloads, using the over-the-bow ramp of the tank landing ship USS *Newport* (LST 1179).

rotated 15 degrees either side of the centerline in order to line up with the causeway or with a better spot on the beach. The 35-ton aluminum ramp is easily handled by the installed multiple wire and winch system.

The stern gate, which is hinged to drop down and act as a stern ramp, is located in the transom and provides a 15-foot-wide opening through which to load or offload amphibious vehicles (LVT and LARC) into the sea, as well as all types of vehicles and cargo from landing craft (LCU, LCM, etc.). The stern gate can receive amphibians up to 45 tons directly from the water, or vehicles up to 75 tons from landing craft married to the stern. In the stowed position the gate forms a watertight closure for the stern opening.

The between-deck ramp is similar in design and function to the "truck ramp" found in older LSTs. It serves, in the "down" position, to carry vehicles, up to 75 tons, from the bow ramp to the tank deck and, in the "up" position, allows transit of vehicles, up to 25 tons, from the bow ramp to the main deck. In the up position the ramp forms a watertight seal for the main deck opening, eliminating the previously used hatch covers, tarpaulins and battens.

The NavShips-designated "auxiliary thrust device" or "side propulsion unit" is called the "bow thruster" by the operators. The bow thruster consists of a constant speed, reversible, controllable pitch propeller, 6 feet in diameter, located in an athwartship cylindrical tunnel near the bow. The bow thruster can apply up to 800 horsepower to move the bow to port or starboard with direct control from the bridge. The primary function of the thruster in this class of ship is to provide a much better method of controlling the bow of the ship during a causeway marriage, i.e., connecting the ship's bow ramp to the end of the causeway, and it is a significant improvement over the previously used "pusher boats." During a causeway marriage, control of the bow thruster can be transferred to the control station on either derrick arm at the bow and operated under the direction of the deck control officer, who is in the best position to observe the relationship of the bow to the causeway. The capability to exercise instant "override," and thus transfer control, remains on the bridge. The bow thruster has proven to be invaluable in shiphandling around a dock or other similarly restricted waters.

A quick-acting cargo hatch (15 feet × 30 feet) is located aft of the superstructure and opens into the tank deck. It is served by two ten-ton booms for loading or unloading disabled vehicles or bulk cargo from over the side into the tank deck. The hatch is operated by a hydraulic-mechanical system which raises it out of the hatch opening and rolls it forward on guide rails on the deck. The hatch and both booms can be operated from the hatch control station above the main deck on the after side of the starboard stack.

The pontoon causeway handling and stowage system is a refinement of the systems used in earlier class LSTs. The ship can carry four sections of 3 × 15 cell (22 feet × 90 feet) pontoon causeways side-loaded on causeway rails along the sides aft of the superstructure. These causeway sections can be self-loaded by the ship and can be "control launched." The "control launch" eliminates damage to the causeways which was experienced by the older "splash" method. The rigging for hoist and launch, as well as the turnbuckles, chains and hooks for securing the causeways on board, belong to the ACB (Amphibious Construction Battalion) who "own and operate" the causeways. The system is designed so that the ship provides only the winch power to hoist or lower these 70-ton causeway sections.

The helicopter-handling facilities and deck structure were designed to accommodate helicopters up to the size of the CH-53, with an operating weight up to 42,000 pounds with a dynamic factor of 2.67 gs. Fueling (JP-5), tiedown, starting power, fresh water, compressed air and fire-fighting equipment have been provided in the landing area. The "flight deck" has been provided with appropriate lighting and communications to permit night helicopter operations.

The single-lever remote control of the propulsion system provides, to the conning officer, instantaneous control of the power and direction of the propulsion system. In a single-lever control for each shaft, the console operator, on the bridge, is able to apply any level of power within the capability of the number of engines in use (1 to 3 per shaft) in either ahead or astern operation of the controllable, reversible, variable pitch propellers. The control system is basically *horsepower* oriented. The operator, by positioning the control lever for each shaft, relays a signal for a specific amount of horsepower in either the ahead or astern direction. This signal goes to the governor on the selected lead engine, which in turn selects the appropriate shaft rpm, propeller direction, and propeller pitch to provide the required horsepower. This in effect gives the operator a very simple single-lever control with which to operate a very complicated propulsion system. The instant response of the system and direct control of the propulsion system by the console operator on the bridge makes the system ideally suited for close maneuvering, such as at a causeway or retracting from the beach.

The hull form which allows high speed also relieves the serious threat of damage from pounding when making way into a head sea. The LST 1179 rides very smoothly at 20 knots into seas which would cause the older LST to come to a dead slow pace. She still rolls like the old LST but, with pounding gone, the danger of shock damage to ship or cargo is greatly reduced.

The amphibious capabilities of the LST 1179 class ship do not differ greatly from those of earlier LST designs except in magnitude. This class can carry a greater tonnage, in larger space, at greater speeds, for prolonged periods of deployment. With long deployments in mind, habitability for both embarked troop and ship's company accommodations has seen significant improvement.

MINESWEEPERS

As a result of the lessons learned during World War II and the Korean War, and to meet the threat of modern mines, new classes of minesweepers have been developed and put into service. The Minesweeper, Oceangoing (MSO); the Minesweeper, Coastal (MSC); the Mineseweeping Boat (MSB); and the Minesweeping Utility Boat (MSUB) are in service today, with the MSO being the largest class of minesweeper in commission. To minimize their vulnerability to magnetic mines, all of these vessels have wooden hulls, special nonmagnetic engines and auxiliaries, and nonferrous hull fittings, and are built to additional rigid specifications which render them virtually nonmagnetic. Since the MSO and MSC are fully commissioned vessels, and the MSB and MSUB are designed for operations within harbors, the following discussion will deal directly with only the first two classes, but the problems faced by all are similar. For comparison the general characteristics of the two largest classes of minesweepers are:

	MSO	MSC
Length	173 feet	145 feet
Beam	35 feet	27 feet
Draft*	10 ¼ feet	8 ½ feet
Full load displacement	780 tons	384 tons
Total shaft horsepower	2,400	1,200
Maximum speed	15.5	14.7
Crew: Officers	5	4
Enlisted	67	35

The MSO

As shown in Figure 16–6, the MSO retains the high "Tuna Clipper" bow and low square counter of the old YMS, though she is considerably longer and broader than her predecessor. She is completely equipped to sweep all moored and influence mines except pressure mines, but she is fitted with a heavy duty towing winch aft for towing special equipment furnished from other sources when it is necessary to sweep pressure mines. Equipped with twin screws and twin rudders, the MSO handles beautifully. She is an oceangoing ship, and, were it not for a limitation in speed, she would be fully capable of operating with the fleet at sea.

Controllable pitch propellers

The MSO has four diesel engines which can be clutched singly or in pairs with suitable reduction gears to corresponding controllable, reversible pitch propellers (CRPs). In principle, the engines turn at a preselected rpm and thus the propellers are turning at a constant speed. Ship speed (or power delivered by a propeller) is changed by changing the pitch of the propellers by means of a remote control hydraulic system. Propeller pitch can be varied from six feet (per revolution) ahead to five feet astern. The equivalent of STOP is achieved by setting the propellers at zero pitch. Pitch adjustments can be accomplished very quickly (12 seconds from six feet ahead to five feet astern), and thus changes in direction and level of power made more quickly than with other propulsion systems.

*Sonar extends below this draft.

FIGURE 16–6. USS *Assurance* (MSO 521), typical of the largest minesweepers in service today.

Actually the situation is a bit more complicated than indicated in the preceding paragraph. Engine speed is determined by throttle setting and output load which varies with pitch at a given shaft rpm. A change in pitch requires a change in throttle settings. As the output power varies, the throttle setting is adjusted to maintain the ordered rpm. A rapid change in pitch can overload the engines, especially if only one engine per shaft is in use. An overload condition is indicated by engine manifold pressures exceeding the prescribed upper limits for the engine rpm. Though there is a wide range of combinations of engine rpm and propeller pitch which will result in a desired ship speed, the propulsive efficiency is affected and, especially on long cruises, it is important to select the combination which results in the highest propulsive efficiency. As a general rule, *select the highest pitch setting and the lowest shaft rpm that will give the required speed but not exceed the recommended engine manifold pressure and that is above critical engine speeds.*

Should the pitch control system become inoperative with a given pitch set on a propeller, the only way to stop the propulsion thrust of the propeller is to unclutch or stop the engine. This can be done moderately quickly with the two inboard engines, but the two outboard engines, which are coupled to generators to provide power when making magnetic sweeps, are also fitted with very heavy flywheels to accommodate power surges and so take some time to stop. For this reason some skippers prefer to maneuver on only the two inboard engines when handling the ship in port. The available power is less, but they are better prepared to handle a pitch casualty.

Handling the MSO

The bridge of the MSO is located well forward above the pilothouse and, because of its height and the shortness of the forecastle, the conning officer has the feeling of being immediately over the bow. From the bridge, the conning officer can easily observe the handling of the four mooring lines and the handling of the minesweeping gear on the fantail.

In addition to normal bridge equipment for a vessel of her size, we find controls and indicators for engine speed and propeller pitch. Normally throttle control is maintained in the engine room and propeller pitch is controlled from the pilothouse, but when sweeping mines, both throttle and pitch control are shifted to the pilothouse so all personnel below decks can be evacuated during a hazardous operation.

The CRPs call for a new propulsion control vocabulary. Instead of ordering, ALL ENGINES AHEAD ONE-THIRD, the MSO conning officer orders, ALL PITCH AHEAD ONE FOOT. Commands include the desired direction and the desired pitch in feet per revolution.

ZERO PITCH is ordered in the place of STOP, but this has effects different from that normally experienced with conventional drives. If the ship is moving through the water, even though pitch is set at zero, the propellers are turning and there will be an angle of attack between the propeller blades and the water as a result of rotation of the propeller and the ship's movement through the water. Consequently, zero pitch results in thrust to *oppose* the longitudinal movement through the water. Ordering ZERO PITCH therefore slows the ship much more rapidly than ordering STOP in a conventional ship, where the propellers would just "idle" with little resulting thrust.

Since the propellers rotate at a relatively high speed even when the ship is dead in the water, the adjustment for zero pitch (i.e., that pitch which will actually produce no thrust when the ship is dead in the water) is quite critical. Perfect adjustment is not normally achieved and MSOs have a tendency to "creep" with their propellers set at zero pitch. The conning officer should be familiar with the tendency of his particular ship.

The twin rudders are mounted directly astern of the propellers and normally afford excellent directional control, especially when ahead pitch is being used. When zero pitch (or a pitch appreciably lower than that for the speed being made through the water) is ordered, the effect of the rapidly rotating propellers is to blank off or even reverse the normal flow past the rudders, so that rudder effectiveness is greatly reduced. When backing, speeds through the water greater than 8 knots must not be used because the rudders are not designed to stand the stress of backing at greater speeds.

With the CRP system, full engine power can be employed ahead or astern, and the load on the engines can be changed rapidly. The conning officer must be aware of the pitch limitations for the engine combination and speed he is using and not overload the engines. For example, if the ship were proceeding through the water at 12 knots with pitch set at ahead five feet and using the corresponding engine speed, and we suddenly shifted the pitch to back five feet, we would increase the load on the engines several fold and would no doubt stall the engines. When operating near the allowable limits of a particular engine combination, the use of a large amount of rudder may add sufficient resistance to overload the engines. This does not imply that the propulsion system is unsatisfactory or difficult to use, it simply means that the conning officer must be familiar with the system and handle it within its limitations.

When going alongside to make a landing, it is better to approach slowly with a small amount of ahead pitch than to use the "stop-and-coast" method common in other types. The MSO has a moderately large sail area for her draft and is sensitive to the wind, and the improved rudder control gained by keeping ahead pitch on as long as practical is quite useful. During the last moments of the landing, an MSO can be stopped quite quickly using astern pitch.

When clearing a berth, opposed pitch will readily walk her stern away from the pier and, since her propellers do not project beyond her sides, clearing a berth by going out ahead is quite normal.

At sea, because of her size and lines, an MSO tends to ride up over the waves like a cork rather than to plow through them. She has no provision for ballasting and the lighter she gets, the more corky she becomes. The sea conditions have a great effect on her performance. When required to steam into the wind and seas, her fuel consumption per mile increases markedly. On long voyages, it is customary to carry a deck load of fuel in a collapsible fuel cell, or in drums, in addition to the load in her fuel tanks.

Minesweeping

A minesweeper with her gear out is not the nimble craft described above. She cannot proceed at top speed because of the drag of her sweep, yet she cannot slow below a certain minimum speed because her sweep will sink to the bottom and be damaged or lost. Her small turning circle cannot be used with her sweep out, and with long multiple sweeps she must use tactical diameters as great as 2,000 yards.

Minesweeping is generally done at speeds of less than 10 knots and in waters of 30 fathoms or less. Frequently the sweeping area contains headlands, islands, reefs, navigation marks, etc., thus complicating the minesweeper's maneuvers and navigation, which must be precise with respect to the minefield. The conning officer must take these factors into consideration, as well as watch his engine loading and keep his sweep properly streamed and off the bottom.

When making turns with gear streamed, it will be found that the tow will tend to oppose the effect of the rudder and that the amount of this opposition may vary during a turn because of the wind and sea conditions. Required to maneuver accurately, the conning officer must be alert to the effect of the sweep gear on the turning characteristics of his ship and compensate accordingly.

In addition to handling her sweep gear, a minesweeper is frequently called upon to lay and recover dan buoys or to act as a mine recovery ship. All of these operations require careful maneuvering and care in the use of propellers because all of the recovery equipment is located on the fantail. However, the ship drifts with the wind directly abeam when stopped, which enables a cable led to an object'to windward to be recovered quite easily and clear of the screws. The object to be recovered should be approached from downwind, snagged at the weather bow and connected to a recovery pendant led aft. Slack is kept from the pendant as the bow is allowed to fall off to leeward until the pendant leads straight out from the hoisting spot. The ship's position is easily maintained with the line tending at right angles by very small changes in pitch.

The MSC

In operation the MSC (Figure 16–7) is very similar to the larger MSO with the exception that she has a normal diesel propulsion plant instead of variable pitch propellers. Through a remote control system her engines can also be controlled from the bridge and engine response is very rapid. She tends to maintain her way when her engines are stopped, and with conning officers accustomed to the braking effect of the MSO at zero pitch, there is a tendency to overshoot when making a landing.

An MSC is not designed for extensive open-ocean operation and severe weather should be avoided when possible. At sea in heavy weather, the MSC plunges and leaps in response to the waves. Proper securing for sea is *essential*. Because of her tendency to roll heavily in the trough, it is better to either steam

FIGURE 16–7. USS *Warbler* (MSC 206), coastal counterpart of the MSO.

slowly into the waves or to run with them. She will ride very comfortably in a following sea, but will yaw considerably and experience a certain loss of rudder control as the crests sweep past. She is short and light enough to ride up over the waves, so the danger of being pooped is not as great as with some other types.

If a really severe storm, such as a hurricane or typhoon, is approaching, an MSC should head for a protected anchorage. If available, a buoy is the safest mooring and she will ride well providing enough scope to the buoy is used to prevent the chain from being pulled taut with a jerk. Mooring to a pier in such a storm is not recommended unless it is certain that the wind will not be blowing the ship against the pier either before *or* after the passage of the "eye" of the storm. Should it be decided to remain alongside a pier during such a storm, the ship's anchor chain and heaviest cables should be used for mooring, but long leads should be used with these to insure that they are not brought up taut as the ship pitches and rolls, and also to provide for the rising storm tide. The MSC is equipped with two good anchors and it is much wiser to attempt to ride out the storm with a two-anchor Hammerlock moor (see Chapter 6) than to take a chance on being damaged against a pier.

THE PATROL GUNBOAT

A very interesting addition to the fleet is the Patrol Gunboat or PG, of the *Ashville* (PG 84) class. These high-performance ships have a combined diesel and gas turbine (CODAG) plant coupled to CRPs. Their general characteristics are as follows:

Length	165 feet
Beam	23 feet, 6 inches
Draft	9 feet, 6 inches
Full load displacement	245 tons
Total shaft horsepower	13,000
Maximum speed	37.5 knots
Crew Officers	4
Enlisted	27

These twin-screw, twin-rudder ships are very fast and maneuverable. Designed for coastal work, their shallow draft has made them particularly useful in the rivers and estuaries of Southeast Asia. At sea in rough weather they have proved to be very hard on their crews even though the ship stands up well to the stresses of the waves. The latest PGs have been equipped with fin stabilizers to reduce their rolling, and this has been a welcome improvement for the men who man them.

17
new hulls and propulsion

HULL FORMS

Thus far we have discussed conventional ships and their characteristics. From largest to smallest, each of the ships we have looked at has had a displacement hull, was driven by conventional propellers and was steered with conventional rudders. But conventional ships can perform only conventional tasks and can be attacked by conventional weapons. In sea warfare there is as much a need for the unconventional solution as there is in any other field of man's endeavor. Modern technology offers many alternatives to the displacement hull and screw propeller—in fact, there is such a large assortment of alternatives that one can but wonder why there has been so little change. High-speed hydrofoil craft were operated successfully in the first decade of this century. The advantage of the catamaran has been known and exploited by the South Sea Islanders as far back as man's knowledge extends. Supporting a hull on a bubble of compressed air and thrusting it forward with air screws instead of water screws does not require the genius of an Einstein—it is a concept quite likely to occur to a first-year physics student. The advantage of the semisubmerged hull has been known since David Taylor first published his treatise on the speed and power of ships, yet no ships exploiting this advantage have come into military service. Jet propulsion has completely revolutionized air travel and resulted in the demise of the transoceanic liner as a prime means of transporting people, but the U.S. Navy is only now venturing to apply the gas turbine to the propulsion of ships. Why does it take so long to introduce a new idea in the marine field?

There are both good and bad reasons why new ideas are accepted so slowly in the design and construction of ships. The bad reasons include all the human failings of limited vision, limited courage, limited ability and limited funds; but probably more importantly, should include the size and complexity of both our Navy and our government. Standarization, organization, logistic support, training, base requirements, personnel levels all militate against change. The special interest groups for aircraft, submarines, amphibious forces, ASW, fire support, and electronics all compete for the same dollar and each becomes the enemy of improvement in the competing camps. The same is true of our civilian government—it tends to work to preserve the status quo; to prevent a "new thing" from disturbing the balance. The larger the organization the greater it is controlled and restricted by its amassed inventory of equipment and ideas. The larger the Navy, the more conservative it becomes.

But there are good reasons for conservatism, too. The sea is cruel and merciless. If the hull cannot stand the stress of the unexpected, the ship is lost. If the power is not there when danger demands, a warship does not get a second chance. The extremes of weather cannot be neglected, they must be lived through. A design might look fascinating on the drawing board, but it has to perform in the angriest moods of an unpredictable sea, whether the designer and builder foresaw such requirement or not.

Of equal importance is the need that a warship be useful in a whole family of situations. It is very infrequent indeed that a navy can afford a special purpose ship, committed to the performance of one duty only. The U.S. fleet must have its major strength in general purpose ships to insure sufficient flexibility to meet the unknown threat of the future. Prudence usually rules out the novel and distates the "tried and true."

But despite a deeply ingrained tendency towards the conventional we are now beginning to see some radically different ship types on the horizon, and some experimental prototypes are already at sea. The first complete class of patrol hydrofoils is about to be built and the first experimental navy surface effect ships are now in existence. These craft embody not only completely new and different concepts of lift, propulsion and control, but they require new design concepts and materials, new and lighter machinery, and many components and systems never seen at sea before. These first ships, as radical and daring as they seem to the eye accustomed to minuscule changes in the conventional, are unquestionably forerunners of new generations of more usual, more capable craft. There is a direct and continuing interaction between fleet requirements and techniques on one hand and the advance of technology on the other. The needed technology is largely here—the "operators" are now beginning to demand its use.

Since only the prototypes of these new craft exist and the actual configuration of the ultimate fleet units has not yet been determined, we cannot yet deal with any authority with the techniques of handling such craft or discuss with any thoroughness the special problems which must be solved when they enter the fleet. The actual operational tasks of such craft will have to be defined before many of the problems which face the shiphandler begin to emerge. On the other hand, it is useful to examine the physical nature of such craft to gain an understanding of the specific characteristics which will affect their operation and maneuvering. But before getting into the details of these interesting craft, we should consider why these new designs have come into being and where they fit in the pattern of fighting platforms.

Speed and payload

The conventionally drawn resistance vs. speed curve for normal warships seems to climb upwards off the chart and towards infinity as the speed/length ratio approaches 2.0 (40 knots for a 400-foot ship). Actually, referring back to Figure 2–11 in Chapter 2, it can be seen that the wave resistance peaks at $V/\sqrt{L}$ of 2.0 and decreases steadily thereafter. When combined with the frictional resistances, the total resistance curves as indicated in Figure 2–12 result. Therefore, for almost all types, there is a reduction in the slope of the resistance curve, and in some cases an actual valley following the wave-making peak at a speed/length ratio of 2.0.

Even displacement hulls tend to rise out of the water as the $V/\sqrt{L}$ approaches 2.0 or better. To capitalize on this tendency to rise and thus reduce the wetted surface of the hull to a minimum, the planing hull has been developed to minimize both wavemaking and frictional resistance. A planing hull must be provided with enough power to get over the "hump" and up on its "step," but once the hull has risen out of the water and is planing smoothly, speed can be increased readily by a relatively small increase in power. Since the hydrodynamic lift on a planing hull is proportional to the wetted surface and the square of the speed, as speed is increased, the wetted surface is decreased rapidly until a suprisingly small area of the bottom is actually engaged with the water. Racing hydroplanes at top speed have only the last few inches of their bottoms touching the water.

Though a smaller and smaller area of the planing surface is required to support the hull as the speed is increased, very strong forces can be applied to the hull as the area of engagement changes as a result of encountering waves. Even modest waves can subject a planing hull to severe jolts. Accordingly, the designer of a planing hull seeks to produce a relatively flat hull area aft to support the boat at her design speed, combined with relatively fine lines for that portion of the hull above the water so that when a wave is engaged, the forward section will slice through the wave with a minimum of upward force which will be experienced relatively gradually, thus eliminating any jolt. This can successfully be done for a given hull and speed up to a certain wave height, but beyond that any hull must be slowed down or it will slam severely. The larger the hull, the greater the wave height which can be handled with comfort. Available power and structural limitations have limited planing craft to ships of PG class or smaller, but one should expect to see larger planing ships as the materials and technology for them become available.

The planing catamaran or hydro-ski craft offers advantages over the conventional planing hull design. With the much greater engaged planing length of the hydro-ski, a wave which increases the engaged length by a few feet produces a much smaller relative change in lift than would be the case with the broader conventional planing hull. Further, the long, narrow hull forward of the wetted planing surface can more easily be designed to slice through oncoming waves with a minimum of additional lift.

From a functional viewpoint all vehicles—land, sea, or air—are cargo platforms designed to transport a payload. In most cases a choice can be made among several possible vehicles and a valid criterion for such choice is essential if the best choice is to be made. For the cargo transport function, the arithmetic product of payload times speed, or cargo transfer rate is a good criterion at the outset, but it, of course, does not include economic considerations. Within the limitations of vehicle range, the possibility of delivering or otherwise utilizing the cargo, and the possibility of operating and supporting the system, a choice between competing vehicles on the basis of relative cargo transfer rate is usually a valid method of choice. if the economics are comparable.

"Payloads," however, are frequently specific inalterable qualities, so after feasibility has been determined, the operational speed of competing vehicles becomes the basis of choice. For aerodynamic and structural reasons, conventional jet aircraft of conventional materials and power must operate at speeds below the speed of sound but above a stalling speed of about 100 knots. The maximum payload for such craft is in the order of 250 tons. As discussed in Chapter 2, the maximum practical speed for a large displacement-hull surface ship is in the order of 40 knots because of the exponential rise of wave-making resistance, while that of the submarine is probably limited to the same region because of difficulties in providing higher power levels within the weight and space limitations imposed by the vehicle. We thus have distinct limited speed regions where each of the vehicles can be used.

In their studies of the place of aircraft in the field of transport, Dr. Von Karman and Professor Gabrielli developed an interesting method of plotting the operational regions of competing systems. The Karman-Gabrielli diagram (Figure 17–1) shows the operational regions of the various transportation vehicles. For example, if one wishes to transport a payload across the sea greater than 10 tons at a speed greater than 50 knots, but not as great as several hundred knots, there is nothing that can do it except hydrofoils or surface effect ships. Displacement ships figuratively run into a wall of water at high speed. Helicopters have not been developed to handle payloads greater than about 10 tons, though there are some experimental ones which can carry up to 20 tons for short distances. The hydrofoils and the surface effect craft have literally been developed to fill a gap in the transportation spectrum.

A significant weapon/sensor suit for a warship operating on the high seas starts at about 15 tons today and can become an attractive general purpose suit at about 40 tons. Operational speed in the vicinity of 50 to 60 knots is very desirable for lightly armed, limited duration warships, since it will permit them to cover a satisfactory patrol area, overtake fleeing adversaries, and also to escape from a stronger opponent when necessary. A hydrofoil craft can meet these requirements, and this is the basis for the intense interest in these craft, but there is a limit to the promise of the hydrofoil. At a given speed the lift realizable from a hydrofoil is proportional to the area of the submerged portion of the foil, hence the realizable lift of a given configuration varies generally as the square of a typical dimension. The weight of the structure on the other hand varies generally as the cube of a typical dimension, so as the size of the craft is increased at a given speed the portion of the lift required to support structure

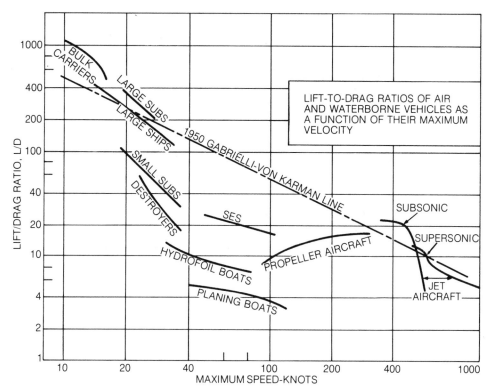

FIGURE 17–1. The Karman-Gábrielli diagram.

increases and the fraction remaining to support payload is reduced. At first larger payloads can be handled by increasing the speed, since lift goes up with the square of the speed, but despite the beneficial shape of the resistance/ power curve for a hydrofoil after surmounting the "hump," the power required to overcome simple fluid foil drag goes up as the cube of the speed, so we are ultimately heading for diminishing returns. The specific limits of size, speed and payload for the hydrofoil will be determined by the available structural materials and power plants, but it is likely that the largest practical craft will be in the order of a few hundred tons with a top speed of about 100 knots.

The factors which limit the growth potential of the hydrofoil do not operate on the surface effects ship. An outgrowth of the air cushion vehicle, the SES depends upon the air pressure in its plenum chamber for lift and this pressure can be raised to significant levels if necessary. Ships in the 5,000-ton region are on the drawing boards, and ships of even greater tonnage are considered practical. Since lift and speed are essentialy independent, they can be considered independently; lift varying as the chamber pressure, speed varying with the interaction of surface and air resistance and installed power.

But there are also other unconventional hull shapes which permit higher operating speeds. If we remember that at high speed a conventional displacement ship expends the greatest fraction of its power-making waves and that the wave-making characteristic of a given hull is dependent largely on the size and shape of the hull at the water line, it is easy to see why the semisubmersible and the displacement catamaran offer superior performance. The semisubmersible reduces its waterplane to an absolute minimum, thus minimizing the wave-making portion of the hull; the catamaran minimizes its waterplane by having exceptionally narrow and deep hulls. Additionally, a catamaran offers an extraordinarily large and stable work platform support on hulls which would be too deep and narrow to remain upright alone.

Finally, combinations of the various hull forms are probably in the offing. The hard sidewall surface effect ship (Figure 17–2) is really a hybrid combination of a planing catamaran and an air cushion vehicle. Hydrofoils as addenda will probably find use in nearly all of the other types to provide additional lift and to adjust trim. Air bubbles can be combined with the catamaran to help it over the "hump" and to provide additional buoyancy and freeboard at low speeds and when dead in the water. The most exciting thing for a shiphandler is that progress is being made to bring more capable and versatile craft into service, and each of these new types will bring with it interesting challenges to the shiphandler.

The hydrofoil

Among the first of the new types to actually reach the fleet is the hydrofoil gunboat. Preceded by a series of research and experimental hydrofoils, USS *Flagstaff* (PGH 1) and USS *Tucumcari* (PGH 2) (Figure 17–3) have entered the service. The new PHM program, being conducted jointly with some of our NATO allies, will bring into being a new class of missile-carrying hydrofoil ships as a permanent part of the fleet. Though the characteristics of these new ships are still in the process of development, they will be powerful and versatile ships. Capable of operating at speeds well in excess of 50 knots in all except extreme sea states, they will be armed with powerful surface-to-surface missiles capable of sinking the largest warships, be well equipped for self-defense with a high performance gun battery, and will be extremely difficult targets for conventional weapons.

Though surface-piercing hydrofoils have been used successfully in certain operations for many years, such craft give a very rough ride as the wave heights increase. As with a planing hull, when the submerged lifting surface is increased abruptly by the encounter of a wave, a severe jolt is felt by the ship. Above a certain modest wave height, the ride in a surface-piercing hydrofoil becomes so rough that foilborne operations cannot be continued and the ship must slow and settle down on its hull for buoyancy. Once on her hull, particularly with fixed non-retractable foils, the craft is a sluggish weapons platform of limited capability.

Fully submerged hydrofoils have been selected for all seagoing hydrofoil warships, since only these can truly isolate the hull from the choppy surface waves. The hull rides above the wave crests and is supported by foils operating deep enough to be fully submerged at all times. The long struts are thin and of

FIGURE 17-2. The SES-100B Surface Effect Ship test craft, pictured on a test run during which it achieved speeds of approximately 40 knots.

essentially uniform cross-section, so there is little change in total lift as the waterplane moves up and down the struts as the ship passes through the waves. Of course, with a short wave of greater height than the length of the strut the crest will hit the hull, but by following the contour of the long swells the ship will ride smoothly with its hull held completely clear of the short chop even in relatively high sea states.

But fully submerged foils require elaborate controls. Since a fully submerged foil is neutrally stable with respect to depth (i.e., it does not change its lift force as its submergence changes as the result of the passage of a wave), it must be equipped with a sensor system to detect the height at which the hull is riding above the surface and a control system to change the angle of attack of at least one foil to maintain the foil submergence at the desired depth. To maintain lateral stability and directional control one of the foils, usually the front foil, must be steerable in the same manner that a bicycle is steered by its front wheel. Finally, at the operating speeds of hydrofoils and with their need for quick maneuverability, aircraft type controls and instruments are employed since normal shipboard controls and instrumentation are not adequate.

But even the most capable hydrofoil ship is normally a rather awkward, underpowered hullborne craft which occasionally mounts its aquatic wings and can then perform extraordinary feats of speed and maneuverability. Below "take-off" speed, usually about 20 knots, the hydrofoil is incapable of rising above the surface, may have its foils retracted, and may be capable of employing only its

FIGURE 17–3. With its foils in retracted position, the 71-foot USS *Tucumcari* (PGH 2) maneuvers near Seattle, Washington.

surface propulsion and control system, which has only a fraction of the power of its foilborne systems. Maneuvering in close quarters and alongside will almost always be conducted with foils retracted and with the low-powered surface maneuvering system.

The takeoff from the hullborne mode to the foilborne mode is surprisingly smooth and quick. The craft simply rises from the surface as it passes through the takeoff speed, and then accelerates rapidly as the hull is released from its friction and wave-making drag. Steering is quick and precise, with the ship heeling smartly inward as the ship banks around a turn. A foilborne hydrofoil ship with fully submerged foils does not roll or pitch in the normal sense, though she does rise and fall gently as she follows the contour of the swells. When properly foilborne, the combined pull of gravity and centrifugal force is always directly down with respect to the deck—again it is like riding a bicycle—so the skipper's dinner can't be thrown into his lap as the result of an OOD's boisterous maneuver. In fact, the at-sea ride of a well-designed hydrofoil ship is so smooth that many operators have found it boring. Rapid deceleration can occur when transitioning from the foilborne mode to the hullborne mode. This can occur accidentally when encountering an unexpectedly high wave or when the craft is driven down to the surface by the action of the foils, whether intentional or not. Driving the craft to the surface is a convenient way to slow down quickly in an emergency.

Surface effect ships

The first experimental prototype surface effect ships (SES) and the larger ones being designed are essentially rigid sidewall air cushion vehicles. The normal air cushion vehicle rides completely clear of the surface of the water, with air escaping around its periphery through the gap between the bottom of its skirt and the surface of the water (Figure 17–4). This reduces its frictional resistance to almost zero, but there is an interaction with the surface which is analagous to wave-making resistance. But one pays for being disconnected from the water by being completely at the mercy of the winds and aerodynamic forces. Thus, an ACV can only be controlled and steered by manipulating the thrust vector of its air propel-

FIGURE 17–4. A typical air cushion vehicle, with air escaping around its periphery.

lers. To turn, the shiphandler must establish the centripetal force to produce the curved path with the power from the vehicle's propellers or by valving "bubble" chamber pressure to the side by manipulating the vehicle's skirt. The ACV is consequently steered with exaggerated movements and is frequently pointing in a different direction from the direction it is moving. It is a bit like trying to steer a castored swivel chair that is rolling across a smooth floor.

In an SES, on the other hand, though equipped with flexible skirts forward and aft, the sidewalls are rigid and extend below the surface to act as keels. This construction permits the use of normal water propellers or hydrojets and the ship can be steered by normal hydrodynamic rudders. Even the skirts generally remain in contact with the water, actually having a planing surface to insure contact, so the amount of air escaping from the plenum chamber is minimized. As waves are encountered, the forward and after skirts move up and down following the movement of the surface, thus reducing the ship's tendency to pitch. The sidewalls act as hydro-skis, giving substantial lift as the speed is increased and adding to both longitudinal and transverse stability.

The SES is, therefore, a much steadier vehicle than an ACV. It steers normally in that it points in approximately the same direction it is moving and it has good platform stability. It can be powered by air screws, water screws, or hydrojets, and it can be equipped with conventional rudders if directional control is not provided as a built-in feature of the propulsion system. In common with the hydrofoil it has two modes of operation, "on the bubble," or "off the bubble, " though it will normally be "on the bubble" when operating. In contrast to the hydrofoil, which loses most of its attractive features when hullborne below takeoff speed, the SES can move at any of its operational speeds, including stop, while "on the bubble." The very large platform area will also certainly be found operationally useful.

There are many questions about the SES which cannot be answered satisfactorily until operational experience is gained. The ship's structure must be light to be efficient and the inverted "U" shape of the hull cross-section with no cross-tie at the bottom may prove fragile. How the ship will behave in heavy seas, whether she can maintain her bubble, particularly with quartering or beam seas, can only be learned satisfactorily when the full-scale ships get to sea. A complete power loss in such a ship means more than loss of propulsion, it also means loss of equivalent buoyancy and freeboard. Obviously, the designers and analysts have thought of these considerations and believe they have satisfactory answers to the challenge. If they have, and the ships perform as well at sea as they seem to in concept, the fleet will find many uses for these novel ships.

NEW TYPES OF PROPULSION

As important to the shiphandler as the new hull forms are several developments in propulsion which are going to affect his ability to control his ship. Some of these developments are already finding their way into the fleet, but others are only in the experimental stage. Any device or change which alters the availability of power, ahead or astern, or offers the capability to apply power in a different direction is of primary interest to the shiphandler.

Already in use in the PG 84 class and soon to see service in the DD 963s is the long-awaited gas turbine. With its basic simplicity, nearly instant availability, and great range of power, a gas turbine seems the perfect solution to the shiphandler who has had to shape his movements and maneuvers to warm-up requirements of a steam plant. Combinations of several sizes of gas turbines or combinations with both diesel and steam plants are at sea in the merchant marine and in other navies and we shall probably see all of these combinations in the U. S. fleet in the future. There are, however, several characteristics of the gas turbine which must be taken into account in its use.

First, a marine gas turbine is not just an aircraft "jet" fitted into a ship. Because it must be used for hundreds of hours without stop and must go thousands of hours between inspections or overhaul, the marine gas turbine must be much more rugged and durable than its airborne counterpart. Though weight is not so critical in a ship as in an aircraft, fuel economy is even more important. Extra care in design and construction must insure maximum efficiency of combustion and maximum utilization of the heat produced. Only the "regenerative" gas turbine, which recaptures the heat normally lost in the exhaust, has fuel consumption rates competitive with a good steam plant or a diesel. Just as much air must flow through a gas turbine as through the furnace of a steam boiler, and it must flow efficiently and relatively quietly. Because of the high velocity of air flowing into the turbine and of the gas flowing out of the turbine, the intake and exhaust system of a gas turbine installation must be large and relatively complex. Finally, backing power from a gas turbine in normally obtained from the use of a CRP or through an electric drive, because the high temperature of the working gas and the rotational velocity of the turbine do not lend themselves to other methods of reversing. Fitting a ship with a gas turbine installation is therefore not a simple matter.

Nuclear power is of course becoming widely used in the fleet with the large number of nuclear submarines and the growing number of nuclear surface ships in service. A discussion of the technical features and operating characteristics of nuclear plants is not appropriate here, but from the shiphandler's point of view, such ships can be considered as being equipped with conventional steam plants wherein the steam is being provided by unconventional boilers.

A promising development on the horizon for ship use is the hydrojet. Its first use within the fleet was in the riverine PBRs, where it has shown great versatility and remarkable shallow-water capability and maneuverability. A hydrojet is essentially a system of ducting, and a pump which draws water in through the intake, accelerates it, and expels it through a nozzle. Reaction from the resulting jet of water pushes the vessel through the water and relatively high propulsive power can be realized from relatively small units. Unfortunately, the higher the velocity of the exit jet as compared to the speed of the vessel through the water, the lower the propulsive efficiency. Nevertheless, in well-designed applications, the efficiency of a hydrojet can equal that of a good propeller system.

FIGURE 17–5. Her sonar dome clearly visible, the destroyer USS *Spruance* (DD 963) rests in her drydock before builder's trials. This ship is one of the first in the U.S. Navy to employ the marine gas turbine.

Almost more important than the ability to couple high power in a small unit is the steering and maneuvering capability of the jet. Steering is accomplished by altering the direction of the jet, either by rudders or by swivelling the nozzle itself, thus altering the direction of the thrust vector, and reversing is accomplished through a "thrust reverser" similar to that used in jet airliners. In some units it is possible to obtain thrust in any direction by combined use of the steering and reversing devices. Thus a single jet, unlike a single screw, can be used to apply force in any direction at the stern of the ship and offers the equal of twin-screw, twin-rudder maneuverability in a craft with no screws and no rudders projecting below its keel. With such characteristics, though hydrojets are only available today in sizes suitable for boats and small, special-purpose ships, it is probable that we will see much more of them in the future.

18
pilots and tugs

Having made our landfall and beaten our way to the harbor entrance, we pause momentarily just before we reach the dangers of the channel to pick up the pilot. The pilot boat swings smartly alongside in spite of the difficult chop. The very presence of this tiny vessel so far from the sheltered port bespeaks the competence of her masters. Catching the surge expertly, the pilot swings aboard by the jacob's ladder and soon is standing on the bridge. His hearty greeting to the captain, his easy habit of command, and his weathered countenance mark him for what he is—a master mariner. "I'm ready to take her, Sir," he says, and we have the feeling that she should be in good hands.

Before we turn the ship over completely to this new master, however, we had better take a look at him and examine the extent of his competence. What is a pilot? Who qualified him? What can he do to assist us? These are good questions and require an answer.

PILOTS

A pilot is an expert on the waters for which he is qualified. He has made a study of the peculiarities of those waters and is required to have had extensive experience handling ships in them. He knows the vagaries of the currents, the latest shifting of the shoals, and the particular problems of each channel and each berth. His knowledge of local conditions extensively augments the information that is available from the charts and sailing instructions. He knows all of the harbor ranges, the landmarks, the habits of the local shipping. He can navigate in and out without a glance at the chart if need be, and he can steer a safe course through the harbor on the most meager visual information.

The licensing of pilots comes under the Coast Guard and is handled by the Marine Inspection Service. To obtain a pilot's license an applicant must give evidence of having served at sea for a minimum of three years in the deck department of a vessel and of having made a certain minimum number of round trips through the waters in question. In addition he must pass an examination on the following subjects, based on *Rules and Regulations for Licensing and Certificating of Merchant Marine Personnel,* CG 191, June 15, 1953.

a. *Pilot Rules* for the waters desired.
b. Local knowledge of winds, weather, tides, currents, etc.
c. Sketch a chart of the route and waters applied for showing courses, distances, shoals, aids to navigation, depths of water, and all other important features.
d. Steering, handling, and maneuvering of steam and motor vessels.
e. Such other written or oral examination as the Officer in Charge, Marine Inspection, may consider necessary to establish the applicant's proficiency.

As noted above, pilots are licensed for a specific locality and route. There is no universal license which is good for *all* waters. A new examination is required for a new route or an extension of an old one. Though a pilot may be licensed for several harbors, for instance, he must be examined for each of them.

In addition to the separate license as a pilot, a pilot's license may be granted as an endorsement to the license of a Master or Mate. This is a normal procedure, because to practice as a pilot it is usually necessary to have Master's papers. To obtain such an endorsement, however, an examination on the same subjects mentioned above must be passed.

Though the *legal* requirements for obtaining a pilot's license are quite rigid, in order to practice his profession (except in his own ship) a pilot must usually pass much more rigid requirements. In most U.S. ports the pilots used by naval vessels are either Civil Service Pilots or they belong to a Pilot's Association. In either case, a Master's license and extensive experience in handling large vessels under all conditions is required. For example, the following is an extract from the requirements for appointment as a Civil Service Pilot in the Twelfth Naval District for the waters of San Francisco Bay and tributaries:

Requirements
Note: It is useless to file application unless you meet the following requirements:
Experience. Applicants must have had at least three years of experience in piloting and moving vessels, in harbor and at berth or dock, which experience must have included handling of vessels of at least 10,000 gross tons and under each of the following conditions:
Entirely under their own power.
Partially under their own power, assisted by tugs.
Entirely with tugs.

Applicants must show in their applications the tonnage of vessels handled and the frequency with which vessels of 10,000 gross tons or more were maneuvered. They must have performed pilot duties at frequent intervals during the year prior to the announcement of this examination, which experience should preferably include acting as pilot for vessels entering or leaving dry docks.
License. Applicants must possess a current license as master of steam vessels of unlimited tonnage, and an unlimited license as first class pilot for vessels of unlimited tonnage, covering waters of navigation described above. These licenses must be submitted with application. . . .

Though the above discussion has been limited to U.S. ports coming under the control of the Coast Guard, similar regulations will be found in foreign ports. Handling ships in restricted waters and in the vicinity of wharves and moorings requires the nicest judgment, and the penalties for errors are costly. Throughout the world the title "Pilot" connotes the highest degree of skill, judgment, and knowledge.

Thus the pilot standing on our bridge is certainly an expert. He is an expert on the harbor in all of its details. He is an expert on handling ships in this harbor, and he has demonstrated his competence as a Master or he wouldn't be standing there. Is he, however, an expert in handling *our* ship?

Though the pilot may have handled many ships of the same type as ours, he is not necessarily an expert in handling this particular ship. As described in the previous chapters, each ship must be studied and calibrated as an *individual* before she can be handled expertly. It takes time to learn her peculiarities and to become accustomed to her behavior. The best "expert" on a given ship should be her own captain. He has lived with her and studied her habits, and he should know her as no one else could.

The question of responsibility arises as the pilot stands there. Though the harbor pilot is quite ready to "take full responsibility for the safey of the ship," this does not in any way decrease the responsibility of her captain. Regardless of who has the conn or what assurances the pilot might have given, the basic responsibility for handling the ship never budges from the captain's shoulders.

Thus the pilot should be looked upon as an exceptionally competent adviser and assistant especially hired for the occasion. He is very familiar with the harbor and the channel, and he can be depended upon as an experienced shiphandler of excellent judgment. He cannot, however, be depended upon to know *our* ship, and his presence on the bridge in no way alters the responsibility of the ship's commanding officer.

The conn

Should we give the conn to the pilot? This must be weighed against the situation. Our decision should be that which will provide the greatest degree of safety and efficiency. When the pilot steps aboard our ship, he is being hired by the ship to assist in a given situation. Though he deserves and should be accorded the respect due a proven captain, he should be used in the manner which can best benefit the ship.

If the situation is one where the intimate knowledge of the harbor is the key, then the *pilot* should be given the conn. If, on the other hand, the intimate knowledge of the ship and her handling characteristics is the key, the *commanding officer* should keep the conn. Unfortunately, this does not completely answer the question, because a full measure of familiarity with both the harbor and the ship is usually required.

A good system for handling the conn is to have the commanding officer give all orders to wheel and engines. In the case where he is maintaining the conn and using the pilot as an adviser, this would be the normal conning arrangement. In those cases where the pilot is given the conn, the pilot would give his commands through the commanding officer. In this system the captain is always in direct control of the ship, and the pilot can be used as an adviser or as a director as the case may require. This arrangement blends the expert knowledge of the conditions possessed by the pilot with the expert knowledge of the ship possessed by her skipper. The captain automatically approves the recommendations of the pilot by the orders he issues. The question of responsibility is clearly solved, because in any case it is always the ship's captain who issues the executive order.

Most naval shipyards and many canals have regulations which state that all ships must be moved "by a pilot" when within certain defined waters. This situation can be met by giving the pilot the conn in the manner described in the above paragraph. In such a situation, however, the commanding officer should follow the orders of the pilot unless he considers the safety of the ship to be in jeopardy. To take over from the pilot on a matter of taste would be a violation of the location regulation. However, no matter what the local regulations may be, the basic responsibility of the commanding officer is not altered.

Aside from the advantages mentioned above, having the commanding officer issue all executive orders is very useful for clarity and consistency of command. Engine orders used in the Merchant Marine such as AHEAD SLOW and HALF SPEED have either no naval counterpart or else carry a different meaning. AHEAD FULL means something different and produces drastically different results when ordered on the bridge of a destroyer than when ordered on the bridge of a Liberty ship. A pilot used to merchant ships is often caught unaware by the power and response of a warship. The ship's captain can rephrase and adjust the pilot's orders until the latter has gotten the feel of the ship.

TUGS

The companion of the pilot is the tug. Without her we could not use the crowded wharves and intricate channels of our modern harbors. This workhorse of the harbor is short, squat, and of relatively deep draft. She is powerful for her size, and she can deliver this power at low speeds through her large propeller. One of her most notable characteristics is her unusually large rudder. This enables her to deflect the discharge from her single screw to obtain adequate side forces even when dead in the water. She is built for the job of getting into and out of tight places and applying her power to the task of moving ships.

The bow of a tug is covered by a large fender to allow her to work against the side of a ship without damage. The newer Navy harbor tugs are being built with rubber fenders which are larger and more durable than the fiber fenders previously in use. The rubber fenders extend beneath the tugs' keels, providing protection when the tugs ride up on low-lying submarines (Figure 18–1). Her superstructure is set forward to allow her "towing point" to be well forward of her

FIGURE 18–1. A large Navy harbor tug of the YTB class under construction, showing typical structure and rubber fenders which extend beneath the tug's keel.

rudder and screw so that her stern can be swung easily even when towing astern. Her fantail is broad and long and her forecastle is short and stubby. She usually has a powered capstan on her forecastle, and from stem to stern she is well equipped with bitts and chocks for handling lines.

A tug can either push or pull. In most harbors of the world, except those in the U.S., tugs habitually pull at the end of a hawser to assist a larger ship. Pulling avoids the ship-to-ship contact that requires large fenders and rubs off paint and fittings, and it insures that the full power of the tug is available in the direction of the hawser. Pulling has the disadvantage that it requires more space (because of the length of the hawser) and can't be used in closed berths where there is no open water from which to pull.

U.S. tugs are usually equipped with bow fenders which they place against the ship's side and secure themselves with one of the "tie-ups" described in Figure 18–2. They are thus ready to push or pull (by backing down), and, by working engine and rudder in combination with their lines, can produce a force in almost any desired direction. They cannot, however, produce as strong and effective a pulling force as a tug pulling at the end of a hawser.

The simplest tug tie-up is the "single headline" or "backing line," shown in Figure 18–2. This is a single line led out through the tug's bullnose and secured to the ship. This tie-up is sufficient when the tug is going to push straight in or pull straight out; or when the tug is going to push steadily either forward or aft. If the tug must provide a force first toward the bow and then toward the stern of the ship, the double headline tie-up should be used. For general purpose use, especially when moving a dead ship, the "power" tie-up should be used. This is the most versatile tie-up and can be readily adjusted to suit the situation. It holds the tug securely in position and allows free use of the tug's engine and rudder without moving the tug relative to the ship. With the power tie-up, the direction of the applied force can be altered over a wide range by simply shifting the tug's rudder.

The tug's skipper usually chooses a satisfactory tie-up, but the situation should be studied and the tug instructed how to tie up, if necessary.

Handling tugs

A case where it is frequently advisable to turn the conn over to the pilot is when the ship is being handled by tugs. In this case the maneuverability is provided by the tugs, and the ship's engines and rudder are of secondary importance. The pilot is familiar with the tugs; in fact, he is often the skipper of one of them. He is accustomed to controlling tugs, and he knows intimately the capacity of each individual tug and her crew. In this case the pilot is certainly the unquestioned expert on both the motive power and the environment, so he is quite clearly the one best equipped to do the conning.

When handling a ship with tugs, a pilot prefers to station himself at the best vantage point on the ship for seeing both the ship and the tugs. This usually means that he is on the flying bridge, air defense station, or other location

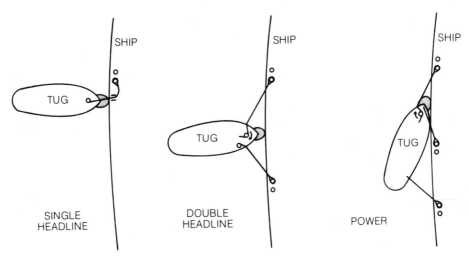

FIGURE 18–2. Tug tie-ups.

removed from the bridge. We must make certain that we have an effective means for putting his orders to the ship into action and of reporting back the action taken. The captain will usually wish to be with the pilot and will be relaying the pilot's orders, so it is desirable to station an officer on the wing of the bridge with the specific duty of transmitting the orders from the captain to the pilot house and reporting back to the captain the action taken.

A pilot high in the superstructure of a large ship on a windy day cannot rely on his voice alone to transmit his orders to the tugs, so a system of hand and whistle signals has been devised to allow the pilot to control his tugs without the need for special communication equipment. Figure 18–3 shows the system of hand and whistle signals which has been approved for use in the United States

TUG BOAT SIGNALS

HAND WHISTLE (POLICE TYPE)

FROM STOP TO HALF SPEED AHEAD	1 BLAST
FROM HALF SPEED AHEAD TO STOP	1 BLAST
FROM HALF SPEED AHEAD TO FULL SPEED AHEAD	4 SHORT BLASTS
FROM FULL SPEED AHEAD TO HALF SPEED AHEAD	1 BLAST
FROM STOP TO HALF SPEED ASTERN	2 BLASTS
FROM HALF SPEED ASTERN TO FULL SPEED ASTERN	4 SHORT BLASTS
FROM HALF OR FULL SPEED ASTERN TO STOP	1 BLAST
CAST OFF, STAND CLEAR	1 PROLONGED 2 SHORT

NOTES:
1. A BLAST IS 2 TO 3 SECONDS DURATION.
   A PROLONGED BLAST IS 4 TO 5 SECONDS DURATION.
   A SHORT BLAST IS ABOUT ONE SECOND DURATION.
2. IN USING WHISTLE SIGNALS TO DIRECT MORE THAN ONE TUG, CARE MUST BE EXERCISED TO ENSURE THAT THE SIGNAL IS DIRECTED TO AND RECEIVED BY THE DESIRED TUG. WHISTLES OF A DIFFERENT DISTINCT TONE HAVE BEEN USED SUCCESSFULLY TO HANDLE MORE THAN ONE TUG.
3. THESE SIGNALS MAY BE TRANSMITTED TO THE TUG BY FLASHING LIGHT. HOWEVER, FLASHING LIGHT SIGNALS SHOULD BE RESTRICTED TO USE ONLY WHEN HAND WHISTLE OR HAND SIGNALS CANNOT BE USED.
4. NORMALLY THESE WHISTLE SIGNALS WILL BE AUGMENTED BY THE HAND SIGNALS GIVEN BELOW.

HAND SIGNALS

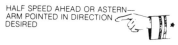
HALF SPEED AHEAD OR ASTERN—
ARM POINTED IN DIRECTION DESIRED

FULL SPEED (EITHER)—
FIST DESCRIBING ARC (AS IN "BOUNCING" AN ENGINE TELEGRAPH)

DEAD SLOW (EITHER)—
UNDULATING MOVEMENT OF OPEN HAND (PALM DOWN)

STOP (EITHER)—
OPEN PALM HELD ALOFT FACING TUG

TUG TO USE RIGHT RUDDER—
HAND DESCRIBING CIRCLE AS IF TURNING WHEEL TO RIGHT (CLOCKWISE) FACING IN THE SAME DIRECTION AS TUG

TUG TO USE LEFT RUDDER—
HAND DESCRIBING CIRCLE AS IF TURNING WHEEL TO LEFT (COUNTER-CLOCKWISE) FACING IN SAME DIRECTION AS TUG

TUG TO RUDDER AMIDSHIP—
ARM AT SIDE OF BODY WITH HAND EXTENDED, SWUNG BACK AND FORTH

CAST OFF, STAND CLEAR—
CLOSED FIST WITH THUMB EXTENDED, SWUNG UP AND DOWN

NOTE: TUG SHALL ACKNOWLEDGE ALL OF THE ABOVE SIGNALS WITH ONE SHORT TOOT (ONE SECOND OR LESS) FROM ITS WHISTLE, WITH THE EXCEPTION OF THE BACKING SIGNAL WHICH SHALL BE ACKNOWLEDGED WITH TWO SHORT TOOTS AND THE CAST-OFF SIGNAL WHICH SHALL BE ACKNOWLEDGED BY ONE PROLONGED AND TWO SHORT TOOTS.

FIGURE 18–3. Tug boat signals.

Navy. Since the captain of a ship often finds himself with tugs to help him but no pilot to control them, it is well worth his while to learn this system.

When we are called upon to handle our ship with non-Navy tugs in the absence of a pilot, we may prefer to rely on verbal orders. The general announcing system, the electric megaphone, or "walkie-talkie" can be used effectively in this case. We should select the system best suited to our ship and make sure that it is rigged and working. When giving orders to tugs by this system, we should preface each order by the tug's name or number. The tug can acknowledge the order with her whistle using the following system, which is nearly universal among tugs:

Tug's Signal	*Meaning*
One toot	Acknowledge all orders and instructions except backing orders.
Two toots	Acknowledge an order to BACK.

Handling a destroyer with tugs

Let's begin our exploration of the use of tugs by considering handling a destroyer with her own engines and a single tug. As we diminish speed in the harbor we commence to lose control of our bow. Even when dead in the water, we can exert whatever side force we may need at the stern by proper use of our engines and rudders, but we have no means of controlling the bow. Obviously, we should place our tug forward to control the bow as we slow down.

Normally we take the tug alongside the forecastle in the location shown in Figure 18–4. She should use the double headline tie-up to allow her to help slow the ship down if necessary, yet be ready to swing her stern out to the side and provide an arthwartships push. As we come abreast the berth, we have the tug swing perpendicular to us as indicated in the figure, and she controls the bow as we move the ship broadside into her berth. The fore-and-aft position of the ship and the arthwartship position of the stern is controlled by the ship's engines and rudders. The tug should be used to maintain the ship parallel to the pier as she is "walked" in with her engines and lines.

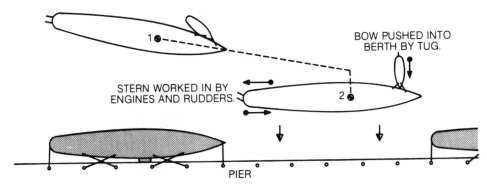

FIGURE 18–4. Berthing a destroyer with a single tug (power on the ship).

When clearing a berth, we take the tug alongside the forecastle and with her stern out in the stream. As we twist our stern out from the dock with our engines, the tug pulls our bow out and keeps it away from the pier. When clear of the berth, we usually back out into the more open harbor, and the tug swings in alongside as shown in Figure 18–5. As she trails us out into safer water, she can be used as a "rudder" operating on the bow. As soon as the ship is clear of the congestion and heading for the channel, the tug can be cast off. Though she helps us for only a brief period, she permits us to utilize berths that would be beyond our reach without her.

With the ship's engines and rudders available for handling the stern and with a tug for handling the bow, a destroyer can be handled nicely at close quarters in all but the most extreme wind or current conditions. However, if the ship's power is not available for handling the stern, it is usually desirable to have a second tug. A destroyer can be handled without power by a single tug, but since the tug can work on only one end of the ship at a time, this is not very satisfactory if the wind is troublesome. A single tug can be considered to afford slightly more versatility than the ship's own engines, but not nearly so much power.

Two tugs afford complete flexibility of control. By placing one at each end of the ship, we can use them in combination to produce any translation or rotation desired. It is normally desirable to have them use the double headline tie-up in order to be ready for any maneuver. Figure 18–6 illustrates a number of the combinations which will be found useful. The top right-hand example of the figure shows a special use of the power tie-up for moving a ship broadside when there is not sufficient room to place a tug perpendicular to the ship's side. In this combination, the two tugs are both turning their engines AHEAD with FULL outboard rudder. The fore-and-aft components cancel, but the athwartship components operate to move the ship broadsides. By various combinations of engine and rudder order on the tugs, the ship can be rotated and translated as desired without shifting the tug's position with respect to the ship.

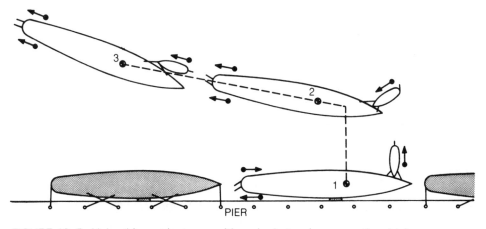

FIGURE 18–5. Unberthing a destroyer with a single tug (power on the ship).

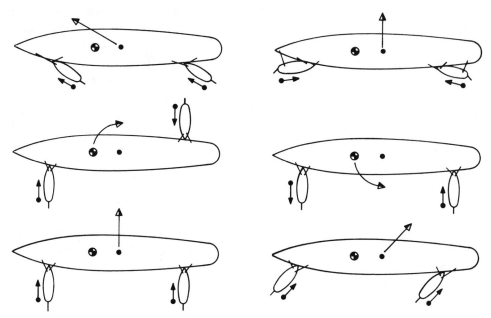

FIGURE 18–6. Movements possible with two tugs working on a dead ship.

Handling large ships with tugs

Two tugs, if properly placed and handled, can be used to maneuver a ship in any manner desired, but with large ships the power available from two tugs is often not enough to overcome the inertia and the forces of the wind and current. With such ships it is customary to use more tugs in order to insure sufficient power.

The principles of handling a large ship with tugs are, of course, the same as for handling a small one. Speeds are so low when tugs are being used that the ship must usually be considered dead in the water. Her bow is at the mercy of the wind, so our first precaution is to provide tug assistance forward. The tugs are usually placed in pairs, so our first two tugs should be spotted one on each bow.

If the ship is being handled dead (no engines or rudder), we must have tugs aft as well as forward. It is common practice to place one on each quarter (using the power tie-up) to replace the engines. By using the engines and rudders of these two tugs just as we would the engines and rudders of the ship, we overcome the lack of the ship's power.

During a move, the tugs are placed and shifted as the requirements of the moment demand. If a ship is being placed alongside a pier starboard-side-to, obviously the tugs on the starboard side must be cleared before the ship is alongside. This might call for quick action on the part of the tugs. If a ship must be taken from her berth, turned around in the channel, and snaked into another berth, any single tug might have to shift her position several times. With each new position and task, a new tie-up might be called for. The tug masters must be on their toes and alert for each new role.

When planning a complex move with a large ship, the pilot usually has a conference with his tug masters. Each phase of the move is examined and the part that each tug must play is explained. If each tug master understands his job, an intricate move can be executed with very few commands.

Though the tugs are frequently required to shift position during the moving of a large ship, it is worthwhile to have a standard arrangement for handling each type of ship. By studying a particular type ship and considering the tugs that might be made available for moving such a ship, a general purpose arrangement can be worked out which will meet most situations, and all other situations can be accommodated by modifying the standard arrangement.

Figure 18–7 shows the standard arrangement used at Puget Sound Naval Shipyard for moving heavy cruisers and transports. Note the tugs on the bow for all cases, and the use of the power tie-up for the tugs on the stern. A YTB is a large yard tug, and a YTL is a small yard tug.

Figure 18–8 is the arrangement for a large carrier. Because of the overhang characteristic of the stern of a carrier, it is difficult to place tugs alongside the quarters. The illustrated arrangement overcomes this difficulty by placing one tug athwartships across the stern and the other working fore and aft against her side.

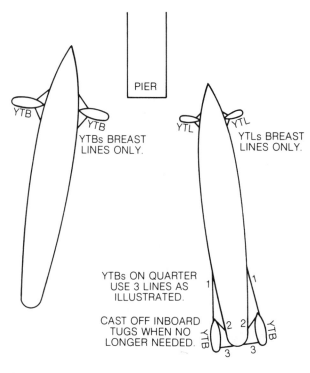

FIGURE 18–7. Tug arrangements for handling a cruiser or an APA.

An ATA is a large seagoing tug, and in this case the single ATA provides all of the fore-and-aft power when the forward tugs are in the breasting position.

In addition to assisting large ships in and out of their berths, tugs can be very useful when negotiating narrow, tortuous channels. If a large ship must make very sharp turns, a tug ahead with a towline to the bullnose can do much to make the job easy. By pulling the bow around in the turn, the normal turning radius of the ship can be considerably reduced. A second tug aft with a line from her bow to the ship's stern chock can augment the action of the tug ahead. Tugs can be used in this manner at speeds of over five knots, and this is especially useful in following a narrow channel with a swift current. The ship's engines provide the main driving power and the tugs add additional force to spin the ship in a tight turn.

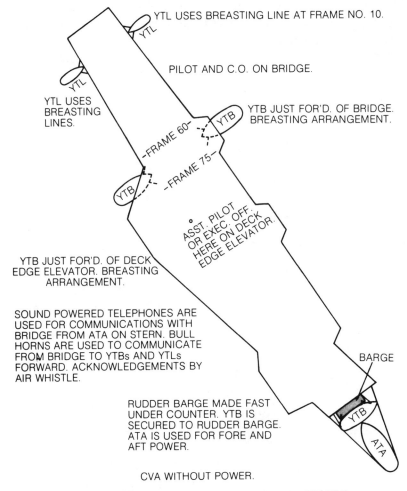

FIGURE 18–8. Tug arrangement for handling a carrier.

FIGURE 18–9. YTB tugs maneuver the carrier USS *John F. Kennedy* (CVA 67) alongside a dock at Norfolk, Virginia.

General

The main reason for the existence of both pilots and tugs is to assist ships in restricted waters. They are provided for the safety and convenience of the ships using the waterway, and it is a foolish shiphandler who does not utilize their services when they could assist him. There is no honor or prestige attached to steaming about a harbor without a pilot, and there is no disgrace in flying HOTEL at the yard. Though a shiphandler should learn a harbor after having entered and departed a few times, he should devote adequate time to studying the chart and discussing the area with a qualified pilot to insure that he has adequate knowledge. The only *valid* reason for not having a pilot on board is that the skipper is so familiar with the harbor that he is absolutely certain he can proceed along his route with safety.

If there is any doubt as to one's ability to maneuver the ship into her berth with safety and efficiency, tug assistance should be requested. The tugs are provided to assist larger ships as needed, and they serve no useful purpose lying alongside a wharf. If tug assistance would materially expedite an evolution or simplify a difficult situation, it should be requested.

As in all other phases of shiphandling, the "smart" shiphandler is the one who uses all of the tools at his disposal. Smartness connotes intelligence, and is measured by the safety and efficiency with which the ship is handled.

19
polar shiphandling

Basically, polar shiphandling (here meaning all shiphandling in the presence of ice, wherever it may be found) is no different from any other kind of shiphandling. Certain amplifications are necessary, however, to safeguard a ship from damage. Though maneuvers are performed at relatively slow speeds, situations change fast. Many things can and do happen during the course of a watch. All require an estimate of the situation and a course of action. But before we begin to deal with polar shiphandling techniques, let us first take a look at the environment which makes all this necessary.

The two general kinds of ice which are of interest to the shiphandler are the iceberg and pack ice. One, because of its concentrated mass, should be avoided. The other usually cannot be avoided by the ship because of its more common origin and far greater abundance. The ship must therefore negotiate it in order to reach her polar destination, selecting the weakest points and observing certain precautions to prevent damage to herself.

Practically everyone has read about icebergs, seen pictures of them, and knows that they are huge, fresh-water ice masses which float in the ocean. But to understand their origin completely we must go back to the Wisconsin Glacial Period—an epoch of low temperatures during which enormous ice sheets covered most of what are today the temperate zones. This so-called ice age had its apex about 100,000 years ago. So much water was scooped out of the sea and piled on shore in the form of ice that sea level the world over was lowered about 400 feet. Even today, if all the ice in the Arctic and Antarctic were suddenly to melt and run off, the water of the oceans would be raised about 130 feet.

Today most of the ice is heaped on the Antarctic continent and on Greenland. In those two regions ice still continues to perpetuate itself, though probably at a diminishing rate. Because of the plasticity of ice and the pull of gravity, the boundaries of the ice caps flow like great white rivers toward the sea. Sometimes, as in the Antarctic, the ice cap pushes itself for great distances out into the ocean. More frequently it sends tongues down valleys into the sea. Wave action and undercutting so weaken projecting sections that they break off from the parent and fall free. Currents then carry these broken-off ice masses, now known as icebergs, far out to sea until wave action and temperature changes eventually reduce them again to water.

Despite their dazzling beauty and excellent photographic possibilities, icebergs are not a mariner's delight. They are dangerous to an average ship and should be given a wide berth. As they are only slightly less dense than the surrounding water, the visible part is only a fraction of the whole. Approximately nine-tenths of the berg lies under water. Dangerous underwater spurs or rams also frequently project from this mass. Bergs, too, have been known to topple or to shift position as a result of change in their center of gravity.

Hence icebergs are best when viewed from a distance. Nevertheless their presence can on occasion be helpful. Because of the terrific amount of water they draw, for instance, they are apt to ground on any shoal spot. Therefore in an area where no hydrographic information is available, the bergs, if abundant, will mark the shoal spots, thus warning the navigator to steer well clear and avoid grounding himself. Another benefit hinges upon the destruction icebergs create. Because they travel at different rates than pack ice (due to being influenced more by subsurface currents than by wind), and sometimes even in a different direction, they literally chew and tear sea ice to pieces, plowing through it as if it were mere cake frosting. The leads and polynas (any nonlinear-shaped opening enclosed in ice) thus produced often come in handy for ships that must proceed through such areas.

To differentiate between the size of icebergs and their smaller derivatives, the following terms are customarily employed:

Berg   100 feet or more across
Bergy Bit   20 feet to 100 feet across—cottage size
Growler   6 feet to 20 feet across
Brash   less than 6 feet across

About 50,000 years ago sea ice covered the North Atlantic Ocean as far south as the latitude of Delaware. With the passing of the earth into an interglacial epoch, sea ice has retreated to the polar regions. There it circulates around the north and south geographic poles. In the Antarctic, the ice moves counterclockwise around the Antarctic continent, peeling off to the northward to join the circumpolar current. In the Arctic, on the other hand, the ice lies in the polar basin. There is but one principal avenue of escape—the East Greenland current. This is because Bering Straits are narrow and shallow; Robeson Channel, between Greenland and Ellesmere Island, is also very narrow. And the Gulf Stream holds the ice at bay between Spitzbergen and the coast of Norway.

In order to better understand the most important element that we will encounter with a ship in the Arctic (Figure 19–1), let us review the mechanics of sea ice formation and disintegration. Fresh water freezes at 32°F. This is not true of sea water because of its salt content. Thus sea water containing 35 parts salt to 1000 parts water does not begin to freeze until it has cooled to 28.6°F. Another deterrent to fast freezing is the effect of convection currents during the cooling process.

FIGURE 19–1. The channel left by an icebreaker.

These currents occur when the cold surface water sinks and is replaced by warmer subsurface water, equilibrium being attained theoretically when all of the water has been cooled to the temperature at which it is densest. Actually, however, surface cooling usually progresses so fast as to mostly overbalance this exchange.

In the sea the first sign of freezing is marked by an oily appearance. The next step is the formation of slush having a thick, syrupy consistency. As freezing continues, the slush separates into pancake forms. Finally the pancakes adhere to each other and form a continuous sheet. (Surrounding brine is entrapped when the foregoing occurs, numerous salt crystals being interspersed in the resulting ice. As ice ages, it begins to lose this salt content, three- or four-year-old ice being quite potable when melted.)

Sea ice, after rapid initial growth (3 to 4 inches in the first 24 hours), continues to develop until its insulating qualities offset the freezing of the water under it. Snow cover increases the insulating qualities. If unbroken through the second winter, then, sea ice may reach a thickness of 7 to 8 feet. In the Arctic Polar Basin three- or four-year-old ice may reach approximately 11 feet in thickness. However, most sea ice with which a ship will come into contact varies from

2 to 6 feet in thickness. "Rafting" (the piling up of blocks or floes forced over each other by pressure) accounts for the thickest concentrations that will usually be encountered.

Essentially there are no physical differences between "fast" ice and "pack" ice, each being composed of sea water which has been frozen. Fast ice, as its name suggests, is attached to land. It forms in sheltered bays, gulfs, and fiords, and, except during the summer months, it remains stationary and does not break up. Pack ice, on the other hand, is sea ice frozen in the open sea. It is continually in motion as the result of wind, tide, and current. In its motion pack ice opens and closes. In winter, lanes of open water soon freeze over with young ice, but in summer, except in very high latitudes, they remain open and allow opportunities for ship passage.

Disintegration occurs from melting and mechanical attrition—the sun, wave action, wind, and pressures all producing effects which cause the breakup and final disappearance of the ice. In the spring, as the sun appears above the horizon for increasing periods of time, the surface of the ice begins to thaw by direct solar radiation and by contact with warm air. In low humidity, most of the loss will pass into the atmosphere through evaporation, but if the relative humidity is higher, pools of water from the melted ice form on the surface. Such pools, being darker than ice, increase the heat absorbed. A further rise of temperature opens cracks which allow fresh water to run down to form a layer beneath the ice, an action that accelerates the rate of melting by reducing the heat normally lost to lower water layers. Warm currents may also contribute heat for melting. Wave action and wind help by providing a mechanical means of attrition which, once started, has a progressively increasing effect. Thus, rubbing action between adjacent floes breaks off small blocks and brash, which enables the sea to come into contact with still greater areas of ice. Also internal pressures, such as those produced by entrapped air and salt deposits, may further speed the disintegration process. In the final stages, ice is reduced to small, water-carved remnants which tinkle like small bells when struck by the steel hull of a ship, and in the end only the appearance of a thin scum marks complete dissolution.

Terms which describe sea ice concentrations and size are as follows:

A. Amount of Ice Covering Water*

Area	Oktas
Open Water	Less than 1
Very Open Pack	1 to 2
Open Pack	3 to 5
Close Pack	6
Very Close Pack	7
Compact Pack	8

*Coverage is measured by the term *Okta*—the ratio in eighths of the sea surface actually covered by ice to the total area of sea surface. For example, 4 oktas is 50 percent ice coverage.

B. Size of Ice

Small Ice Cake	Less than 6 feet across
Ice Cake	6 to 60 feet across
Small Floe	60 to 300 feet across
Medium Floe	300 to 1,500 feet across to 1 mile
Big Floe	1,500 feet across
Vast Floe	1 to 5 miles across
Giant Floe	Over 5 miles across

There are other important environmental elements which affect the ship in one way or other. A brief summary here may aid the shiphandler in becoming familiar with some of his forthcoming duties while his ship is in polar regions. Even though temperatures during some days of summer are mild so that personnel do not require additional clothing other than a standard foul weather jacket, more often greater warmth is needed. In the winter, when temperatures are considerably lower, the providing of sufficient protection from the weather for men stationed topside will ensure that they will perform at an accepted level of efficiency. The greatest deterrent to keeping warm is the wind. Actually, a man can feel much colder at 20° *above* zero Fahrenheit with 25 knots wind, than at 20° *below* zero Fahrenheit with no wind—the reason being that wind removes body heat as soon as it is manufactured. This is called *wind chill* (Figure 19–2). Low temperatures have their effect on materials, too, some of the resulting shipboard problems being freezing of electrolyte in storage batteries; loss of lubricating qualities with normal oils and greases; freezing of water left in firemain risers above main deck; coating of ship's rigging and decks with ice and snow. In each instance appropriate publications advise as to remedial or preventive action.

In the polar regions the ship's compasses will be affected by the weakening of directional and stabilizing forces. As a result, the magnetic compass (depending upon the proximity to the North Magnetic Pole, where the horizontal component of earth's lines of force is zero) becomes sluggish and unreliable. At the terrestrial poles, the conventional shipboard gyrocompass loses its effectiveness. Hence, beyond 70° North or South Latitude, a special correction table is necessary so that corrections can be applied to the latitude and speed adjustments on the gyrocompass.

Another disheartening feature of the Arctic, apart from ice and low temperatures, is its propensity for magnetic storms. The resulting conditions (radio blackouts) cause great difficulty in sending and receiving radio traffic, sometimes preventing it entirely. Radio Washington, however, broadcasts the schedule of such storms, so one knows when to expect them.

Ships in polar regions

Let us take a look at the ships themselves (Figure 19–3)—or, better yet, at the characteristics which have a direct bearing on operating capabilities in polar

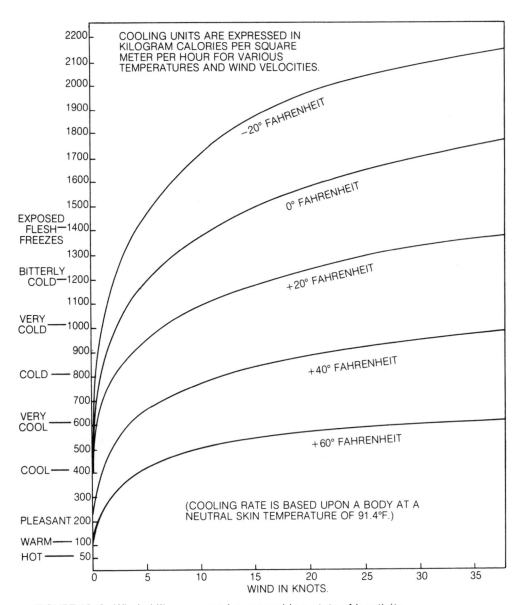

FIGURE 19–2. Wind chill on exposed personnel in a state of inactivity.

regions. Almost all types of ships have at one time or another been in either the Arctic or Antarctic. What we are really interested in is what makes one ship perform better in the ice environment than another. We will therefore list those characteristics which affect polar operating ability, and will show in what way they affect it.

Length. In the ice fields, a long ship has difficulty in negotiating the sharp turns of the ice-free channels and in following the cleared channels made by an icebreaker. Since the hull of the normal long ship is thin and relatively unbraced

FIGURE 19–3.   The 269-foot U. S. Coast Guard icebreaker *Burton Island* (WAGB 283) keeps a path open through McMurdo Sound.

amidships, it is not well designed to withstand the stresses of fending off the ice. When making a turn, a ship pivots about her pivot point, and her bow and stern are forced sideways into the ice alongside. A long ship swings her extremities farther to the side for a given turn, and can thus more readily be damaged from this cause.

Size. A large ship, with its greater mass, is usually more difficult to stop or to decelerate than a smaller ship. The sudden appearance of a floe ahead of such a ship may mean that damage would occur before she could slow down enough to take avoiding action.

Propellers. Protruding as they do outside the hull, propellers are very vulnerable to damage by the ice. Besides being poorly formed to resist damage from solid objects, the rotation of the propeller increases the force of any impact with the ice and insures the likelihood of damaging *all* of the blades when a piece of ice enters the propeller arc. The conventional propeller, constructed of bronze of relatively low tensile strength, can be deformed rather easily. Resulting dents and bends are quite troublesome because they cause an unbalance of the side forces (symptom—vibration) which can result in bearing failures and possible shaft misalignment. Cast steel propellers are much better for a ship operating in ice because their stronger blades can better resist the effect of impact with the ice. Before installing them in a ship, however, it must be determined that a "safety link" still exists—that is, they should not be so strong that when a very heavy piece of ice strikes a blade, the propeller shaft itself will be twisted off or the reduction gears themselves damaged. A single-screw ship offers much more protection to her single propeller than a twin-screw ship does to hers, because of its centerline location behind and below the bulk of the ship.

Power. Generally, the greater the power, the more ability the ship possesses in maneuvering to avoid ice. Tug-type ships which develop maximum power at low speeds have the advantage, as speed in the ice must necessarily be low. The ability to effect quick power changes is also important. Bursts of power used in conjunction with the rudder greatly assist in turning the ship.

Beam. A narrow ship offers less resistance to ice when moving directly ahead or astern than one of greater beam does, and such ships also are able to follow astern of wider ships with relative freedom from striking ice with the hull. A wide ship, on the other hand, gives more protection to her propellers by forcing the ice further to the side.

Hull cross-section. The ideal ship for polar operations has a hull of distinctive cross-section. The sides begin sloping inward immediately below the waterline and continue to the keel, giving the ship a nearly semicircular underwater cross-section. This lends itself to great structural strength and prevents the ice from exerting its full pressure normal to the ship's side. Since the greater bulk of the ice is below the surface of the water, ice-pack pressure on such an underwater shape will cause the ship to be forced up and out of the ice like a pea being squeezed from its pod. When heavy ice bears against such a ship, the ship tends to ride up on the ice and its weight operates to break the ice and relieve the pressure. Nansen's *Fram*, which successfully drifted across the Arctic Polar Basin, had this desired cross-sectional characteristic. Lieutenant DeLong's *Jeannette*, which was crushed in the ice off northern Siberia, did not.

Tumble home. The form of the above-water hull structure and the rigging is important in a ship which is to operate in heavy ice. Projections from the ship's side could catch on the jutting pieces of the pack ice in a heavy ice field and either be damaged or retard the ship. For this reason, icebreakers and other ships which normally operate in ice-infested waters are usually built with marked tumble home to insure that all projections at the ship's rail and above are well within the extreme beam in the vicinity of the waterline.

Rudder. The more rugged and the more deeply mounted the rudder, the less chance it has of becoming damaged or deranged. Since it is mandatory that a ship in the ice be able to steer at very low speeds, the rudder(s) should be mounted directly behind the propeller(s) to insure that the full force of the screw current can be brought to bear for steering.

Draft. As stated before, the deeper the draft, the more protection afforded the propellers from floating ice. Shallow-draft ships, however, may at times have advantages over deep-draft ships since they can cruise closer to the coastline, where the ice-free channels first appear.

Special modifications. Ordinarily the first step in modifying a ship for ice operations is to strengthen that part of the ship which will bear the brunt of the ice. This is the bow. Strengthening can be accomplished by installing timbers or metal longitudinals to brace the stem; by adding additional stanchions; by adding extra frames; and by welding on additional side plating (this should extend at least four to five feet above and below the waterline and should extend aft to the turn of the bow). The second step is to provide stronger propellers, as mentioned before. They should be of cast steel, stainless steel, high tensile strength bronze, or of similar composition. The third step is to strengthen the entire length of the hull, mainly by adding frame members and welding steel plating externally along the waterline to augment that of the bow section. Further steps may consist of installing screens over sea chests, building shelters for lookouts and conning personnel, piping of steam topside to use when ridding the ship of ice accumulations, and so forth.

Icebreakers

A well-designed icebreaker embodies all the good characteristics required for operations in ice-infested waters. Since 1966, the Coast Guard has operated all the nation's polar icebreakers. Presently there are three types, or classes, whose general characteristics are as follows (Figure 19–4):

Class	*Wind*	*Glacier*	*Polar*
Length	269 feet	310 feet	400 feet
Beam	64 feet	74 feet	83.5 feet
Draft (full load)	29 feet	29 feet	31 feet
Displacement	6515 tons	8450 tons	12,000 tons
Horsepower	10,000	21,000	18,000/60,000
Propulsion	Diesel-electric	Diesel-electric	Diesel-electric/gas turbine
Maximum speed	16 knots	17.5 knots	17 knots
Endurance	38,000 mi/10 kts	25,000 mi/12 kts	28,275 mi/12 kts
Helo platform	yes	yes	yes
Icebreaking Capability	3.2 feet con-tinuous	4 feet con-tinuous	6 feet con-tinuous
	11 foot ram	14.5 foot ram	21 foot ram
Built	1944-47	1955	1975/1976
Number in service	5*	1	2**

*Three *Wind*-class icebreakers will be decommissioned when the new *Polar* class becomes operational.
**Under construction.

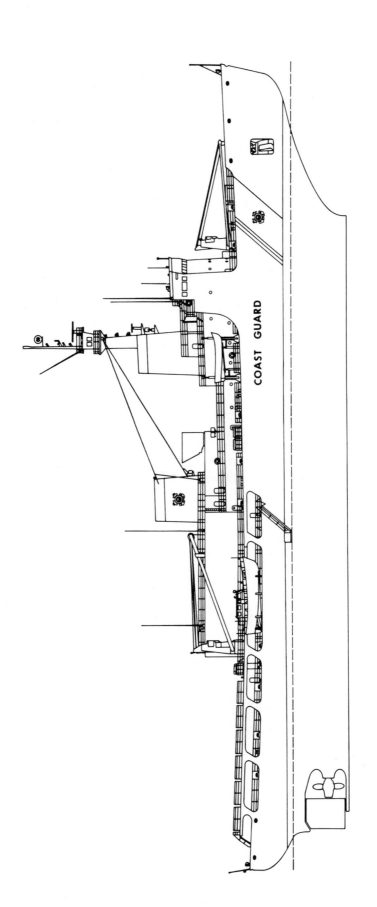

FIGURE 19–4. Side view of the new 400-foot *Polar*-class icebreaker, soon to be put into service.

All icebreakers have modified spoon bow with a sloping forefoot. When the ice is of sufficient strength and thickness to resist the forward horizontal crushing force of the ship, the inclined forefoot permits the ship to slide up on the edge of the ice a little way and thus exert a vertical force which tends to break pieces off the ice edge. The stern is roughly similar to the bow to facilitate breaking ice astern.

Occasionally the icebreaker wedges into the ice and is unable to move ahead or astern. In this situation, heeling the ship breaks the hull loose from the grip of the snow and ice and permits the ship to back clear for another try.

A "quick roll" automatic feature is provided in these ships to heel the ship from side to side. Using high-speed pumps, seawater ballast is shifted from one set of heeling tanks to the other set on the opposite side of the ship to induce the necessary heel. The transfer of this water ballast can be made in about one minute. Admiral Peary, not provided with this luxury, had his crew rush from one side of *Roosevelt* to the other in order to break her out of the ice (a practice known as "sallying ship").

Icebreakers are equipped with an electrically heated crow's nest which has glare-proof glass and room for the observer(s). In the ice, the conning officer operates from this position where he can control the ship's course and speed by a rudder angle indicator to the bridge and an engine telegraph direct to the engines. He also has sound-powered telephone communication with the bridge and the other control stations.

One feature which gives great speed and maneuvering flexibility to the icebreakers is the installation of engine *controllers* in three different locations on the bridge. These permit *direct* control of the propeller drive motors in speed and direction. When not in the ice, the conning officer usually controls his engines with normal engine order telegraphs, but in the ice this direct control is very desirable.

Modern icebreakers are equipped with a small flight deck, for helicopters. For scounting ahead, finding open leads, and reporting on the conditions to be encountered, these aircraft are invaluable. They can see much farther ahead than is ever possible from the ship alone, and they can explore a full day's run in a fraction of the time it will take the ship to cover it. In heavy ice, an observer in the helicopter can assist the icebreaker to find the best course and to take advantage of openings in the ice which would otherwise be undetected. With the help of the helicopter, the icebreaker need not dash blindly into promising leads, uncertain whether they will lead to open water or to a dead end.

How is icebreaking, or more properly "ice clearance," accomplished by the icebreaker?

It may be accomplished by one or all of the following means:

a. The weight of the ship exerts a downward bending moment on the edge of the ice, tending to break the ice off in chunks. This is made possible by the inclined forefoot of the bow below the waterline, and by the flare of the bow.
b. The shock of ramming (Figure 19–5) tends to crack and split the ice.
c. The shouldering or pushing action of the bow thrusts the small floes and debris to the side.

FIGURE 19–5. The Coast Guard icebreaker *Northwind* (WAGB 282) charges the ice pack, making a passage for the thin-hulled vessels which follow.

To break ice, the shiphandler has the following available to assist him:

a. Stern propellers.
b. Bow propellers (if installed). Bow propellers set up a suction current forward of the ship, which suction draws the water out from under the ice ahead, causing it to sag and be more easily broken by the bow. The discharge current produced by such a propeller is also helpful in clearing the ice debris from the ship's sides as she makes her way through the ice. If desired, the bow propeller can be reversed while the ship is still being driven ahead. This throws water over the ice ahead, clearing it of snow and removing the cushioning effect from this source. A bow propeller is naturally very susceptible to damage because of being mounted at the end of the ship normally used for breaking the ice, and its use is usually restricted to fiords, inland waterways, and lakes, where the ice is level and

homogeneous. No U.S. polar icebreakers have bow propellers.

c. Rudder.

d. Heeling system.

e. Capstans.

If the ship's power is insufficient to clear the ice, it may be necessary to resort to explosives. Often, however, the passive course of waiting for the forces of nature to do the job may be the best solution to the problem.

All U. S. icebreakers have diesel generators supplying power to each of their two main drive motors and are capable of differing main propulsion combinations. Utilizing a two-engine combination has the advantage of low fuel consumption, lessened possibility of damage when the propellers strike ice, and good opportunity for the ship's force to adjust and repair non-operating engines. Use of more engines has the advantage of greater icebreaking ability, better maneuverability, and more rapid completion of the given mission. Usually the two-engine combination is employed in the open sea, and more engines are used when icebreaking, towing, or in a close maneuvering situation such as going alongside a dock or another vessel.

By shifting seawater ballast from the after to the forward trimming tanks, or vice versa, the icebreaker's trim can be changed. When the ship is down by the head, the added weight forward has the effect of increasing its ability to break hard ice, e.g., as the bow rides up on the ice, the greater the weight, the greater the pressure on the ice. The disadvantages of being trimmed forward are that the ship does not answer her rudder as well, and the propellers and rudder are more vulnerable to damage from the ice.

As mentioned before, pilothouse engine control should always be employed when breaking ice, since the conning officer has the advantage of instant use of his engines. He can push the controllers ahead when he feels that the ship is slowing, or he can reverse engines for backing before the ship actually becomes deeply wedged into the ice. The engines can be quickly brought to bear when it is desirable to use them to assist the rudder in a turn.

How much ice can an icebreaker break? Icebreaker skippers are continually being asked this question. If they say three feet or twenty feet, either is correct, for icebreaking ability depends not so much on the thickness of the ice as upon other factors. A snow cover will cushion and dissipate the icebreaking effect. Solid or ten-tenths solid ice slows the icebreaker because it continually resists the ship's advance, besides allowing no opportunity for escape of ice displaced by the hull of the icebreaker herself. Ten-tenths slush can hold the ship back more than six-foot-thick ice of three-tenths concentration. If ice has water space into which it can be shoved, very thick ice can be broken. To elaborate further, young ice is more plastic than old ice. Annual antarctic ice is like a bed of feathers, compared to old arctic ice. Even the temperature has its effect, the hardness of ice increasing with decreasing temperatures. At 32°F, ice has a hardness of 2 on Moh's scale; this increases to 4 at 50 degrees below zero, and 6 at about 80 below. The hardness of mild steel plate is about 5½ and of glass about 6 on the same scale. To answer the question truthfully about how much ice an icebreaker can break, one should say, "It all depends." The answer must always be qualified.

The shortest distance between two points in the ice is seldom the most expedient for the icebreaker. The conning officer must often select leads and polynas which, although they do not lie along the desired base course, save time in the long run. If one has a choice between going through a gate or hopping a fence, he will naturally ascertain by which method he will conserve the most energy. The same is true when following leads. The choice between following a divergent lead or bulling through the ice by brute force often confronts the conning officer of an icebreaker (Figure 19–6).

Following leads at the expense of pushing through ice-bridges, however, can be carried too far. Unless the conning officer watches his compass closely, he may find that his ship is describing a circle or working away from the intended destination. Therefore, it is a good thumb rule not to follow leads which diverge more than forty-five degrees from the base course.

FIGURE 19–6. Where is the lead? The Coast Guard cutter *Northwind* anchors in a field of grounded ice.

Air reconnaissance is the best means of determining which leads to follow. Long-range aircraft give the over-all ice picture as well as the conditions in certain selected areas. Helicopters give the close-up picture. We should not hesitate to use the helicopters. The pilots like to fly and to contribute to the success of the mission, and the aircraft serve no useful purpose sitting on deck.

When considerable brash is present, an icebreaker can clear her wake by "fishtailing" or slanting the screw currents at an angle to the channel to plaster the loose ice to the sides of the channel. Reversing the engines and "fishtailing" violently is also effective, but, when doing this, care must be taken to ensure that the ship never actually gains sternway. When the engines are backing, no screw currents are going astern to disturb the ice once it has been shoved aside. Fishtailing also widens the cleared path by levering the bow and stern against the ice. If a heavy concentration comes in astern between the icebreaker and a following ship when in soft ice, the icebreaker can back down to disperse the concentration. Whenever paleocrystic (old) ice is present, however, this maneuver is not recommended as it may result in damaging the propellers.

When an icebreaker wedges herself in ice so securely that she cannot move by use of her engines alone, she must rely on heeling or automatic roll. As the ship begins to free herself as a result of the rolling motion, the engines should be backed FULL. As soon as momentum astern is gained, the engines are eased and the heeling discontinued. When about fifteen yards clear, the controllers are pushed ahead to low speed to clear out the ice debris in the ice "dock," or opening made by the icebreaker's battering. When the ice dock is once again clear, the breaker is in position and can make another ram.

Should the breaker become so fast in the ice that heeling and ice anchors cannot free her, explosives must be employed to relieve the pressure of the ice. To accomplish this, charges should be planted about thirty feet to leeward of the bow. The charges should parallel the keel from the bow back to about the bridge and just before the blast is touched off, the engine controllers should be pushed FULL AHEAD. We must of course be sure that all men are under cover and that the helicopters are away from the ship or securely hangared before touching off blasts.

Going north

To explore the shiphandling techniques required in the polar regions in a manner easier to understand, suppose we steam a hypothetical ship northward from an eastern U.S. port to the Arctic and allow the problems to present themselves in logical order. As situations develop, we will pause to observe procedures which should be employed. We will assume that our ship has been adequately prepared for cold weather operations, and that all necessary planning has been accomplished. We are sailing in July.

During the first few days we set speed at fifteen knots and maintain a course that will provide a safe margin for clearance of land and shoal areas. As the sea remains calm, visibility good, and nothing out of the ordinary occurs, we decide to spend this period instructing officers and crew about what to expect on the coming cruise. Accordingly, we break out all manuals on cold weather operations, have top personnel with previous cold weather experience conduct lectures, and show appropriate films on polar operations.

The *Oceanographic Atlas of the Polar Seas* (Part II-Arctic), a U.S. Naval Oceanographic Office publication (H.O. 705) gives colored illustrations depicting general ice conditions over the entire Arctic for each month of the year. In it we will note that ice spreads over a considerable area, and that maximum coverage exists during February and March. Beginning in March this ice area commences shrinking, reaching a minimum during August and September. We observe that the maximum growth of sea ice lags in the coldest period of the Arctic year, and that the least ice occurs quite a bit after the sun has reached its zenith during the Arctic summer. This lag accounts for the fact that the most favorable period for ship operations in the North is between 1 August and 15 October.

Areas in which heavy glaciation occurs, and where strong currents are prevalent, have heavy concentrations of bergs, particularly in shoal areas. These berg concentrations may prevent certain operations in these regions from the middle of September through October due to the absence of sea ice which hitherto had limited the effects of wind and sea current upon these berg concentrations. We should study the reports of previous expeditions and talk with experienced personnel who have operated ships in the areas into which we are going. There seems to be a general tendency to begin Arctic operations too early in the year, and to depart just when best operating conditions prevail. Commencing operations at a later date, particularly during bad ice years, will pay off in reducing the possibility of ice damage to the ships.

No two years are ever exactly the same with regard to ice conditions in the Arctic. Seemingly, there exists no plausible explanation for an especially bad ice year. Sometimes the winter ice has been very light and a break-up has actually commenced ahead of schedule, so that everything points to a good ice year for the summer months. But something happens. Somewhere along the line, either lack of bad storms (which break up ice), undue amounts of cloud cover (which shields the warming effect of the sun), sudden and unexpected drops in temperature, small variations in current, or something else, apparently unrelated, causes the disintegration process to be slowed or even halted. Today, more and more is being learned about this. Arctic weather stations and special ice observers on long-range aircraft pool information so that forecasts can be made and transmitted to ships. In the past, ships took their chances in the Arctic; today they are much better prepared.

Meanwhile, our ship is receiving daily ice broadcasts compiled by Fleet Weather Facility Suitland. Ice charts are also being produced on our facsimile equipment. A plot of this information on an overlay covering the applicable Arctic chart should provide an up-to-date presentation and a history of ice in the operating area, as well as pointing out ice trends to all conning personnel.

Ice broadcasts usually include:

a. The sea ice coverage expressed in oktas in relation to total sea area. Area limits are given by latitude and longitude coordinates.
b. Thickness of sea ice.
c. Presence of icebergs. The presence of bergs is usually reported by the words "many" or "few."
d. Forecasts. These consist of statements concerning the trend of ice conditons in general and specific areas. (Whether leads will improve because of an impending period of clear weather or will close because of unfavorable winds is of definite value. Long-range forecasts assist ships in seizing favorable opportunities for Arctic operations when time is a factor to be considered.)
e. Recommended routes for ship passage. Points along recommended routes are usually expressed by distances and bearings from navigational landmarks, distances and bearings from previously selected coordinates, or by latitude and longitude. Average direction and length also may be given. (Open water often exists adjacent to land because of early breakup of fast ice and the effect of offshore winds. In other areas the direction and flow of comparatively warm water currents may cause early breakup.)

On the fourth day the ship enters into marginal or subarctic waters and the lookouts begin to report the presence of bergs. The outside air temperature falls to forty-two degrees Fahrenheit, and the water injection temperature goes down to thirty-five. Various articles of cold weather clothing make their appearance above decks. Appetites improve. Hot coffee and soup are most popular with all hands. Cameras are taken out of lockers. Everyone is anxiously looking ahead to what the Arctic has to offer. Then fog closes in so that we can barely make out the outlines of our jackstaff. We set special fog lookouts and reduce speed to five knots.

The stationing of lookouts during periods of low visibility is of the utmost importance when the ship is navigating in waters where icebergs are present. One lookout should be stationed in the bow, in a post sheltered from the wind. This lookout may provide us with our first warning of impending danger close ahead, because bergs are notoriously poor radar targets. Recent tests have indicated an iceberg has a reflective coefficient of approximately 0.33 and will reflect radar waves 60 times *less* than a steel ship of equivalent physical cross-sectional area. Some ships make it a practice to station two bow lookouts, with instructions for one to watch ahead to starboard and the other ahead to port. Another lookout should be stationed in the crow's-nest in order to take advantage of layers in the fog or of a sudden clearing at mast height. Sometimes objects can be sighted from the crow's-nest when they are still obscured from sight at lower levels. Other lookouts, of course, are stationed on the wings of the bridge, as is normally done. All lookouts should be dressed warmly, should have ready communication with the bridge, should be instructed in detail about their duties and their importance, and should be relieved at intervals generally of no greater than thirty minutes duration.

Icebergs produce "pips" on the radar scope the same as land masses do. We should make sure that the bridge scope is set on the proper scale and that the "gain" is properly adjusted. All bergs lying in the forward quadrant should continually be plotted both in CIC and on the bridge. A plot will prevent confusion when the ship is proceeding through an area of heavy berg concentration.

A watch should also be put on sonar, if a ship is so equipped. Have the operator search the sector from ahead to thirty degrees on either bow, reporting any contacts immediately. If an iceberg is within range, a good solid echo will result. Sometimes growlers which are too low in the water to show on the radar can only be detected by sonar.

The fog clears. We secure the special fog lookouts and change ship's speed back to fifteen knots. We make sure to give each iceberg a wide berth, approaching no closer than 500 yards. As we proceed north, we notice that the sun remains above the horizon more and more each day so that now there is only a short period of twilight at midnight. The navigator relies more and more on crossing sun lines for his celestial fixes. Generally, radar provides us with an excellent presentation of the shoreline, but the charts are old and have been known to be of poor quality on past occasions. Because of this Loran, Omega, NavSat and other means of electronic navigation become more important. We see mirages frequently, and we begin to see the oddly distorted bergs that are common in the Arctic.

Finally our ship approaches the remnants of the pack ice, while ahead is a seemingly impassable barrier of ice. Speed is reduced and we proceed with caution. Closer, we begin to see the true picture. Instead of an apparently solid mass of ice, there are large areas of open water between the floes. This is the outer fringe of the pack—rotten ice and floes in the last stage of disintegration. We estimate the ice concentration to be about two oktas. Though a ship can operate unescorted in concentrations of two to three oktas or less, we lie to in accordance with our previous instructions. This is where we rendezvous with the other ships and the icebreakers.

The ice convoy

On arrival of the other ships, we take our place in column in the "ice convoy" (Figure 19–7) and begin Arctic shiphandling in earnest. Our job is to get our ship through to its destination in the far North without damage to the ship. The task, if correct shiphandling techniques are observed, will be interesting—and can be without mishap.

For an ice convoy, the column is the only practical formation. Icebreaker assistance is required to get a number of ships through an area containing two to eight oktas coverage under summer conditions, and, naturally, the ships must follow in the path of the icebreaker if they are to benefit by the path she opens. Also, in a column each ship benefits by the action of the ships ahead in keeping the lead open.

When only one icebreaker is available, she should be placed ahead of the leading ship of the column (Figure 19–7), but she should be free to range ahead as necessary to break tough sections of ice. Frequently a particularly thick ice

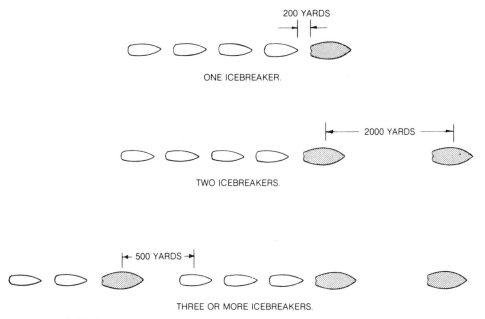

200 YARDS

ONE ICEBREAKER.

2000 YARDS

TWO ICEBREAKERS.

500 YARDS

THREE OR MORE ICEBREAKERS.

FIGURE 19–7. Organization of an ice convoy, using various icebreaker combinations.

bridge will require extra work by the icebreaker in order to clear a channel through it. At times it will be necessary to stop the convoy and wait while the icebreaker makes repeated charges at any unusually tough section.

For these reasons, the first ship in the column astern of the icebreaker should be designated as formation guide. She should follow in the wake of the icebreaker, but should maintain as steady a speed as possible. The icebreaker will normally have little trouble staying ahead of the formation, but she should not range out too far ahead when in the ice. A station two to three hundred yards ahead of the leading ship is ideal when in heavy ice. This short distance is required, because the ice, once cleared by the icebreaker's hull, has a tendency to slide back into its original position because of the pressure being exerted upon it by other ice.

When two or more icebreakers are available for the convoy, one should be stationed two or three thousand yards ahead of the convoy to reconnoiter the pack. In this position she is free to search out promising leads and to make trial penetrations without retarding the main convoy. If other icebreakers are available, they should be interspersed at intervals in the convoy column to widen leads and keep them clear of ice. In such positions they will be readily available to help ships when they get stuck in the ice, thus avoiding the necessity of sending an icebreaker back from the head of the column.

The most powerful and rugged escorted ship should lead the column astern of the icebreaker. This is necessary because there are frequent bends in the channel left by the icebreaker as she seeks out the most favorable path. These changes in the ice channel must be widened and straightened after the passage of the icebreaker to allow the passage of longer and wider ships. The largest and most powerful ship is the one for this task, because if she can negotiate the channel, any of the other ships should be able to pass with no trouble. A weak ship in the lead position might hold up the entire convoy by getting stuck in a turn that a stronger ship could have passed through.

Because of her position in the column, the leading escorted ship is an excellent ship for the convoy commander. She is the convoy guide and the first escorted ship to encounter each new problem. With variable ice conditions, however, the convoy commander may find that a station aboard the leading icebreaker will give him better control of the situation.

The icebreaker naturally assumes course guide. Course signals are unnecessary and impractical because the course is the clearly marked channel left by the icebreaker. The leads between floes often vary from a few degrees to ninety degrees from the base course. Numerous changes of course, both voluntary and involuntary, will be made by the icebreaker to take advantage of the weakest sections of the ice. The "shortest" distance between two points in the ice is seldom a straight line between them. Time can be gained by taking the clearest course, even though it does not lead directly toward our destination. The conning officer of the icebreaker should remember, however, that the other ships are "following the leader," and he should proceed as directly and with as few turns as the ice conditions allow.

After a day or two in the convoy, we begin to lose our initial fear of the ice. Although some of the other ships have lagged behind or strayed from the course, our ship has been on station all the time. When we hear that one of the ships has suffered hull damage and another has bent a screw, all of our old fears come rushing back.

We notice, however, that the ships that were damaged were the ones that have been the worst offenders in station keeping. They have often been out of column, and they have been slow in answering the signals. Maybe this damage can be avoided by alert, smart shiphandling.

The damage reports emphasize that we have already begun to learn certain of the fundamentals in this ice business. Perhaps we can begin to enumerate the lessons we have learned.

We should never strike the ice *at high speed*. Hard shocks can rupture the hull plating and distort frames and strength members. We must never strike the ice with any part of the ship except the *stem*; it is the strongest part of the ship. Experience has shown that a speed of two or three knots in heavy ice and four or five knots in light ice are best. These speeds insure the maneuverability required for a safe passage, and spurts of higher engine speeds can be employed momentarily when greater rudder forces are required.

Our ability to push through a tough stretch of ice is dependent on our *momentum*. Our momentum is the product of our mass and our speed, so we must keep up our speed. When pushing through the ice debris left by the breaker, it may be necessary to use a good deal more power to maintain a given speed than is normal in open water. Once headway is lost in pushing through brash, we may soon find ourselves stuck and calling for an icebreaker.

All conning officers must be throughly instructed on the danger of allowing chunks of ice to foul the propeller. Special precautions should be taken to prevent the propellers and rudders from striking hard cakes of ice. It is useful to station men, equipped with police whistles, on the wings of the bridge to warn the conning officer when ice approaches the propellers. If the situation warrants, these men may be given permission to actually operate the engine telegraphs to stop the shafts. If, because of the construction of the ship, the water in the vicinity of the propellers is not visible from the bridge, men should be stationed aft to warn of this danger. This is a situation calling for STOP SHAFTS. Even with no power on the shaft, the rotational momentum of the propeller as she idles is enough to cause damage when a piece of ice enters the propeller arc. STOP SHAFT should be ordered promptly as soon as it is seen that ice is going towards the propeller.

Danger to the propellers and rudder also exists when the ice tends to squeeze under the ship due to the pressure of a dense pack. When the ice concentration is eight oktas, broken ice presses tightly against the sides of a ship. Often, as ice becomes pinched by the forward motion of the ship, chunks of ice upend and present their longest dimension downwards. Such chunks are very dangerous to the screws and rudders. The lateral motion of the stern as the ship pivots in a turn may also throw the ship hard against the ice.

Conning officers should make every effort to keep the ship *in the middle of the path* left by the ship ahead. Sometimes one may be forced to maneuver to avoid heavy ice which has come back into the channel, but the ship should be brought quickly back to the center as soon as the obstruction has been passed. Variations of course for any reason make it more difficult for the ship astern. It is the path traced by a ship's stern which determines the cleared channel, and course variations tend to increase in amplitude from the van to the rear of the column. Tail-end ships may find themselves unable to negotiate turns as a result of these increasing course deviations.

We should conn the ship from the *highest practical position*. The higher one gets, the better perspective one obtains of the ice ahead. From a high conning station one can estimate the action the ice will have on the ship, and can take preventive measures as necessary.

We must *keep closed up*. Ice has a tendency to close in astern of the ship ahead. The closer a ship follows, the better chance it has of finding a free channel. In close ice, a ship should never be more than 300 yards from the ship ahead.

Experienced shiphandlers only should conn. The ice is no place to learn the fundamentals of shiphandling. On most ships the commanding officer and the executive officer spell each other, so that one of them is on the bridge at all times.

Breaking ships out

On our imaginary trip all has gone well for perhaps two hours. The ship ahead finally is slow in making a turn to follow the channel cut by the icebreaker, and she "hangs up" on the ice. We see that she is in trouble, back our engines promptly, and notify the ships astern of our action. Fortunately we did not wait for the report from the ship in trouble, because her conning officer was so engrossed in trying to push through the ice that he forgot to notify the other ships that he was stuck. But we can't stop indefinitely in the ice without getting stuck ourselves, and soon the wind drifts us down against the ice to leeward and we too are caught in the grip of the ice. One by one the other ships report that they also are stuck and request icebreaker assistance.

Soon one of the icebreakers comes charging back, crashing through the pack as if it were nothing. We admire the purposeful way she goes about her job. One by one she breaks the ships out of the ice, and soon the whole convoy is moving once again.

To best perform the task of breaking out a convoy of ships, a brief estimate of the situation is necessary. As the object is to get all of the ships under way, in the shortest possible time—and to do so without damage—a review of the factors involved is in order.

A first consideration is the number of icebreakers we have at our disposal. If only one icebreaker is working the convoy, the job is more difficult because the breaker must end up in a position ahead of the lead ship in time to handle the next tough section of ice. In this case the icebreaker normally goes all the way to the stern of the column and then works forward, breaking out the ships in succession until finally the whole column is free and the icebreaker is again in her proper position ahead.

A ship can be freed from the ice by opening a channel close to her on her leeward side, and then providing means for her to get into this channel (Figure 19–8). The wind will help carry the icebound ship into the cleared channel, since it is to leeward. A good system for the icebreaker to use when breaking out a column of ships is as follows:

a. Pass close to the lee side of the last ship in column on a converging course.
b. Cut in as close as practical to her bow, and, when dead ahead, swing parallel.
c. Have the stuck ship turn over her propeller for FULL SPEED AHEAD.
d. There will be a last cake of ice between the icebreaker's stern and the stuck ship's bow. Back down and crack this piece.
e. Kick ahead with plenty of power to get out of the way as the stuck ship begins to move.
f. Proceed ahead to as near the stern of the next vessel ahead as practical, turn out to leeward, and repeat the process. Continue the process until all ships are free and the icebreaker is once again in her place at the head of the formation.

When more than one icebreaker is available, one can be left to her job of breaking ice ahead of the column at reduced speed and the other can be utilized for breaking out ships in succession from van to rear. As soon as ships are broken out, they should quickly work up to speed to close up on the icebreaker working ahead. This tends to keep the convoy moving and may result in fewer ships becoming "restuck," especially if the convoy is a long one. On completion of the breaking-out operations, the icebreakers take their former

FIGURE 19–8. "Busting 'em loose"—*Northwind* breaks *Mt. Olympus* out of the pack ice.

positions in the column. The series of maneuvers used when breaking out a column from astern or from ahead is shown in Figure 19–9.

Normally a ship can extricate herself if the ice accumulation ahead of her bow is broken and cleared, but she may have diffiiculty returning to the convoy course if her stern is not free to move or if the wind is holding her hard against the ice. In such circumstances it becomes necessary to clear the ice away to leeward. This can be accomplished by the icebreaker coming up astern and paralleling the ship on her leeward side. Enough clearance should be allowed to prevent the ship from drifting down on the icebreaker. If this fails because the wind is blowing too hard, the icebreaker can tow the ship to a more favorable location. Several tries may be necessary before the convoy is clear and moving again.

But to get back to our imaginary convoy, our ship is back in position and we begin to think about turning in for a well-deserved nap, when suddenly the fog closes in and we can't even see the other ships. A signal is received to stop until the fog lifts. As no icebergs are closer than two miles, we take advantage of

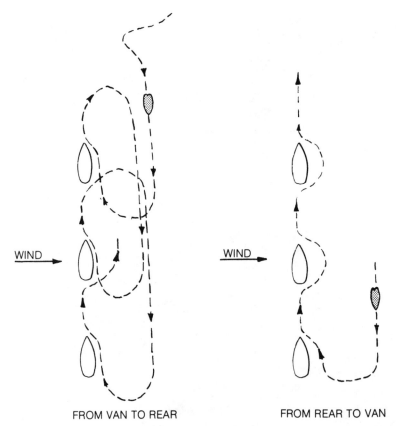

WIND →

WIND →

FROM VAN TO REAR

FROM REAR TO VAN

FIGURE 19–9. Breaking-out techniques.

this lull, and turn in for the much needed nap. Once we vaguely hear the OOD report that two ships are readjusting positions, but nothing else disturbs us. This is a moment of rest, not the harrowing experience of fog in a busy seaway.

After several delightful hours the fog lifts, and the convoy gets under way once more. The sea ice conditions improve so that the convoy speed is boosted to five knots. We begin to notice the natural characteristics of the ice pack which can aid the ship. For instance, we can estimate the distance our ship has travelled through the ice by taking ranges and bearings on the icebergs in the pack. We learn to notice the distinct white and dark splotches in the overcast. These are made by ice reflection or "ice blink"; open water makes a dark or "water" sky. If we head toward the highest dark spot in the sky, we will end up in the closest area of open water. The radar also works well for detecting open leads; open water is indicated by the absence of pips on the scope.

About this time, perhaps, the leading icebreaker launches its two helicopters for ice reconnaissance. One aircraft proceeds out ahead about 30 miles to scout the general area to be encountered while the other works at short range with the icebreaker to assist in locating favorable leads. By tuning in on the helicopter voice radio circuit, we can keep abreast of the information being passed to the mother breaker.

Now our ship is approaching the Arctic Circle and we prepare for the Crossing-the-Arctic-Circle ceremonies (similar to Crossing the Line except that Polaris Rex replaces Neptunus Rex, and the Court is composed of Arctic land and sea creatures). Bright sunlight around the clock which glints from the white ice and snow reminds us to have all personnel wear sunglasses topside. When one is "snowblind," his eyeballs feel on fire. All ships going to the Arctic should make sure that they have plenty of sunglasses for all hands.

Towing in the ice

The ship with the damaged propeller finally reports that she has wiped a shaft bearing and must stop. The whole convoy is halted while one of our guardian icebreakers goes back to take her in tow.

Towing in the ice is a very important evolution. In addition to the necessity of towing when a convoy ship has sustained damage to her propulsion or steering equipment (a common enough occurrence), towing may be advantageous under other conditions. When transit through an ice area is urgent, or in an area where the ice is very thick or very dense, towing may be the best method of getting a single ship through. An icebreaker can break through a heavy pack with a relatively large ship in tow.

The towing problem with an icebreaker is complicated by the necessity of keeping the tow close to the breaker's stern. If this were not done, the ice passage might close before the tow got through. All icebreakers are equipped with a towing engine.

When towing a ship by the conventional *short scope method*, it is best to use both anchor chains as a towing bridle in order to provide some weight to the short catenary. A scope of 50 to 100 yards can be maintained with use of the towing engine. With this method the towed ship's engines cannot be used steadily, because they would cause the towed ship to overrun the breaker. It is necessary to use the towed ship's rudder, however, to keep the towed ship in the icebreaker's path, and occasional kicks with the propeller may be necessary to obtain a sufficient twisting force. It may also occasionally be necessary to back the towed ship to keep from riding up on the icebreaker's stern, but usually the wash from the breaker's propeller is enough to hold the towed ship back.

In a convoy with only a single icebreaker, towing will have to be done by one of the convoy ships. While in the ice, all ships should be kept ready for towing and for being towed, for towing is frequently resorted to, and any time that can be saved means less chance of getting stuck.

With our broken-down companion safely in tow, the convoy once again proceeds. The leads are more open, no more ships get stuck, and our general progress is more rapid. At last we reach our destination. We enter the harbor, find our assigned berth, and commence off-loading our valuable cargo. In a few hours, however, we begin to become alarmed about the floes and growlers which are drifting down upon us.

Currents in a harbor will often carry bergy bits and floebergs down upon an anchored ship, and there is real danger that they may foul the anchor chain or damage the ship. If we cannot move away from them, we must find a means to move them away from us. The ship's boats can be used for this task.

No matter how large a bergy bit may be, it can always be rotated by a good shove with a boat. If we keep such a body rotated so that it doesn't engage either our chain or our hull, the current will eventually carry it away. When using the ship's boats for this purpose, the boat coxswains should be instructed not to ram the ice at high speed, as the sudden shock can cause boat damage or the capsizing of an unstable bergy bit which also could result in possible boat damage and/or injury to personnel. Contact should be made with bare headway and then the engine speed increased slowly. We must be very careful to keep the boat's propeller from being damaged by the ice (Figure 19-10).

Sometimes it is more convenient to move the ship than to move the berg. At times simple veering and heaving on the chain will avoid the ice, but at other times it will be necessary to employ the ship's engines and rudder to swing the ship clear. If persistently troubled with drifting ice, we should shift berth to a

FIGURE 19-10. Bergy bits like this must be pushed or towed away from moored ships.

safer anchorage. A few hours' observation will disclose the flow patterns of the ice and indicate the spots that are untroubled by this menace.

In some regions of the Arctic in the winter—and in most locations in the Antarctic in the winter and summer—off-loading of ships must be accomplished over sea ice platforms. In the Bay of Whales in the Antarctic, ships moor directly against the edge of the bay ice just as they normally would along the side of a pier or sea wall. The mooring lines are secured to the ice with sea anchors or by using buried timber (deadmen) as indicated in Figure 19–11. Deadmen are usually preferred because the timbers can be left in the ice upon departure and need not be dug up again. A method occasionally employed by icebreakers when mooring to the edge of the ice shelf is to force the ship into the ice until she is jammed securely from the bow back to about amidships. Ice anchors can then be set to keep the ship from sliding back out of its dock, as shown in the figure.

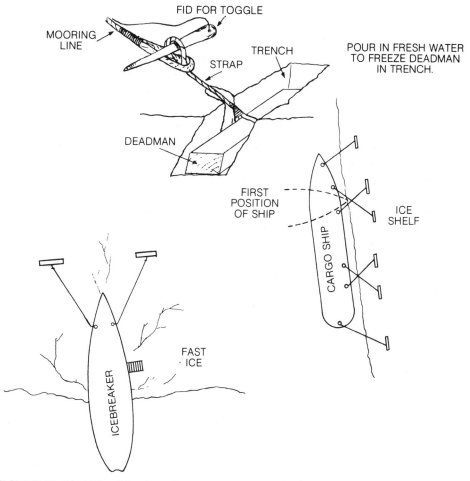

FIGURE 19–11. Using "deadmen" to moor to the ice shelf.

In the Arctic patience many times pays off better than anything else. Generally it is one's nature to want to get things finished as soon as possible. Consequently we use power and strong arm methods, trying to force our way through ice when sometimes just the opposite is needed. The power of modern ships gives us the impression of great ability. Remember that the wind and current can move more ice in a few hours than the most powerful icebreaker can penetrate in several days. Ice leads tend to open up during high tides and to close during low tides. Let nature work for us, not against us. We should study each situation thoroughly and then do it the easy way.

Conventional ships in the ice

Though icebreakers and specially reinforced polar ships are built to work in contact with even hard, multiyear ice, the ordinary unreinforced ship is not. Neither her skin nor her ribs are strong enough to take the shocks and pressures of ramming into a solid ice floe. Yet whether by plan or accident, many ships find themselves in the presence of ice and the conning officer must know how to handle the situation. The key to a safe passage is to stay out of contact with the ice, but often this is not easily done. Remember, though, new sea ice is soft and mushy, old ice is hard, and a piece of an iceberg is like solid concrete. Unless you are sure of the consistency, treat any ice as dangerous to your ship's hull.

If the ice is clearly scattered ice (4 oktas or less) it is usually safe to pick successive channels through the clear areas between the floes and proceed at a moderate speed. Such a transit is like following a narrow, tortuous channel and the conning officer will normally use rudder commands instead of giving courses to steer. He must be looking ahead constantly, picking his next opening before he runs out of the clear water in which he is steaming. This type of steaming is quite common in fjords or along the edges of the main ice pack and can be handled readily by an alert and careful conning officer. If ice is there, one can see it and the ship will be quite safe so long as she is in clear water.

When the ice is broken or close (greater than 4 oktas), it may be impossible to find enough clear water to completely avoid contact with the ice. The conning officer is then faced with the unattractive choices of waiting for the ice to clear, waiting for icebreaker assistance if that is available, or of attempting to proceed ahead making contact with the ice. If the ice is consolidating from wind or current, the ship may soon find herself completely closed in with the pressure of the floes building up on her sides. If more open water is in sight, it may well be the best decision to try to work the ship through the ice.

To accomplish movement of the ship through the ice, the conning officer should proceed slowly and deliberately. Normally a small floe of solid ice can be found which can be used as a "ram" or "fender" to push ice out from ahead and to clear a path for the hull of the ship. The ship's bow should be placed against the floe gently and when well seated, power should be applied slowly up to about AHEAD ONE-THIRD. With luck the ship can move ahead quite a distance before the ram floe cracks and passes down the ship's sides, after which it will be necessary to select another small floe. When maneuvering or twisting to contact the selected floe or to enter leads which develop, screw wash can be used effectively to clear brash and small floes away from the ship. A short bell will send a surge of water to move the ice away without getting appreciable way on the ship. Special care should be taken not to back the screws into ice floes near the stern. A normal bronze propeller is quickly damaged when in contact with hard ice. Further, when backing, ensure that the ship's rudder is amidships to lessen the possibility of damage.

The best solution with an unprotected hull is to stay completely clear of ice. Even a few inches of river ice in temperate climates have been known to dent sides and crack plates. The brash one sees at the edge of the pack may be debris from a berg or a multiyear floe and if so, it is dangerous to your ship's hull and screws.

20
mariners at work

Although we have explored shiphandling throughout the entire field of normal operations, our work would not be complete if we neglected to mention the little scraps of information and advice which make up the "folklore" of shiphandling. Most of these items would be supported by logic if they were traced to their source, but some of them clearly fall into the category of personal preference. They are the little rules that are picked up as one's experience broadens at sea, and they are the things that prevent one from repeating mistakes. They might be called the safety precautions of shiphandling.

In listing these shiphandling tips, no attempt has been made to record them in order of their importance, nor has any attempt been made to arrange them in groups. They are listed piecemeal for what they are worth.

KEEP YOUR SHIP'S STERN AWAY FROM DANGER. If the propellers and rudders become damaged, you are crippled. If the stern is free to maneuver, you can work your ship out of trouble.

DON'T TAKE A CHANCE. If you recognize it as a chance, it is probably too risky.

WHEN ORDERING RUDDER, LOOK IN THE DIRECTION YOU INTEND TO TURN. This is as good at sea as ashore.

CHECK TO MAKE SURE THAT THE RUDDER MOVED IN THE DIRECTION YOU ORDERED. Watch the helmsman move the wheel if you can see it. Check the Rudder Position Indicator to see what the rudder actually did. Check the compass for direction and rate of turn.

WHEN ORDERING RUDDER, TELL THE HELMSMAN YOUR INTENDED FINAL COURSE. You may be distracted during the turn, and the ship will continue to swing.

WHEN SWINGING TO A NEW COURSE, BRING THE RUDDER AMIDSHIPS A NUMBER OF DEGREES BEFORE REACHING THE NEW COURSE EQUAL TO ONE HALF THE RUDDER ANGLE BEING USED. When using 30° rudder, order the rudder amidships when you have 15° to go. This works remarkably well for coming smartly to a new course.

BEWARE OF A SHIP LYING TO. She is often moving imperceptibly.

DON'T TRUST YOUR SENSE OF DISTANCE IN A FLAT CALM. This sense is bad under any conditions, but it is at its worst across a glassy sea.

DON'T ATTEMPT PRECISE MANEUVERS WHEN GOING ASTERN. Ships handle awkwardly when going astern, and occasionally veer erratically.

GIVE BUOYS A WIDE BERTH. You can't see the cable to the buoy anchor from the surface. Many a screw has been damaged on a buoy which had been "cleared."

IF YOU ARE CONFUSED, CONSIDER THAT THE OTHER SHIPS IN THE FORMATION ARE, TOO. When the situation seems confused, a normal maneuver by another ship may catch you by surprise.

WHEN UNCERTAIN WHAT TO DO, COME TO FORMATION COURSE AND SPEED. This will give time to clarify the situation.

DURING A COMPLEX FORMATION MANEUVER, REMEMBER THE DIRECTION TOWARDS OPEN WATER. This is the avenue to safety; you may need it.

WHEN COLLISION IS IMMINENT AND A SAFE COURSE OF ACTION IS NOT APPARENT, BACK EMERGENCY AND TURN TOWARD THE DANGER. The backing will delay the collision and reduce the impact. The turn toward the danger will reduce the target presented, and the ship can withstand the impact better forward. A head-on collision crumples the bow; but the ship can be cut in two when hit from the beam.

NEVER TRUST A COMPASS OR A CHART. Keep checking the ship's heading by landmarks and auxiliary compass. A compass doesn't announce its departure when it goes out. And all charts have minor inaccuracies; some have major ones.

IF BLOWN AGAINST A SHIP OR DOCK WHEN GOING ALONGSIDE, STAY THERE UNTIL COMPLETE PREPARATIONS HAVE BEEN MADE TO GET CLEAR. The ship is normally quite safe resting there, but can do major damage trying tó pull clear without assistance.

NEVER TRUST A MOORING; CHECK IT. Anchor chains part, mooring shackles break, buoys break adrift, even bollards pull out of docks. Check the position regularly.

IN LOW VISIBILITY, KEEP THE RADAR TURNED FOR SHORT RANGE. The power setting and tuning of the main control console should be selected for best coverage of the band 0—5,000 yards. Though we can expand the presentation by changing the scale setting on the remote scope on the bridge, we can't get optimum results unless the main console is properly adjusted. Remember, it is the contact at short range that presents the danger!

WHEN SOUNDING FOG SIGNALS, SHORTEN THE INTERVAL ONCE EVERY FEW MINUTES. We may be synchronized with another ship and not hear her signal because of our own.

SOUND THE DANGER SIGNAL EARLY. This is legal, and it declares that you do not understand the other ship's intentions. It will prompt her to commit herself and thus clarify the situation.

A SHIP ON A STEADY BEARING IS ON A COLLISION COURSE. Take precise bearings on approaching ships, and check the trend.

TAKE AVOIDING ACTION EARLY. Signal your intention early by taking a positive action that is clearly visibie from the other ship.

AVOID PASSING STARBOARD-TO-STARBOARD CLOSE ABOARD. The other ship may evaluate the situation as being nearly head-on and cause a collision situation by altering her course for a port-to-port passing. It is safer to alter course to starboard at an early stage and pass port-to-port.

JOIN OTHER SHIPS BY COMING UP FROM ASTERN. Relative speeds will be less and the whole maneuver will be more comfortable for yourself and your formation mates.

THE FASTER THE SHIP IS MOVING THROUGH THE WATER, THE BETTER CONTROL YOU WILL HAVE. The rudder force and the hull stability depend on speed. Wind and current are little felt by a ship moving at a good speed.

WHEN ADJUSTING POSITION ALONGSIDE WITH THE LINES OVER, DON'T WAIT FOR THE SHIP TO BEGIN MOVING BEFORE STOPPING THE ENGINES. The time lags are too long for this.

STEER YOUR SHIP AS YOU WOULD STEER A BOAT. Look ahead and steer where good sense indicates. Orient to the real world of landmarks, channels, buoys, ships and obstructions. Keep your head up and your eyes open. Charts, maneuvering boards and compasses are aids, not substitutes. If the navigator's recommended course doesn't look right, stop your ship and "let her soak" until you are sure the the course you are taking corresponds both with the indications of the chart and the physical situation which you can see.

WHEN FOLLOWING A TORTUOUS CHANNEL OR THE MOVEMENTS OF ANOTHER SHIP, STEER WITH RUDDER ANGLES INSTEAD OF ORDERING SUCCESSIVE COURSES. You are fitting curves to curves and you must adjust as you move along the curved path.

WHEN ENTERING A NARROW CHANNEL, TRY TO ADJUST YOUR SHIP'S HEADING TO COM-PENSATE FOR THE CROSS WIND AND CROSS CURRENT BEFORE GETTING INTO THE NARROW PART.

WHEN REQUIRED TO MANEUVER BY THE RULES OF THE ROAD, TURN EARLY AND TURN PLENTY. Make your intention completely clear to the privileged vessel; you can refine your course later.

WHEN THE SHIP'S BOW GOES TO PORT, THE STERN GOES TO STARBOARD: MAKE SURE YOU HAVE ALLOWED ROOM FOR IT.

IN A TIGHT PLACE WHERE EVEN A SMALL MOVEMENT IN THE WRONG DIRECTION SPELLS TROUBLE, LEAVE A SPRING LINE SECURED TO CHECK A FAULTY MOVEMENT UNTIL THE SHIP IS ACTUALLY MOVING IN THE RIGHT DIRECTION.

IF YOUR SHIP LOSES POWER OR STEERING, NOTIFY ANY SHIPS IN THE VICINITY IM-MEDIATELY SO THEY CAN STAND CLEAR.

KEEP THE JACKSTAFF UP WHEN MANEUVERING IN PORT. IT IS A VALUABLE AID IN VERIFY-ING THE SHIP'S HEAD WITH RESPECT TO SHIPS AND LANDMARKS AND TO JUDGE THE RATE OF SWING OF THE BOW IN A TURN.

SHIPHANDLING APPLIED

The following pages describe thirty-five different shiphandling situations involving everything from minecraft to battleships—in all kinds of weather, tidal conditions, crowded anchorages, restricted channels, and tight berthing spaces. Do not be lulled into a sense of security by the fact that some of the ships mentioned here are no longer in existence. Adverse conditions of wind and current still exist, and the best shiphandler in the Fleet may suddenly find himself in a predicament he has never faced before, where only knowledge of how someone else got out of exactly that same predicament years before will help him save the day.

Example 1

Problem

USS *Thomas J. Gary* (DER 326) was moored stern to the quay at Admiralty Dock, Port Said, with a slightly modified Mediterranean moor. Because of the proximity of other ships, the anchors had been dropped nearly dead ahead, well out in the Suez Canal. As the ship prepared to depart, a 15-knot wind sprang up, blowing *Gary* down on the the other ships moored to the quay. A British submarine was next adjacent to leeward. The wind was too strong to allow the moor to be broken in the normal manner without the ship being set hard against the submarine lying only 5 yards to leeward. No tugs were available and departure could not be delayed until the wind subsided.

Solution (Figure 20–1)

Gary commenced heaving on her windward anchor as she eased her stern line. As soon as the stern began to come away from the quay, the engines were opposed; the starboard engine BACK TWO THIRDS and the port engine AHEAD ONE THIRD. This kept the stern upwind and maintained a steady strain on the chain while heaving short, thus keeping the bow away from the ships to leeward. As the stern line was eased, it was found that the stern actually walked to port (upwind). By the time the stern was abreast the conning tower of the submarine, 15 yards of clear water showed between the ships, and *Gary* was still working farther to windward. When the stern was abreast the sub's bow, the stern line was cast off, and the starboard engine was slowed to BACK ONE THIRD. With this combination the anchor was readily heaved to short stay and held thus for a moment. The engines were stopped and the ship swung to the wind, with the stern clearing the submarine and the other ships quite readily. The first anchor was then picked up and the ship was allowed to ride back with the wind while the second anchor chain was shifted to the wildcat. The ship rode well clear of the other moored ships, the second anchor was weighed easily, and *Gary* proceeded on her way.

Example 2

Problem

USS *Thomas J. Gary* (DER 326) and USS *Finch* (DER 328) were assigned to a single buoy in Hong Kong Harbor. Upon arriving at the assigned berth it was found that the berth was fouled by two wrecks and an improperly anchored Liberty ship, as

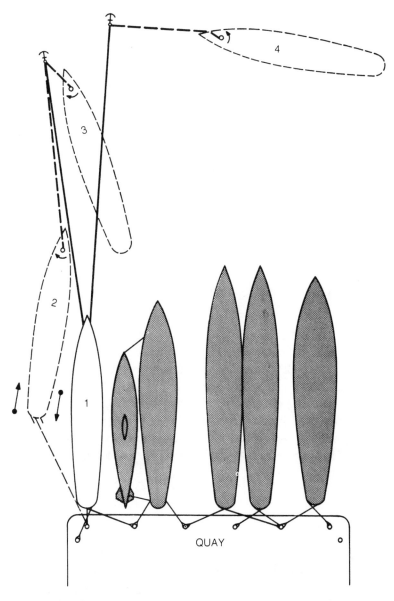

1. *GARY* MOORED STERN TO DOCK WITH ANCHORS NEARLY DEAD AHEAD WELL OUT IN THE CANAL.
2. HEAVING ON FIRST ANCHOR WHILE TWISTING STERN UPWIND WITH ENGINES.
3. FIRST ANCHOR AT SHORT STAY. SWINGING TO THE WIND.
4. APPROXIMATE POSITION WHILE HEAVING IN SECOND ANCHOR.

FIGURE 20–1. USS *Thomas J. Gary* clearing at Port Said.

indicated in the figure. Because of minesweeping operations going on at the time, berths were in short supply, and the American ships did not wish to complain to the British SOPA. How could they make a safe mooring in this berth?

Solution (Figure 20–2)

Gary snatched the buoy and kept it snubbed to the bow while *Finch* came alongside bow to stern. As soon as *Finch* had doubled up, *Gary* began veering chain and twisting her stern away from the closest wreck. She veered about 75 fathoms of chain, using more power on her backing engine than on her ahead engine in order to keep the chain taut. When sufficiently clear, *Finch* dropped her anchor and the moor was equalized between the bouy and *Finch's* anchor. This mooring proved snug and safe during several days of windy weather.

When the time came to break up this improvised moor, the above procedure was simply reversed. After weighing her anchor, *Finch* cleared by going out ahead around *Gary*'s stern.

Example 3

Problem

USS *Cogswell* (DD 651) was ordered to load ammunition at the Naval Ammunition Depot, Charleston, S.C., during daylight. The Ammunition Pier is located at a sharp bend in the Cooper River a few miles north of the Navy Yard, and the current conditions in the river are severe. At maximum ebb, the current runs at a full 5 knots, and at maximum flood it passes the Ammunition Pier at more than 2 knots. Because of other schedules the arrival had to be made at maximum flood, and the departure made while 3 knots of ebb tide was running. Tug and pilot assistance, normally provided, were not available.

Solution (Figure 20–3)

Cogswell approached upriver, with the flood current of 2 knots as indicated in the figure. As her bow passed over a carefully preselected point 120 yards (60 fathoms) abreast the pier, she dropped her port anchor. She swung to her anchor nicely, and working against her anchor, made a smooth controlled landing in spite of the current. As soon as her lines were doubled up, the anchor chain was slacked to the bottom to clear the channel.

On departure (the current now running at 3 knots downstream), the stern was walked away from the pier with the engines while the bow was controlled between the chain and number two line to the pier. As the ship moved broadside into the channel, she was held parallel to the current and in the desired fore-and-aft position by using the engines. As the bow came over the anchor, number two line was cast

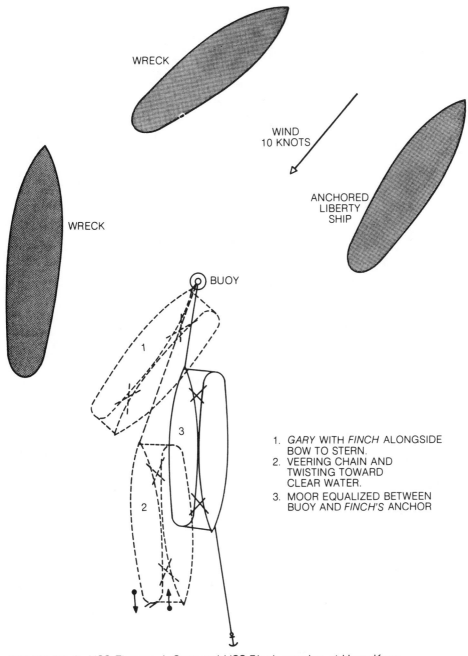

WRECK

WIND
10 KNOTS

ANCHORED
LIBERTY
SHIP

WRECK

BUOY

1

3

2

1. *GARY* WITH *FINCH* ALONGSIDE
   BOW TO STERN.
2. VEERING CHAIN AND
   TWISTING TOWARD
   CLEAR WATER.
3. MOOR EQUALIZED BETWEEN
   BUOY AND *FINCH'S* ANCHOR

FIGURE 20–2. USS *Thomas J. Gary* and USS *Finch* mooring at Hong Kong.

off, and the ship was held in place with her engines alone while the anchor was
weighed. Care had to be exercised during this part of the evolution to avoid any
athwartships strain on the anchor chain which might twist the ship cross-current.
Once the anchor was in sight, the ship could proceed downstream with ease from
her position well out in the channel.

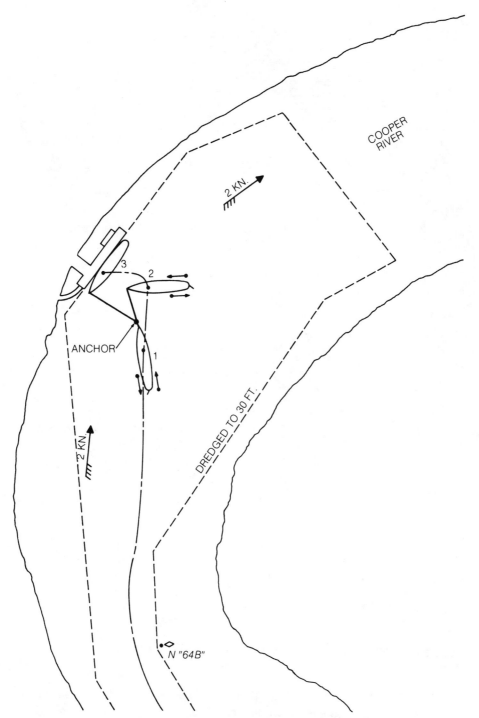

FIGURE 20–3. USS *Cogswell* going alongside at NAD, Charleston.

Example 4

Problem

USS *Cogswell* (DD 651) was moored outboard of USS *Eaton* (DDE 510) at Railway Wharf, Kingston, Jamaica. Just before the ships were to depart, a 30-knot wind sprang up from the starboard quarter, forcing *Cogswell* hard against *Eaton*. No tugs were available to assist. How could *Cogswell* clear without raking *Eaton*?

Solution (Figure 20–4)

Cogswell dipped her port anchor as a first precaution to eliminate any possible damage from this source. Next, she ran her "strong line" to the next pier to

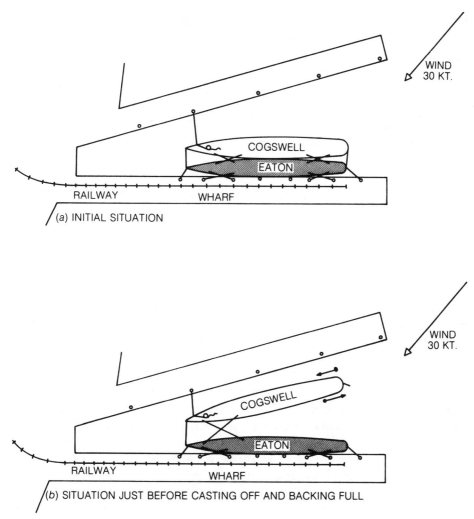

FIGURE 20–4. *Cogswell* clearing *Eaton* at Kingston, Jamaica.

windward and heaved her bow about 10 feet upwind with her capstan. Casting off the after lines, her stern was walked upwind by opposing the engines at TWO THIRDS. The forward lines were used for control as the stern slowly worked to windward.

When the stern was sufficiently upwind, all lines to *Eaton* were taken in and BACK FULL was ordered. Just as the ship began to move astern, the strong line to the windward pier was slacked and cast off (provision had been made to let the bitter end of this line run out in case the men on the pier were unable to cast it off). The ship backed clear beautifully, never closing *Eaton* appreciably.

Example 5

Problem

USS *Coral Sea* (CVA 43) was moored starboard-side-to the stone breakwater at Mers-el-Kebir (the Naval Harbor), Oran, Algeria. At the time set to get under way, a 23-knot wind was blowing steadily against the port bow, setting the ship hard against the camels on the face of the breakwater. The harbor entrance was about 700 yards astern, as shown in the figure, but it was desired to turn the ship inside the harbor and proceed to sea going ahead rather than to back through the entrance. A sunken battleship 300 yards ahead prevented maneuvering in that area, so it was decided to turn the ship in the clear area abeam to port. Two French tugs and a pilot were provided, but when the pilot attempted to breast out the ship directly, using one tug on the bow and one on the stern, the pressure of the wind held the big ship solidly against the face of the breakwater. How could the ship get clear and turn?

Solution (Figure 20–5)

Both tugs were put on the bow. The stern was moved out by opposing the ship's engines at ONE THIRD and pivoting the ship against the forward camel. When the ship reached an angle of about 10° with respect to the breakwater, all engines were backed FULL with the rudders LEFT 30°, and the tugs were directed to pull straight out at maximum power. The ship came away from the breakwater nicely, with the stern moving rapidly into the wind. The pull of the tugs, assisted by the wash of the backing screws along the solid face of the breakwater, held the bow clear of the breakwater as she backed into the wind. As soon as clearance forward permitted, the port engines were worked ahead and the rudders shifted to RIGHT 30° to increase the rate of turn, but care was taken to insure that the ship did not move toward the breakwater.

When the ship had finally been worked perpendicular to the breakwater, the tugs were cast off and the turn completed with the engines and rudders alone. By using more ahead power than back power during the last part of the turn, sufficient headway was achieved to insure good rudder control for passing through the harbor entrance.

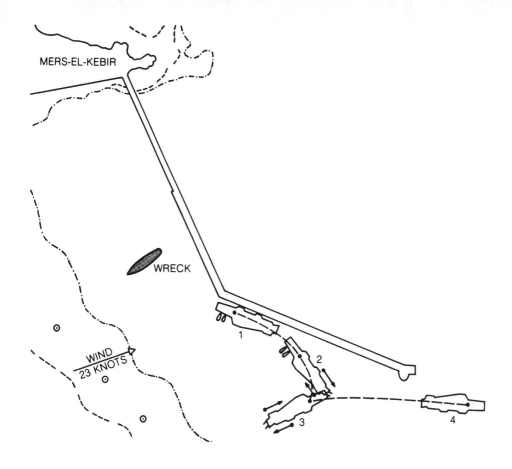

MERS-EL-KEBIR

WRECK

WIND
23 KNOTS

1

2

3

4

FIGURE 20–5. USS *Coral Sea* clearing at Mers-el-Kebir, Algeria.

Example 6

Problem

USS *Princeton* (CVA 37) was moored port-side-to the pier at Alameda, California, heading out into the channel. At the time set for getting under way, a 10-knot wind was setting the ship against the pier, but the pilot with two tugs at his disposal, thought he could handle the job.

Solution (Figure 20–6)

The pilot placed the tugs as indicated in the figure, and when the ship had been breasted only about a yard clear of the face of the pier, he ordered ALL AHEAD ONE THIRD. As the ship commenced to move forward, the tugs trailed aft and were unable to supply as great an athwartships force as previously because of their inclination. With the breasting force thus reduced, the wind carried the ship down against the pier and she scraped against the end of the pier for about one-third of her length. Fortunately, little damage was done.

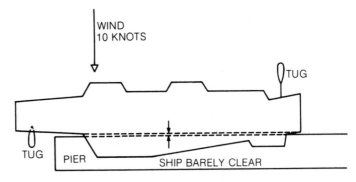

(a) SITUATION AS ENGINES ORDERED AHEAD ONE THIRD.

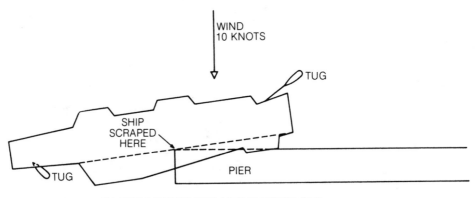

(b) SHIP AGAINST PIER AS SHE MOVED OUT.

FIGURE 20–6. USS *Princeton* clearing pier at Alameda, California.

Criticism

With tug power barely sufficient to move the ship from the face of the pier, the pilot should have waited until he had a much greater margin between the ship and the pier, and then he should have moved the ship ahead very slowly in order to avoid the loss of his breasting force as the tugs trailed aft. Additional tugs or the use of "Pinwheel" would have insured a safe operation.

Example 7

Problem

USS *Pluck* (MSO 464) needed to go to Berth 62, Pier 6, U. S. Naval Station, Long Beach, to exchange her magnetic minesweeping cable. This involved placing the stern against the quay wall at the head of the pier in what is a fairly tight berth. While many MSOs normally used tugs to make a dead plant move to this berth, it was felt that this berth could be easily made and left unassisted despite prevailing winds of 10–18 knots across the slip which tended to set the ship hard on the pier. Two factors complicating the situation were (1) a large ARD moored in the adjacent berth (64) which left a working area of about 250 feet for the 170-foot MSO, and (2) a cluster (10–12) of camels moored immediately adjacent (80 feet) to berth 62 with shoal rocks reportedly directly beneath. Backing into the berth with the twin screw/rudder, variable pitch versatility of the MSO was no particular problem, but clearing the berth with the camels and shoal water on the starboard quarter and without the ability to go astern posed a bit of a problem.

Solution (Figure 20–7)

The ship was twisted at the mouth of the slip (on another occasion twist was accomplished in the slip) and backed to position #3 using engines opposed (position #2) where necessary to alter ship's head. At position #3 the starboard anchor was let go and the chain veered as the ship backed into the berth; engines opposed and anchor were used to keep the ship from being set hard on the pier by the wind (position #4). When ready to clear the berth the ship was breasted out by twisting the stern gently to starboard while heaving around on the anchor (position #4). When the bow was clear of the ARD ahead the anchor was recovered and the ship headed fair out of the slip.

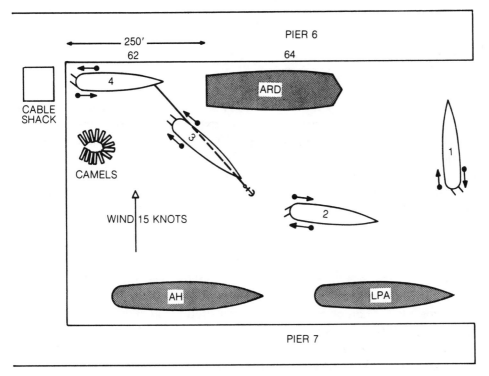

FIGURE 20–7. *Pluck* uses her anchor to make and clear a tight berth.

Example 8

Problem

USS LST 859 was required to go inside the harbor at Canton Island to unload cargo alongside the pier. The entrance channel is about 150 feet wide, the turning basin is small, and beyond the turning basin are dangerous coral heads. A strong current flows through the channel at all times except at high water and low water slacks (which last only about twenty minutes), and it was undesirable to wait for slack water. The tide was flooding through the entrance and a wind of 15 knots was blowing from the east. How could the ship enter the harbor and go alongside the dock without being swept into the coral heads?

Solution (Figure 20–8)

The initial intention was simply to enter and go alongside port-side-to, without turning. Once in the channel, however, the current was found to be so strong that the ship was swept past the pier and into the center of the turning basin in spite of her engines. To keep from being swept into the coral heads, the anchor was dropped and the ship spun rapidly to her anchor. Once heading into the current, the anchor was heaved in, and a starboard-side-to landing made at the pier with no trouble. To hold the bow against the wind, the anchor was dragged at short stay during the last part of the approach.

Example 9

Problem

In a small undeveloped port in Korea, LSTs bringing in supplies are confronted with a difficult shiphandling problem. The harbor is exposed to the prevailing wind and the ships must unload through their bow doors onto a sea wall which is nearly parallel to the wind. The busy little harbor is usually congested with numerous barges and small craft, and, in the winter, the wind may have a velocity as high as 25 knots. How can an LST be handled to moor crosswind under a typical situation as depicted in the figure?

Solution (Figure 20–9)

As the LST approaches the harbor, both her LCVPs are lowered to act as tugs. The approach up the channel is made at 6 knots to insure good control, and, as the ship turns into the harbor, the stern anchor is dropped in mid-channel about 700 feet from the intended berth. As the ship moves into the restricted part of the harbor, the two LCVPs are placed on the port bow to push the bow to starboard. As the ship comes abreast the sea wall, she is inclined to the wind by a combination of the engines, rudders, and the boats working on the port bow. As soon as

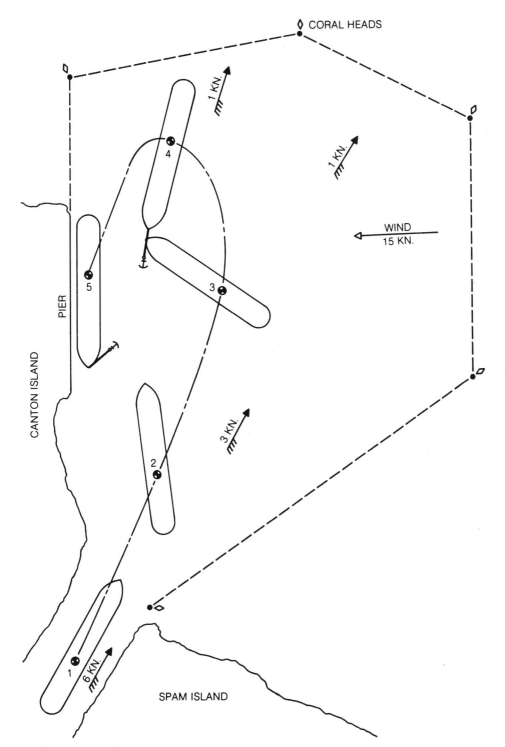

FIGURE 20–8. LST 859 recovers at Canton Island.

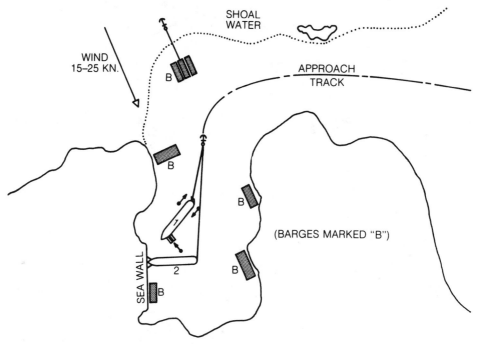

FIGURE 20–9. Tight situation in Korea.

possible, the starboard bow line is passed to the sea wall, and the bow is worked gently in to the sea wall by the combination of the bow line and the boats. Once the bow has been secured, the ship can be brought perpendicular to the sea wall by adjusting the stern anchor cable.

In clearing, the reverse of the above procedure is used, with the addition of using the bow anchor to help hold the bow from being swept to leeward after the bow lines are cast off. If control is lost when getting clear, the wind will carry the bow down on the lee shore, so care must be taken to insure that every shiphandling aid is ready for use. When the stern anchor has been picked up, the ship can back into the wind to the edge of the shoal water to insure sufficient room to square away on her departure course.

Example 10

Problem

During World War II an LST was stuck on "Brown" beach, Nakagasuku Wan (later Buckner Bay), Okinawa, and could not retract. She was enveloped in a cloud of diesel smoke for a long time as she tried every trick in the book to get free. Several tugs had been used singly and in combination to try to get her off, but she wouldn't budge. How to get her off?

Solution (Figure 20–10)

After having taken careful soundings to insure there was sufficient water alongside the LST, two LSMs were backed in alongside, as indicated in the accompanying figure. The stern anchor wires of the LSMs were secured to the forward bitts on the LST, and the ships were securely married with mooring lines as indicated. The stern anchor of the LST had already been recovered.

When all was ready, the engines of all three ships were applied to the task of getting the LST free. By alternately reversing the LSMs, a strong twisting motion could be applied, and when all engines were working together, a very strong force was applied to pulling the LST off the beach. After a moderate amount of effort, the balky LST was pulled free.

Example 11

Problem

USS *Carpellotti* (APD 136) was frequently required to berth between two other APDs at the finger piers, Naval Amphibious Base, Little Creek, Virginia. The usual procedure for the three ships was for the first ship to go alongside the windward pier, the second ship to moor to the leeward pier, and the third ship, usually

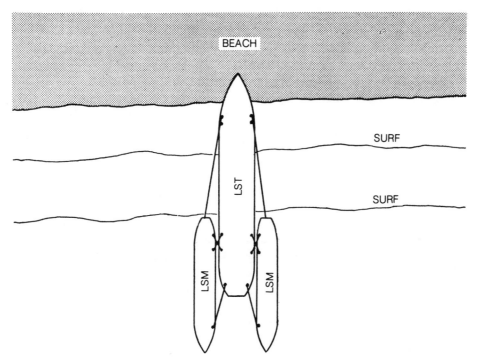

FIGURE 20–10. Retracting an LST at Buckner Bay.

Carpellotti, to slide in between the two and moor to the ship alongside the windward pier. The space remaining after the first two ships were alongside was only about a ship width and a half, and *Carpellotti* often had to "thread the needle" with a strong crosswind. How could she make her berth without raking one or both of the other ships? Her cross wind angle, even for a fast approach, would be so large that she could not fit into the remaining space.

Solution (Figure 20–11)

Having passed the cable crossing and arrived at a position with her bow in line with the slot, the windward anchor was dropped and snubbed at short stay. The remainder of the approach was made working against this anchor at relatively high power and dragging the anchor as the ship moved into her berth. This moved the pivot point forward near the bow and allowed a controlled approach to be made into the tight berth. The restraint at the bow, coupled with the much higher side forces from the rudders and propellers allowable with this method, easily countered the side force from the wind, and the ship could move into her berth on a heading nearly parallel to that of the other two ships.

Example 12

Problem

USS *Edsall* (DE 129), alongside a pier at Miami, Florida, on a windy day had to get under way and proceed to sea through the main ship channel astern. A brisk breeze was blowing from astern, and the situation was complicated by a slight current from the Inland Waterway which cut across the small turning basin. The tendency of a destroyer escort to back into the wind, and the difficulty of twisting such a ship in the confines of the basin, had just been demonstrated by a sister ship. After much unsuccessful backing and filling, this ship had ended up against the end of one of the piers, still not turned around, and with a damaged side to show for her efforts.

Solution (Figure 20–12)

Edsall backed into the wind until clear of the piers and then started a turn to her port—the direction the current tended to carry her stern. When she neared the opposite extremity of the basin, her engines were kicked AHEAD with the rudders RIGHT FULL, and, as the ship commenced to move ahead, the starboard anchor was let go and snubbed underfoot. As soon as her stern was sufficiently across the wind, her engines were stopped, and the wind and the current carried the ship completely around until she was headed fair for the main ship channel. Once squared away, the anchor was weighed and the ship proceeded to sea.

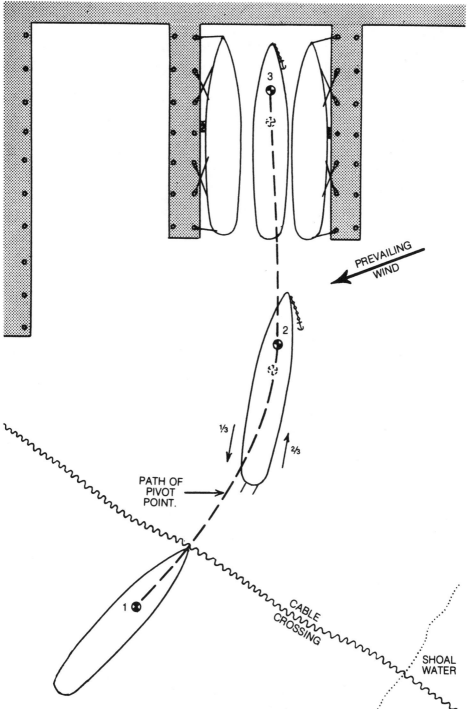

FIGURE 20–11. *Carpellotti* makes a tight berth at Little Creek.

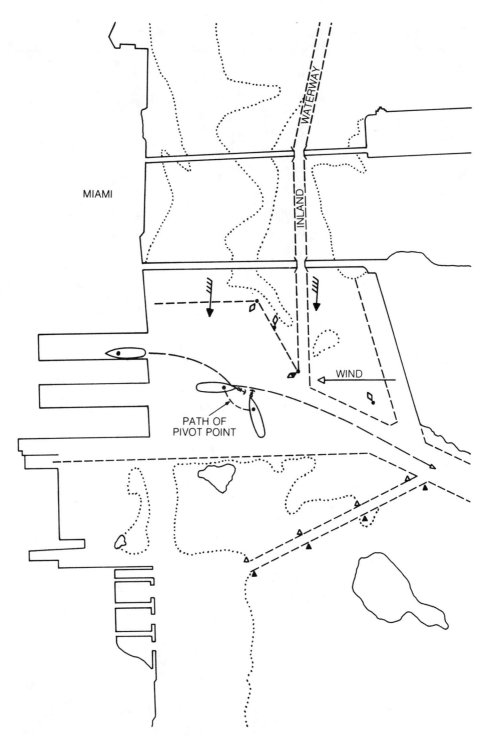

FIGURE 20–12. Working a DE out of harbor against wind and current.

Example 13

Problem

A division of DDEs, returning from operations off the coast of Korea, upon arrival at Yokosuka was ordered alongside the destroyer tender. A strong wind was blowing and the tender lay with her stern so close to a point of land that there was scarcely a boat passage between her stern and the adjacent sea wall. The first ships had backed in alongside the tender, but the operation had been awkward, hazardous, and time consuming. How could USS *Taylor* (DDE 468), the last ship to go alongside, make her landing more efficiently and with less hazard?

Solution (Figure 20–13)

As the ship next ahead of her was backing in alongside, *Taylor* made a broad sweep and came up nearly abreast the nest, heading into the wind. As the other ship was getting her lines over, *Taylor* was inclined to the wind and "controlled" in, half sailing and half twisting, as indicated in the figure. When the other ship was ready to receive her, she moved in alongside under complete control, never having been exposed to the awkwardness and hazard of a sternward approach.

Example 14

Problem

The destroyer USS *Taylor* (DDE 468), was in a narrow slip congested with other craft, and had to be moved across the basin from the submarine base at Pearl Harbor to the Naval Shipyard where she was to be squeezed through a narrow opening near the head of a slip and then worked broadside into a berth. There was not room at either slip for a tug to swing perpendicular to the ship and push against her side. The move called for moving broadside as well as fore-and-aft, and the margin allowable for error was only a few feet. How to handle a dead ship under such conditions?

Solution (Figure 20–14)

The pilot placed two tugs on the port side of the ship, one at the bow, the other at the stern, heading in opposite directions with their sterns towards the ends of the ship. The tugs secured firmly with the "power tie-up" parallel to the ship and snubbed in so nicely under the flare of the bow and against the quarter that the three ships were scarcely wider than the destroyer alone. With this arrangement the pilot could produce motion in any direction he desired without requiring either tug to shift its position.

    With the rudder of the lead tug amidships, and steering with the trailing tug, the pilot snaked the ship out of its narrow berth, across the channel, and into the

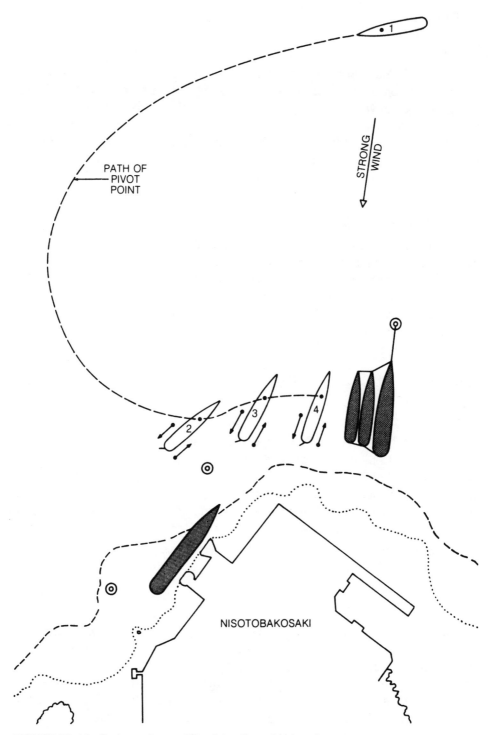

PATH OF
PIVOT
POINT

STRONG
WIND

NISOTOBAKOSAKI

FIGURE 20–13. *Taylor* makes a difficult landing at Yokosuka.

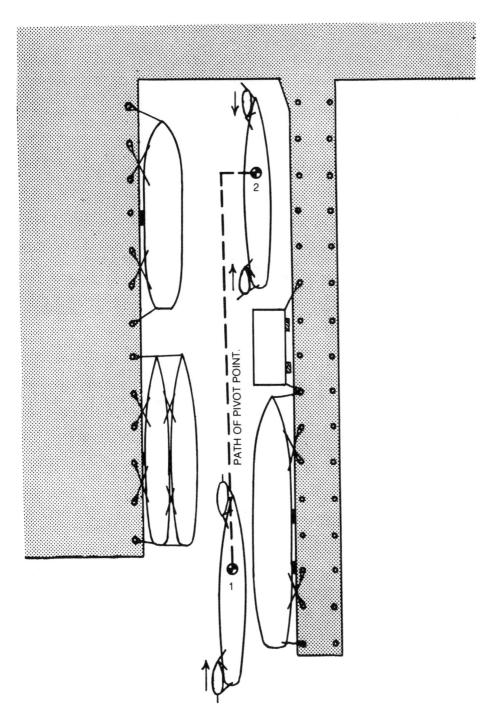

FIGURE 20–14. Broadside berthing with a dead ship.

slip on the opposite side. She skinned through the restrictions without a hitch, but the most interesting part of the move occurred as the ship was brought opposite its new berth. The pilot ordered both tugs to drive ahead with their rudders full outboard, as seen from Taylor. The forward components of the tugs' propeller thrusts cancelled, but the sidewise component, controlled by the rudders, breasted the ship into her berth perfectly.

Example 15

Problem

The amphibious group had arrived in the transport area for the landing exercise and each ship was anchored in its assigned berth, but a 30-knot wind, gusting to 50 knots, threatened to upset the entire operation. Though the boats could manage the choppy sea when clear of the ships, it was nearly impossible to load them alongside. How could the ships provide a lee so the off-loading could continue?

Solution (Figure 20–15)

USS *Sarasota* (APA 204), riding to 60 fathoms of chain to the port anchor in the 8 fathoms of water, kicked AHEAD into the wind at ONE THIRD until the chain tended directly astern. Throwing the bow to port with FULL LEFT RUDDER, the engine was slowed to about 2 knots, and as the ship continued to work against the chain, the wind on the starboard bow carried the ship downwind. This movement carried the ship across the anchor chain, and a state of equilibrium was finally reached with

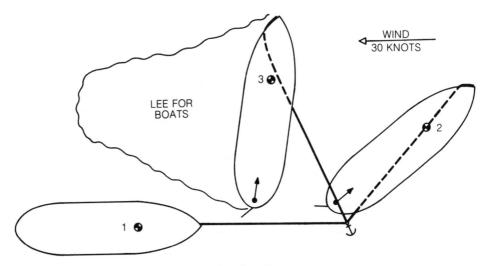

FIGURE 20–15. *Sarasota* makes a lee for offloading.

the chain tending under the ship at Frame 30. The chain under the keel provided the equivalent of a fulcrum against which the ship could be levered with her engine and rudder. By this method the ship could be held steadily at a constant angle across the wind, with no yawing. This maneuver provided an excellent lee for loading the boats, and the ship's operations went off on schedule. It was interesting to note that as a result of eliminating the yawing, the anchor never budged, though several other ships were dragging alarmingly.

Example 16

Problem

Ships mooring to the piers at the Minecraft Base, Charleston, South Carolina, are required to moor bow downstream. On a full ebb tide the current sweeping down past the ends of these piers may be as fast as 6 knots, so a conventional landing, moving with the current, adds the ship's way to the velocity of the current and results in a dangerously fast landing.

At full ebb USS *Towhee* (AM 388) was standing up the Ashley River to moor to Pier B at the Minecraft Base. There was a breeze of 10 knots blowing from across the river. How to make this tough job easy?

Solution (Figure 20–16)

Selecting the last suitable turning basin before arriving at the Base, *Towhee* headed into the wind and made her turn in the mouth of Wappoo Creek. She then commenced backing upstream to her berth. When the ship had built up to about 6 knots sternway through the water (1 knot over the ground), she began moving upstream, and except for carrying a little rudder to compensate for the wind, she answered her helm satisfactorily. She was backed upstream to a point about 100 feet abreast her berth and held there with her engines while her lines were sent over. When all lines were set, she was worked in slowly toward the pier, and finally, when nearly against the pier, her engines were slowed and the strain was taken by the lines. This method of making the landing allowed a controlled evolution instead of a frantic "grab" at the pier as the current swept the ship downstream.

Example 17

Problem

USS *New Kent* was often faced with the problem of making a landing unassisted, with the wind blowing directly against the face of the pier. She had her landing craft available, but these would have to work on the windward side during the last stages of the landing and a more expeditious method was desired.

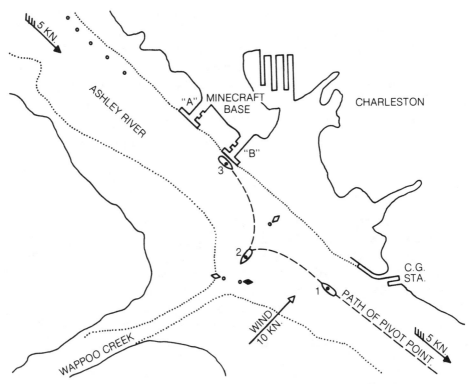

FIGURE 20–16. *Towhee* avoids a too-fast landing at Minecraft Base, Charleston.

Solution (Figure 20–17)

When still well clear of the pier, the windward (off-pier) anchor was dropped and veered to about 30 fathoms. Working against this anchor at an engine speed of 8 knots, the ship made a wide approach, dragging her anchor, at about 1 or 2 knots to a point about 100 feet abreast her berth. At this point the engines were slowed to 4 knots, the dragging ceased, and the ship was held dead in the water, parallel to the pier, by working her engine and rudder against the taut chain. In slowing the engine speed from 8 to 4 knots, the ship had "sagged" downwind until now she lay only about 30 feet from the face of the pier and slightly astern of her berth. From this position her lines could be run to the pier as desired. When all lines were in place, the ship was eased in against the face of the pier by veering the chain and adjusting the engine speed to achieve the desired fore-and-aft position. Once in her berth, her chain was slacked to the bottom, and she had a friend in mid-channel ready to help her when the time came to get under way again.

Example 18

Problem

The new skipper was handling the ship for the first time, and he had been ashore for

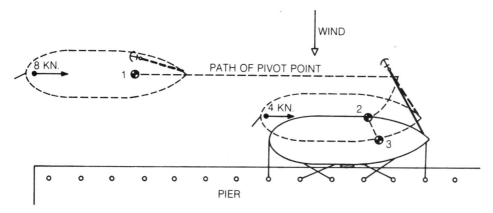

FIGURE 20–17. *New Kent* makes an unassisted landing with the wind blowing directly onto the pier.

the past two years. USS *Cushing* (DD 797) lay alongside a nest at Yokosuka, Japan, a fresh breeze was blowing from nearly astern, and she had to depart through the entrance to windward. She cleared the nest nicely, threaded her way between the tender and a line of station ships as she backed into the wind, and reached a clear area to the northward where she could turn. The skipper put her stern to port, opposed the engines, and commenced to turn her into the wind. Twisting with the engines alone would not do the trick. She would come almost broadside to the wind, and then she would turn no further. The shoal water astern and the ships ahead limited her motion, and as she backed and filled with high engine power, the wind was carrying her relentlessly to leeward. Soon she was in a veritable cul-de-sac between the tender and a nest of minecraft. The sea wall was getting ominously close, and in spite of twisting at maximum power the ship was not going to make-it. The new skipper was getting desperate.

Solution (Figure 20–18)

Sensing the mounting tension, the commodore whispered "Don't forget your anchor." The starboard anchor rattled to the bottom, the ship pivoted smartly into the wind, and in a few moments the ship was standing safely towards the entrance—a lesson in shiphandling permanently engraved in the new skipper's mind.

Example 19

Problem

USS *Wisconsin* (BB 64) was ordered to moor bow and stern to Buoys A and B in Berths 5 and 6 in the Hudson River, New York City. In this part of the river, that part of the channel deep enough for a battleship is only slightly wider than the *Wisconsin*'s length. It was desired to moor the ship heading downstream.

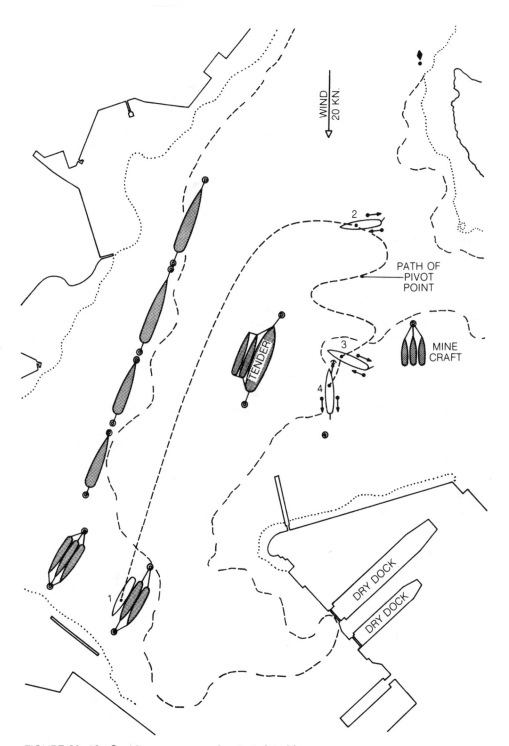

WIND
20 KN.

PATH OF
PIVOT
POINT

TENDER

MINE
CRAFT

DRY DOCK

DRY DOCK

FIGURE 20–18. *Cushing* uses an anchor to twist ship.

Solution (Figure 20–19)

A pilot and 8 tugs were on hand. The mooring was timed to coincide with the changing of the tide from ebb to flood, and as the ship arrived at Buoy A, heading upstream, there was still a slight downstream current running.

The tugs, working in pairs, held the big ship in position while a heavy wire was secured to Buoy A. When this was completed, the ebb had ceased, and the first part of the flood commenced to carry the ship upstream. The bow wire was slacked to allow the bow to move near the Jersey side while the ship was turned by the tugs. The wire to Buoy A provided a positive control on the cross-channel position of the ship (her draft was 36 feet, and the Naval Base had provided a special chart to show the exact location of the 36-foot depth contours).

Upon completion of the winding, with the ship now heading downstream, the tugs moved her stern near Buoy B, and four heavy wires were secured to this buoy. Finally, the bow was heaved close to Buoy A and the port anchor chain was secured to the buoy. The moor was made taut by heaving in on the chain, and the big ship lay safely in her berth, having used all of the tools available to the shiphandler.

Example 20

Problem

USS *Richard E. Kraus* (DD 849) was again assigned an end berth at one of the piers at Naval Base, Norfolk, Virginia. A full ebb tide combined with a southwesterly wind of 25 knots gave an off-pier wind and current. It was known from previous experience that though the bow could be brought in with the capstan, it would be impossible to twist the stern in with the engines and rudders alone. No tugs were available, and operational commitments required a landing without delay.

Solution (Figure 20–20)

Kraus had a trick up her sleeve. Long experience with this situation had caused the crew to carefully reexamine their resources. The strongest mooring line was made ready on the fantail, and Mount 53 was trained around into her starboard stops.

A fast approach put her close alongside, and the lines were quickly passed to the pier. The bow was snubbed and under control in the usual way, but the stern began to move away from the pier in response to the wind and current in spite of the engines being opposed at TWO-THIRDS.

The stern was snubbed by holding all after lines as soon as they were secured on the pier and turns were taken with the extra mooring line about the moving part of the base of Mount 53. When ready to move the stern in, a strain was taken on the special mooring line aft by training Mount 53 slowly to the right in "local." The powerful train drive of the 5"/38 twin mount provided adequate force to move the stern in against the pier in spite of the wind and tide. The stresses of such use are small compared to the stresses of firing, and this unusual employment of a gun

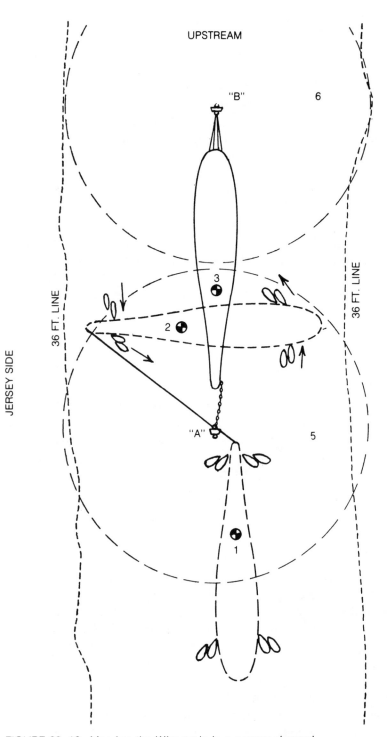

FIGURE 20-19. Mooring the *Wisconsin* in a narrow channel.

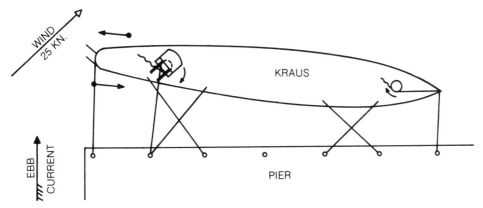

FIGURE 20–20. *Kraus* uses a gun mount for a capstan.

mount did not harm the mount in any way. Had the mount trained all the way into its port stops, the stern could have been held with the other lines while the mount trained back to starboard and a new purchase was taken on the line. The use of the gun mount provided a solution to a troublesome shiphandling problem.

Example 21

Problem

A "Med Relief" was in progress, and most of the ships of the Sixth Fleet had crowded into the Harbor of Naples. *Yellowstone* was already in port when the others arrived, and *Newport News* (NN), *Goodrich* (G), *Larsen* (L), and *Grand Canyon* (GC), had Med-moored in the locations indicated in the figure. A 25-knot wind complicated the situation when the time came for *Yellowstone* to get under way.

As *Yellowstone* cast off her after lines and commenced heaving in on her anchors, backing to hold her stern up against the wind, things began to happen. About the time her stern was even with the bows of the adjacent destroyers, their stern lines commenced to part from the combination of high wind, the strong screw currents from *Yellowstone*, and the strain on *Goodrich*'s anchor chain (mentioned below). Soon both destroyers had broken free from the sea wall and were drifting across the harbor. As *Yellowstone* heaved in her port anchor she found it fouled by *two* anchor chains (*Newport News*' and *Goodrich*'s); when she tried her starboard, she found it had fouled *Grand Canyon*'s chain. Three chains fouled, two destroyers adrift—now what?

Solution (Figure 20–21)

Every man for himself! Luckily *Goodrich* and *Larsen* had steam up, and before they had drifted into *Newport News* or into the shoal water on the opposite side of the harbor, they were gotten under control with their own engines. Maneuvering nested

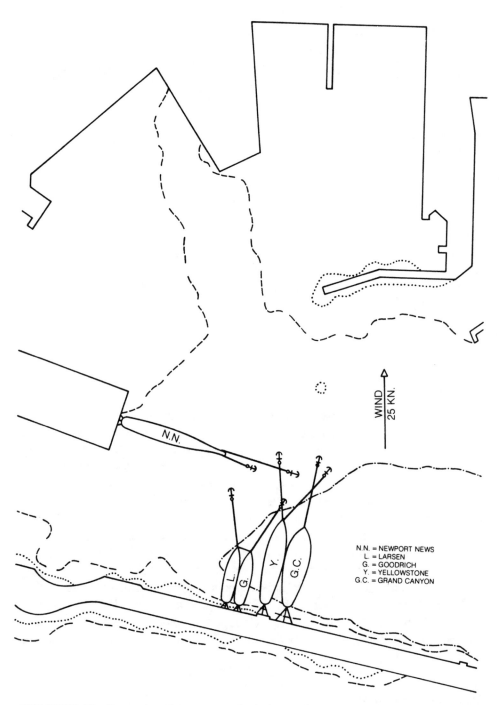

FIGURE 20–21. Crossed anchors mean a fouled-up getaway.

N.N. = NEWPORT NEWS
L. = LARSEN
G. = GOODRICH
Y. = YELLOWSTONE
G.C. = GRAND CANYON

WIND
25 KN.

together, they could exert a tremendous twisting moment as well as move fore-and-aft, and soon they had backed up to the sea wall and were securing again.

Yellowstone held herself in position, stern into the wind, and cleared her chains one at a time. This was accomplished by heaving the anchor clear of the water to work on it. By passing a wire under the bight of chain which had caught in the anchor's flukes and securing the wire back on deck, the offending chain could be held suspended while the anchor was again lowered. When the anchor had been gotten past the chain by hoisting it a second time, the chain could be released by slipping the wire. Soon *Yellowstone* was on her way clear of her entanglements, but all who had observed had learned a lesson about fouled anchors.

Comment

Had the anchors of all ships been clearly marked and had all concerned been alert to the danger, the anchors of all ships could have been placed in such a way that no anchors would have been fouled.

In cases where it is necessary to cross anchor chains, fouling is usually avoided if the last ship to arrive is the first to depart.

Example 22

Problem

The night of 28 November 1943 had been a tough night for cruisers. It is now called the Battle of Tassafaronga, but most of that night it was a confusing nightmare. *Northampton* had been sunk, *Pensacola* nearly cut in two by a torpedo, and *Minneapolis* and *New Orleans* had their bows blown off! The destroyers had been called back from the attack to stand by the stricken cruisers, and dawn found *Maury* (DD 401) shepherding *New Orleans* (CA 32) into Tulagi Harbor. As they approached the anchorage, it was suddenly realized that the anchors were in that part of the ship which had disappeared (she was sheared off between turrets one and two). How to secure the cruiser?

Solution (Figure 20–22)

New Orleans maneuvered to the spot where she wished to anchor, and stopped. *Maury* came alongside, and as she secured to the larger ship, she dropped her inboard anchor. Both ships rode to *Maury's* anchor.

When *Maury* had veered to the desired scope of chain, a strong wire was run from the chain outside the hawsepipe to the foremost remaining set of bitts on *New Orleans*. The chain was secured with a detachable link just inboard of *Maury's* stopper, so *Maury* could quickly get free by breaking her chain and tripping her stopper. In this manner *Maury* would be free to get under way in case of attack without leaving *New Orleans* adrift.

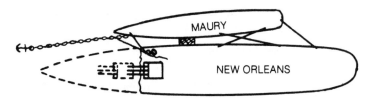

FIGURE 20–22. *Maury* provides a jury anchor for an anchorless ship.

Example 23

Problem

The five ships of TransDiv 128 (APDs) were assigned to berths at the finger piers at the submarine base, St. Thomas, Virgin Islands. A 20-knot breeze was blowing across the piers. *Tolberg* (APD 103) was third in column and the only ship assigned to a berth on the leeward side of a pier. The two following ships could not berth until *Tolberg* had cleared the area between the piers, and the crews of all ships were looking forward to a well-earned liberty. How could *Tolberg* expedite her landing and make way for the other ships?

Solution (Figure 20–23)

As she approached the finger piers, *Tolberg* put all four of her LCVPs into the water and had them follow just off her port side. She made a fast approach and stopped with her bow close to the pier abreast her berth. As soon as the ship had come to rest, all four LCVPs were called in alongside and ordered to push on the port quarter. Heaving on number one with her capstan, twisting with her engines, and being pushed by the four powerful boats, the ship moved rapidly in against the pier and the lines were quickly secured. As soon as they could be spared, the boats were ordered to clear the side and the basin was ready for the next ships to enter.

Example 24

Problem

USS *Black* (DD 666) was moored port-side-to *O'Hare* (DD 889) at Buoy 2, Hampton Roads. A fresh breeze was blowing from the north, but the strong ebb tidal current held the ships stern-into-the-wind. Under way time was 0800, and this could not be varied because *Black* was to take part in a scheduled sortie. Just before casting off, the wind overcame the weakening current (slack water was approaching) and the nest swung broadside to the wind and the remaining current. An LST, more sensitive to the wind than the current, had already swung to the wind and lay across *Black*'s stern about 200 yards away. The time for departure was rapidly approaching. What to do?

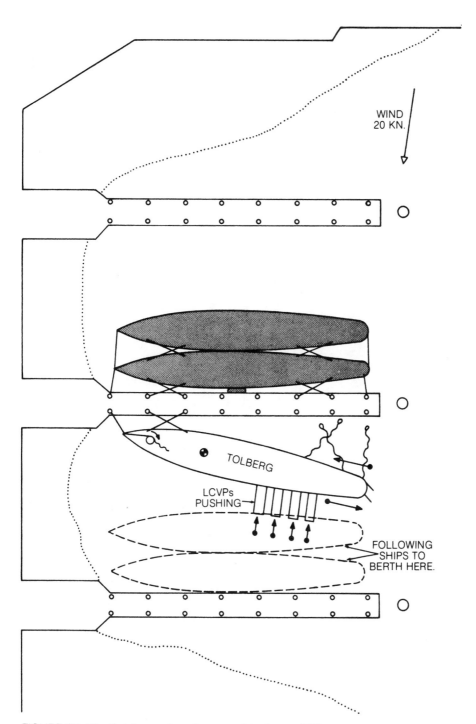

FIGURE 20–23. Quick mooring close quarters for an APD.

Solution (Figure 20–24)

Black dipped her port anchor and all available fenders were made ready along the port side. The chief engineer was notified of the entended maneuver to insure that the throttlemen would be ready for it. All lines were cast off simultaneously and both engines were backed FULL. As soon as she had moved slightly astern, the rudder was ordered LEFT FULL to counter the tendency of the stern to go upwind and to keep

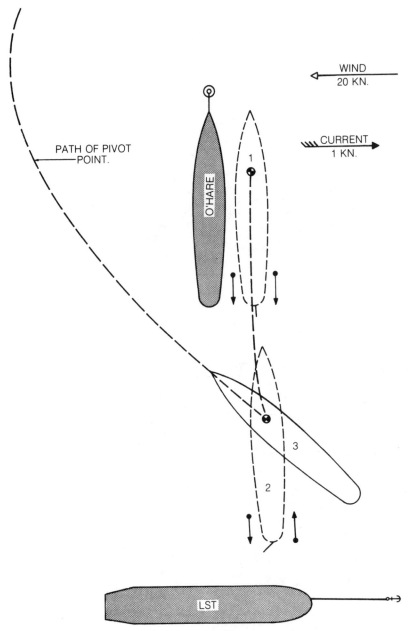

FIGURE 20–24. Getting under way in variable wind and current.

the bow clear of *O'Hare*. As her bow came abreast of *O'Hare's* quarter, all engines were ordered AHEAD TWO-THIRDS and the ship was brought to a stop about 50 yards clear of *O'Hare's* stern. Once dead in the water, the engines were opposed, and the bow was twisted downwind easily. *Black* executed a broad sweep to leeward and stood out toward the channel on schedule.

Example 25

Problem

USS *Stormes* (DD 780) had been damaged on Picket Station Fifteen at Okinawa. After waiting for a full two months, she was finally placed in a floating dry dock (an ARD) for emergency repairs to make her safe for the long trip home. In the interim, however, the summer of 1945 had worn on and it was now typhoon season. *Stormes* had been extensively damaged aft by the Kamikaze, and though the major structural members had been replaced, her hull plating had not been completely replaced. A typhoon was approaching, and Buckner Bay was in the center of its path. Sensing the imminent danger, the SOPA ordered the bay evacuated—that is, except for *Stormes* and her ARD. Deserted, she lay there alone as the velocity of the wind mounted. All hands donned lifejackets. The crew of the ARD seemed to be drifting aboard the destroyer; the crew of the destroyer seemed to be drifting over to the ARD. Anxiety seemed to say that the combination would certainly roll over in a typhoon—but the question was, would the destroyer fall out of the dock and sink, or would the dock founder and the destroyer float free?

Solution (Figure 20–25)

Anticipating severe rolling and heavy seas, a conference was held to decide upon measures to minimize the danger. It was decided that the real danger lay in the ship coming loose in the dock and rolling off the keel blocks. The spur shores were the key to the situation.

It was estimated that no amount of wedging could keep the ship from moving to some small extent with respect to the dock, and it was anticipated that should the destroyer roll away from one of the sides of the dock ever so little, the spur shore would thereby be released and fall to the bottom of the dock. If the spur shores began to go, the ship would most certainly slip off the blocks. The solution could not lie in tighter wedging alone.

After several suggestions were explored, it was decided to construct a small retainer frame around the ends of the shores. Thus, if the ship moved momentarily, the spur shore would be held in place and would not fall out from between the ship and the dock. The spur shores were backed up by "preventers" to hold the shore in place should the opening become larger than the retaining frame.

The storm came on, and though the center passed many miles away (over the center of the formation of ships which had evacuated Buckner Bay), the wind and

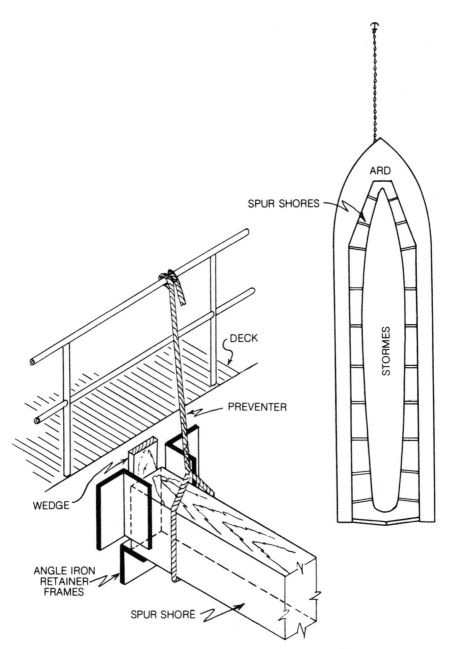

FIGURE 20–25. Securing a ship in a floating dock against typhoons.

waves were severe. The dock and ship rolled as much as 15° to a side, and half-inch gaps were observed between the ends of the spur shores and the side of the ship at the extremity of the roll. Each time a gap would appear, wedges would be driven between the end of the shore and the ship (or dock). By this means, all shores were held in place and kept bearing throughout the storm.

The ship didn't roll out of the dock, and the dock didn't founder. A severe situation had been alleviated, however, only by careful forethought and positive action.

Example 26

Problem

The second Battle of Kula Gulf had gone poorly for *Gwin* (DD 433). She had been torpedoed aft, and she was awash for the after one-third of her length. *Maury* (DD 401) and *Ralph Talbot* (DD 390) had been ordered to stand by her, but as the morning wore on and the Japanese air attacks became more troublesome, it became apparent that they would never get her back to the now safe waters of Iron Bottom Bay (between Guadalcanal and Tulagi). After repeated attempts to tow her had been thwarted by the appearance of Jap planes, the Commodore finally decided to abandon her and ordered *Maury* alongside to take off the salvage detail. (Most of the crew had been taken off earlier by *Ralph Talbot*.)

Approaching a ship, the after third of which is submerged, presents its problems. If we get our screws over the submerged part of the ship, perhaps we too will become crippled and at the mercy of the dive bombers.

Solution (Figure 20–26)

The captain selected a spot on the *Gwin*'s forecastle which was about the same height as *Maury*'s forecastle, and made a one-point one-line landing. Approaching smartly, he placed the flat of *Maury*'s forecastle against this point (abreast No. 1 gun), passed a single mooring line, and kept *Maury*'s stern away from *Gwin*'s by gentle use of the engines.

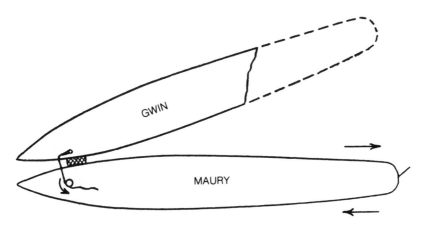

FIGURE 20–26. Rescue work under enemy threat.

After a few minutes alongside, all survivors had been transferred and *Gwin*'s captain had made his inspection to be sure that none had been forgotten. With all safely on board, *Maury* backed clear. Twenty minutes later *Gwin* had been sent to the bottom by a torpedo from *Ralph Talbot* and the two surviving ships were headed down the "Slot" at top speed. Coolheaded shiphandling had been essential in a hot situation.

Example 27

Problem

In December 1944, *O'Neill* (DE 188) in Ulithi was ordered to the ammunition anchorage at the far end of the lagoon to load ammunition. The weather was marginal with 25 to 35 knots of wind and five to eight-foot swells. On approaching the AE, a converted Liberty ship, the commanding officer to *O'Neill* informed the master of the AE that it would not be advisable to come alongside under existing weather conditions since damage to the DE's superstructure and gun sponsons was certain to occur.

Solution (Figure 20–27)

At the suggestion of the master of the AE, *O'Neill* proceeded to a point about 100 yards 60° on the starboard bow of the AE and dropped her *port* anchor. Then slowly paying out chain, she eased aft and worked in, using opposed engines and *in* rudder, until she was abreast the AE and mooring lines could be passed. With her bow controlled by the mooring lines and anchor chain, and her stern by the engines and rudder, *O'Neill* was brought in parallel to the AE until about 6 feet of water separated the ships. Lines were secured and *O'Neill* was held in her position by the combination of lines and chain and by maintaining low power ahead on the starboard engine, backing slowly on the port engine, and using left rudder.

Though the ships rolled heavily and *O'Neill* pitched moderately, they never touched and the transfer was made safely and expeditiously.

Example 28

Problem

Stormes (DD 780), in shakedown training at San Diego, was ordered to moor bow and stern to a pair of buoys near the Sonar School. The buoys were just off the mouth of a creek from which a strong current was flowing, and 20 knots of wind was blowing across the buoys to add to the difficulty. The bow was secured to the first buoy easily enough, but when the conning officer tried to work the stern up to the other buoy with the engines and rudder he didn't come close. After a half an hour of twisting and sweating, the conning officer gave up, declaring that it just couldn't be done.

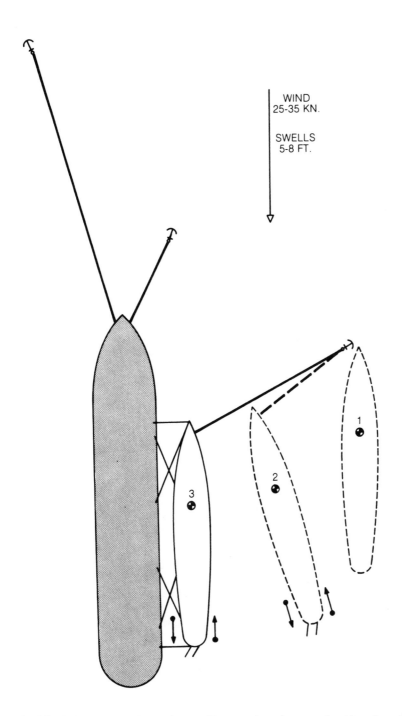

WIND
25-35 KN.

SWELLS
5-8 FT.

FIGURE 20–27. How to keep from rolling against the supply ship when the weather is difficult.

Solution (Figure 20–28)

The skipper, who had a better comprehension of the forces acting on the ship, stepped in and pointed out that the chain to the first buoy was countering the twisting action of the engines. To eliminate this restraint on the vessel he veered chain and moved the ship forward, into the wind and current, until the chain led aft and the buoy was abreast the pivot point. Then twisting the ship with engines opposed with lots of power and full rudder, he turned the ship 180° until her stern was into the wind without putting any significant strain on the buoy. Once her stern was into the wind, he veered chain and "sailed" cross-wind, controlling the ship's orientation with engines and rudder, until the stern was in the vicinity of the other buoy. Once the stern was secured to the buoy, the engines were stopped and the ship brought into her proper position between the buoys by heaving in on the chain.

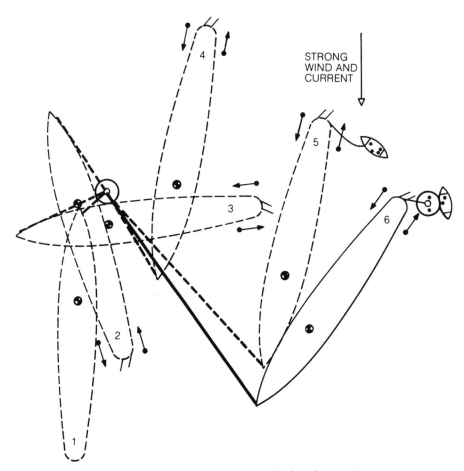

FIGURE 20–28. Snatching two buoys in a strong wind and current.

Example 29

Problem

Forrest Sherman (DD 931) was ordered to Washington, D.C., for the Presidential Inauguration. She made her way up the frozen Potomac, often with only inches between her sonar dome and the bottom, and finally moored in the ice-clogged slip at the Municipal Pier. The visit was enjoyable, but when the time came to depart, a new problem arose. The channel was not considered wide enough for backing clear of the slip, and then turning and proceeding down the channel. Backing out all the way was unattractive because of the ice on the river and the great distance to the closest suitable turning basin. Though a tug was available, there was little room in the slip and the sheets of ice made maneuvering difficult.

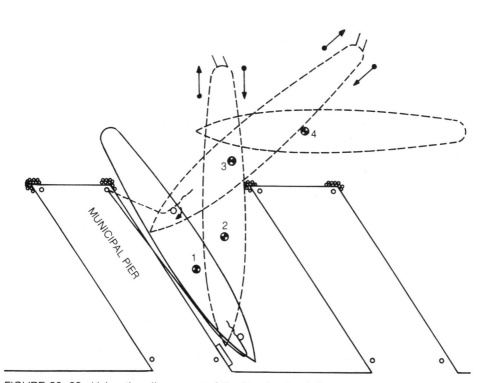

FIGURE 20–29. Using the slip as part of the "turning basin."

Solution (Figure 20–29)

A line was run from her bow to the channel end of the pier. The ship was then twisted, pivoting on a camel, until her stern had crossed the slip and her port side was close to the head of the adjacent pier. A strain was then taken on the line leading to the head of the Municipal Pier, and as the bow moved toward the channel, the stern was worked up channel with the engines keeping the port side close to the head of the other pier. As the ship came parallel to the channel, the bow line was cast off, the ship backed up channel slightly to clear the pier heads, and she finally proceeded down channel normally. The trick had been to use the slip as part of a turning basin and to find a means of moving the bow out to the end of the pier.

Example 30

Problem

USS *Garcia* was ordered to moor bow out, outboard of the USS *J. A. Furer*, on the south side of Pier One, U. S. Naval Station, Newport, R. I. USS *Talbot* was to moor outboard of *Garcia* and was waiting in line. The wind was from the south at 20 knots.

Solution (Figure 20–30)

Two Naval Station tugs were available and used. One tug was made up forward with a headline and starboard quarter line and the second tug made up similarly aft, both on the port side. The approach was made at a ONE-THIRD bell parallel to the pier, well to the south side, until the ship was about 200 yards from the pier. At this time the ship's rudder was put hard left and the bow tug ordered to back easy (A). When the ship had turned about 45 degrees, the after tug was ordered to come ahead full (B). When the ship was perpendicular to the pier at a distance of about 100 yards, the ship's engine was stopped. Both tugs continued as originally ordered until the ship had turned 135 degrees, at which time the ship's engine was backed ONE-THIRD (C). This was continued until the ship was in the approximate fore-and-aft position for mooring. The engine was then stopped, followed by a brief AHEAD bell to stop the ship, which was then parallel to the *J. A. Furer* and drifting smartly down on her because of the wind. Both tugs were backed intermittently to make a gentle mooring (D).

Example 31

Problem

USS *Lexington* (CVT 16) was required to go into Mobile, Alabama, harbor alongside a shipyard pier. The Mobile River is about 1,100 feet wide where the piers are located, and the piers are perpendicular to the river flow. How could the ship, which

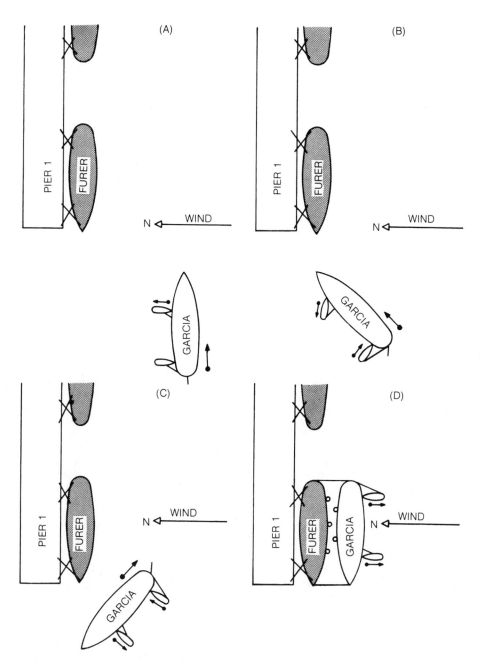

FIGURE 20–30. Tugs maneuver *Garcia* to a mooring outboard of *J. A. Furer*.

is 840 feet in length at the waterline, go alongside the pier, starboard side to, with the bow facing the river, and avoid the pier to port and a floating drydock directly across the narrow river from the slip?

Solution (Figure 20–31)

The pilot positioned the tugs as shown in the photograph, and maneuvered the ship perpendicular to the pier and close aboard to starboard to allow sufficient room for the ship to swing in the river so as to avoid the floating drydock. A camel was placed 45 degrees across the corner piling of the pier to evenly distribute the force of the ship against the pier, and also to act as a fulcrum in twisting the carrier to line up with the slip. The abreast tugs kept the ship close aboard the end of the pier, while the bow and stern tugs twisted and maneuvered the ship to line up with the pier. Then the stern tugs pulled the ship back into the slip alongside the pier.

Example 32

Problem

USS *Howard W. Gilmore* (AS 16) is assigned a berth alongside the south quaywall at Key West, which is most convenient to permit her to service her charges, but

FIGURE 20–31. Tugs maneuver USS *Lexington* (CVT 16) alongside a shipyard pier in the Mobile River.

rather tight for a ship of her size. She gets under way infrequently and has the assistance of tugs, but there is hardly room for a ship of her length; Pier one blocks any motion astern and is almost too close to permit side motion of the ship. How best to get in and out of this berth?

Solution (Figures 20–32 and 20–33)

As with most shiphandling problems, careful advance planning solved the problem. The skipper constructed a transparency showing the outline of his ship to the scale of the harbor chart. He then experimented with various maneuvers and motions of his ship until he was satisfied that he had developed the most practical solution to his problem. His solution:

Getting under way: Holding *Gilmore*'s after lines and working against carefully placed fenders and a camel, he ordered the tugs to pull the ship's bow out until she was heading fair for the entrance of the basin. The skipper then cast off the after lines and proceeded to sea.

Coming alongside: Picking up the tugs as the ship approached the basin, the skipper brought *Gilmore* slowly to a point where her bow was just clear of the quaywall and the bridge was in line with the face of Lighthouse Pier. Careful measurement beforehand had assured him that if he kept the centerline Pelorus on the line of the face

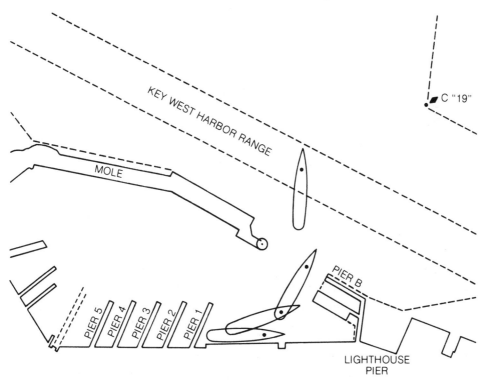

FIGURE 20–32. USS *Howard W. Gilmore* (AS 16) gets under way from a tight berth.

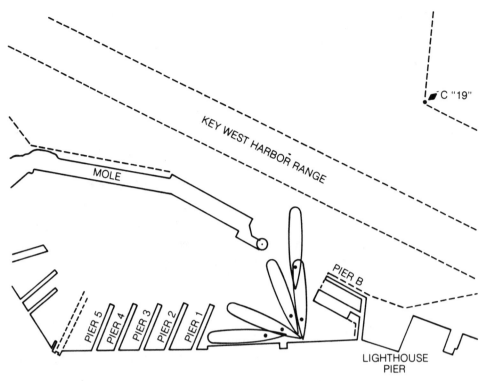

FIGURE 20–33. USS *Howard W. Gilmore* maneuvers into her tight berth alongside the south quaywall at Key West.

of Lighthouse Pier and approximately abreast the end of Pier B, the ship's bow would be well clear of the quaywall and the stern would clear Pier one when he twisted the ship in. Both port and starboard bow lines were passed to the quay to snub any motion along the quaywall as the ship twisted. Once the ship was alongside with lines over, her fore-and-aft position could be adjusted.

Example 33

Problem

USS *Garcia*, moored starboard side of USS *Compton* in berth 153, U. S. Naval Station, Newport, R. I., was instructed to get under way at 0900. A nest of three destroyers is berthed directly astern in the 13 berth. One tug is available. Wind is from the NNE at 22 knots. Because of the large bow-mounted sonar dome in the *Garcia*, the bow could not approach *Compton* without risk of striking the dome. Further, a backing bell on this class ship twists the stern to port rapidly. This, coupled with the brisk NNE wind, increased the danger of scraping *Compton* if this ship were to back.

Solution (Figure 20–34)

The tug was moored for power on the port bow and was ordered to put on left rudder. With the ship's rudder amidships, a BACK TWO-THIRDS bell was ordered and, simultaneously, the tug ordered to come ahead. *Garcia*'s stern swung smartly to port while, at the same time, the bow was pulled away from the DD by the tug. The tug at this point was used to steer *Garcia* and, after clearing the slip, the tug assisted in turning *Garcia*. The tug provided sufficient force to control the ship's bow against the wind and the ship's engine.

Example 34

Problem

USS *Koelsch* (DE 1049) was required to moor bow out at berth 112, pier one at Newport Naval Base. The night was dark with winds of 20 to 25 knots coming from the northwest.

Two tugs were available, but communications could not be established and it was too dark to use hand signals.

Solution (Figure 20–35)

Since a port-side-to, ahead landing is relatively simple even with a wind setting the ship onto the pier it was decided to use this method to moor. The ship came in past

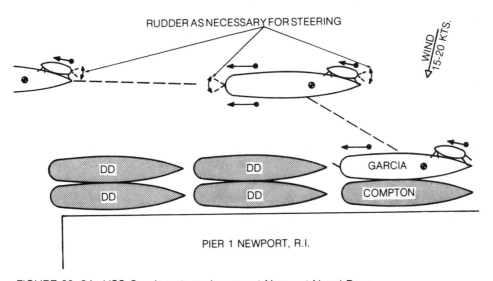

FIGURE 20–34. USS *Garcia* gets under way at Newport Naval Base.

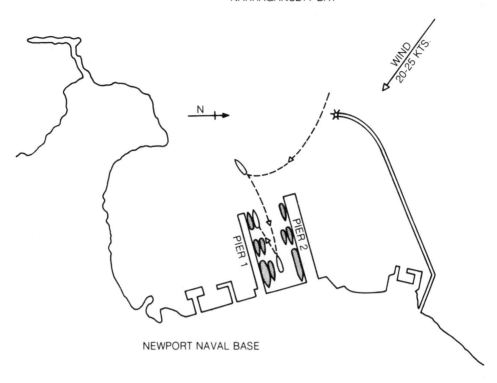

FIGURE 20–35. USS *Koelsch* (DE 1049) makes a port-side-to landing at Newport Naval Base.

the breakwater, made a hard right turn and then backed down between pier one and pier two. Once the ship was in position it was a simple matter to come ahead and make a normal port-side-to landing at the end of the pier.

Example 35

Problem

USS *Koelsch* (DE 1049) was required to moor bow out at the north side of pier Victor in Guantanamo Bay, Cuba. The wind was from the southwest at 15 to 20 knots, and no tugs were available.

Solution (Figure 20–36)

The approach was made in a southeasterly direction at ten knots. Just before the bow came abreast of the pier, the rudder was put over HARD RIGHT. After engine was backed TWO-THIRDS. When all way was lost, the ship was south of the pier and

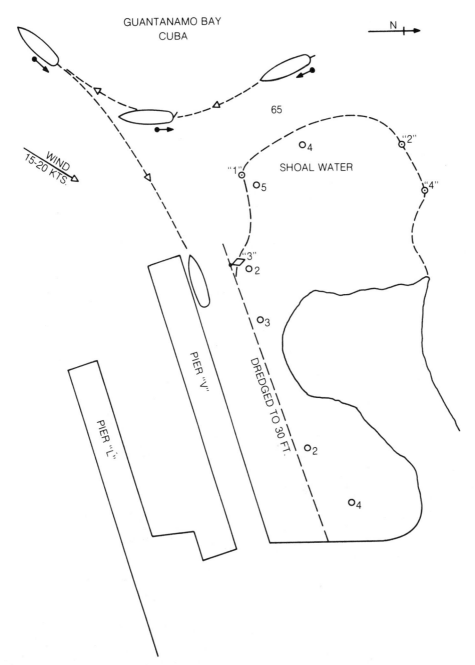

FIGURE 20–36. USS *Koelsch* (DE 1049) moors bow-out at Guantanamo Bay, Cuba.

heading about 20 degrees to left of pier heading. the back TWO-THIRDS bell was left on, and as a result of the combination of propeller forces pushing the stern to port and wind pushing the bow to starboard, the ship arrived at her berth parallel to the pier and about ten feet out.

21
rules of the road

Since thousands of vessels meet along the busy trade routes and in the teeming harbors of the world each day, the safety of such encounters cannot be left to chance. Ships are designed economically and are no more rugged than necessary to withstand the stress of the elements; the hull of a ship is proportionally no tougher than the shell of an egg. Ships are not built to stand up to the shock of a collision and the history of marine accidents is full of examples of seemingly minor collisions which resulted in the sinking of one or both of the vessels involved.

Individual judgment, even among experienced mariners, cannot be depended upon to provide for the safe passage of ships. The possibility always exists that just when one master decides on a certain turn to avoid another ship, the skipper of the second, sizing up the situation differently, might order a turn which exactly cancelled the precautionary maneuver of the first, and a collision would result. Personal judgment is too variable to be relied upon exclusively to prevent collisions.

The safe passage of ships can be assured, on the other hand, by the use of a universal system of rules which will insure that all ships maneuver predictably and consistently so that each mariner can know what he can expect of others and what is required of him. To provide such a universal system, the modern Rules of the Road were adopted by Great Britain and France jointly in 1863. The United States adopted these same rules the following year, and by 1885 most of the other major maritime powers had accepted them. These rules have been kept up to date by periodic revision and have always stood as the cornerstone to safety at sea. The International Rules of the Road are the effective law on all the high seas and in most of the coastal waters and harbors of the world—they are the governing law for more than 90 percent of the navigable water of the world.

In 1972, upon the invitation of the Inter-Governmental Maritime Consultive Organization, a conference was held in London among the principal maritime nations to revise the International Regulations for Preventing Collisions at Sea, 1960. This conference produced a very much improved set of "International Rules," not only from the viewpoint of completeness, but also the presentation and organization of the rules were greatly improved. The provisions for adoption of these new rules are such that it is expected they will become effective in all international waters on 1 January 1976.

For the navigation of the Inland Waters of the United States, Congress has established the Inland Rules of the Road. In the same act that established these rules, Congress directed the Commandant of the Coast Guard to "establish such other rules . . . not inconsistent with the provisions of this act . . . as he may from time to time deem necessary for safety." Accordingly the Commandant of the Coast Guard has published the Pilot Rules for Inland Waters, which for the mariner have the same authority as the Inland Rules. The Inland Rules of the Road are couched in broad terms and generally give the regulations applicable to the normal vessels which frequent inland waters. The Pilot Rules re-state most of the Inland Rules, sometimes elaborating for greater clarity, and they also cover a great variety of special vessels and operations not provided for by the Inland Rules. Unfortunately, neither set of rules can stand alone and the overlap is extensive.

In addition to the rules above for navigating the high seas and the coastal waters of the United States, there are the following rules for particular inland water systems:

1. Great Lakes Rules
2. Pilot Rules for the Great Lakes
3. Western River Rules (for Mississippi and tributaries)
4. Pilot Rules of Western Rivers
5. Corps of Engineers, Department of the Army, Rules and Regulations for the Great Lakes and Western Rivers
6. Panama Canal Rules

These rules are similar to the Inland Rules in scope but provide for the special conditions encountered in their respective areas. Since the normal naval vessel will traverse these waters only infrequently and will ordinarily employ a local pilot who will be thoroughly conversant with the special local rules, these special sets of rules are considered beyond the scope of this discussion.

The complexity of the system of rules and regulations for navigation of the Inland Waters of the United States has long been a concern to both mariners and the governmental officials responsible for such matters. As a part of the legislation adopting the new International Rules, the Commandant of the Coast Guard has proposed a set of new Inland rules conforming almost entirely to the new International Rules and it is expected that they will be authorized and go into effect either simultaneously or shortly after the effective date for the International Rules. Consequently, in this chapter, we will present and discuss the new International Rules and then follow with a brief discussion of the few differences which will remain after the adoption of the new Inland Rules. Until the new International Rules and new Inland Rules go into effect, the reader must rely on other publications for reference to the older rules.

The new International Rules are a tremendous improvement over the old rules and when the Inland Rules are brought into conformance with them, the task of the mariner operating in and out of United States ports will be greatly simplified. In fact, the new rules rectify all of the matters previously criticized in earlier editions of this book and therefore much of the text required to explain the rules in action has been eliminated.

INTERNATIONAL RULES OF THE ROAD

In the following pages, the new International Rules of the Road will be quoted rule-by-rule, followed by comments as indicated.

INTERNATIONAL REGULATIONS FOR PREVENTING COLLISIONS AT SEA, 1972

PART A—GENERAL

RULE 1
Application
(a) These Rules shall apply to all vessels upon the high seas and in all waters connected therewith navigable by seagoing vessels.
(b) Nothing in these Rules shall interfere with the operation of special rules made by an appropriate authority for roadsteads, harbors, rivers, lakes or inland waterways connected with the high seas and navigable by seagoing vessels. Such special rules shall conform as closely as possible to these Rules.
(c) Nothing in these Rules shall interfere with the operation of any special rules made by the Government of any State with respect to additional station or signal lights or whistle signals for ships of war and vessels proceeding under convoy, or with respect to additional station or signal lights for fishing vessels engaged in fishing as a fleet. These additional station or signal lights or whistle signals shall, so far as possible, be such that they cannot be mistaken for any light or signal authorized elsewhere under these Rules.
(d) Traffic separation schemes may be adopted by the Organization for the purpose of these Rules.
(e) Whenever the Government concerned shall have determined that a vessel of special construction or purpose cannot comply fully with the provisions of any of these Rules with respect to the number, position, range or arc of visibility of lights or shapes, as well as to the disposition and characteristics of sound-signalling appliances, without interfering with the special function of the vessel, such vessel shall comply with such other provisions in regard to the number, position, range or arc of visibility of lights or shapes, as well as to the disposition and characteristics of sound-signalling appliances, as her Government shall have determined to be the closest possible compliance with these Rules in respect to that vessel.

Rule I Comment:
It should be emphasized that these rules apply to *all* warships at *all* times when they are on the high seas and connected navigable water. Also, though *additional* special lights and sound signals are permitted for warships, warships are not relieved of complying with the basic minimum requirements for lights and sound signals; slight deviations are permitted when the "special construction or purpose" of the ship prevents full compliance.

A most important point is that a warship is not relieved of its obligation under these rules because of the nature of its operations, whether it is steaming singly or under the orders of higher authority in a military formation. The *official* character of a warship or participation in naval operations is no excuse for violation or noncompliance with the Rules of the Road.

RULE 2
Responsibility
(a) Nothing in these Rules shall exonerate any vessel, or the owner, master or crew thereof, from the consequences of any neglect to comply with these Rules or of the neglect of any precaution which may be required by the ordinary practice of seamen, or by the special circumstances of the case.
(b) In construing and complying with these Rules due regard shall be had to all dangers of navigation and collision and to any special circumstances, including the limitations of the vessels involved, which may make a departure from these Rules necessary to avoid immediate danger.

Rule 2 Comment:
This rule clearly states that the conning officer is never relieved of his responsibility to be prepared for emergencies. to use good judgement, and to take all practical steps to prevent a collision. In these cases where special circumstances create a situation where strict compliance with the rules would not be adequate to prevent a collision, a departure from the rules is permitted. Any departure, of course, should be on the "safe side," such as stopping and backing or sounding the danger signal before such action is required.

RULE 3
General definitions
    For the purpose of these Rules, except where the context otherwise requires:
(a) The word "vessel" includes every description of water craft, including nondisplacement craft and seaplanes, used or capable of being used as a means of transportation on water.
(b) The term "power-driven vessel" means any vessel propelled by machinery.
(c) The term "sailing vessel" means any vessel under sail provided that propelling machinery, if fitted, is not used.
(d) The term "vessel engaged in fishing" means any vessel fishing with nets, lines, trawls or other fishing apparatus which restrict maneuverability, but does not include a vessel fishing with trolling lines or other fishing apparatus which do not restrict maneuverability.
(e) The word "seaplane" includes any aircraft designed to maneuver on the water.
(f) The term "vessel not under command" means a vessel which through some exceptional circumstance is unable to maneuver as required by these Rules and is therefore unable to keep out of the way of another vessel.
(g) The term "vessel restricted in her ability to maneuver" means a vessel which from the nature of her work is restricted in her ability to maneuver as required by these Rules and is therefore unable to keep out of the way of another vessel.
    The following vessels shall be regarded as vessels restricted in their ability to maneuver:
    (i) a vessel engaged in laying, servicing or picking up a navigation mark, submarine cable or pipeline;
    (ii) a vessel engaged in dredging, surveying or underwater operations;
    (iii) a vessel engaged in replenishment or transferring persons, provisions or cargo while underway;
    (iv) a vessel engaged in the launching or recovery of aircraft;
    (v) a vessel engaged in minesweeping operations;
    (vi) a vessel engaged in a towing operation such as renders her unable to deviate from her course.
(h) The term "vessel constrained by her draught" means a power-driven vessel which because of her draught in relation to the available depth of water is severely restricted in her ability to deviate from the course she is following.
(i) The word "underway" means that a vessel is not at anchor, or made fast to the shore, or aground.
(j) The words "length" and "breadth" of a vessel mean her length overall and greatest breadth.
(k) Vessels shall be deemed to be in sight of one another only when one can be observed visually from the other.
(l) The term "restricted visibility" means any condition in which visibility is restricted by fog,

mist, falling snow, heavy rainstorms, sandstorms or any other similar causes.

Rule 3 Comment:
These new, clear definitions are most welcome and need no clarification. The special acknowledgment that a warship, when replenishing and a carrier when launching or recovering aircraft, is "restricted in her ability to maneuver as required by these rules and is therefore unable to keep out of the way of another vessel" is a generous concession to naval operations.

PART B—STEERING AND SAILING RULES

SECTION I—CONDUCT OF VESSELS IN ANY CONDITION OF VISIBILITY

RULE 4
Application
Rules in this Section apply in any condition of visibility.

Rule 4 Comment:
These rules in Section I apply at all times, whether you can see any other vessel or not.

RULE 5
Look-out
Every vessel shall at all times maintain a proper lookout by sight and hearing as well as by all available means appropriate in the prevailing circumstances and conditions so as to make a full appraisal of the situation and of the risk of collision.

Rule 5 Comment:
The conning officer is required by this rule to maintain a *proper lookout* by sight, hearing and all other available means appropriate to the prevailing circumstances and conditions. Though no numbers are specified, sufficient lookouts are required to provide sight and sound coverage all around the ship, augmented by the use of radar and sonar when appropriate. A "proper lookout" implies alertness, proper instructions, effective communications and sufficient judgement to insure a full appraisal of the situation and evaluation of the risk of collision.

RULE 6
Safe speed
Every vessel shall at all times proceed at a safe speed so that she can take proper and effective action to avoid collision and be stopped within a distance appropriate to the prevailing circumstances and conditions.
    In determining a safe speed the following factors shall be among those taken into account:
(a) By all vessels:
    (i) the state of visibility;
    (ii) the traffic density including concentrations of fishing vessels or any other vessels;
    (iii) the maneuverability of the vessel with special reference to stopping distance and turning ability in the prevailing conditions;
    (iv) at night the presence of background light such as from shore lights or from back scatter of her own lights;
    (v) the state of wind, sea and current, and the proximity of navigational hazards;
    (vi) the draught in relation to the available depth of water.
(b) Additionally, by vessels with operational radar:
    (i) the characteristics, efficiency and limitations of the radar equipment;
    (ii) any constraints imposed by the radar range scale in use;
    (iii) the effect on radar detection of the sea state, weather and other sources of interference;
    (iv) the possibility that small vessels, ice and other floating objects may not be detected by radar at an adequate range;
    (v) the number, location and movement of vessels detected by radar;

(vi) the more exact assessment of the visibility that may be possible when radar is used to determine the range of vessels or other objects in the vicinity.

Rule 6 Comment:
In the absence of a collision or other damage judged to have been caused by excessive speed, it is difficult to put a numerical limit on speed which is safe. The framers of this rule wisely outlined the factors which should be considered by the conning officer, with and without radar, in determining that he is proceeding at a safe speed. The conning officer should therefore make sure that he has considered all of these factors and proceed at a speed no greater than that at which he is sure that he can detect and avoid all shipping, large or small, which he might encounter regardless of the other vessel's alertness or maneuvers.

RULE 7
Risk of collision
(a) Every vessel shall use all available means appropriate to the prevailing circumstances and conditions to determine if risk of collision exists. If there is any doubt such risk shall be deemed to exist.
(b) Proper use shall be made of radar equipment if fitted and operational, including long-range scanning to obtain early warning of risk of collision and radar plotting or equivalent systematic observation of detected objects.
(c) Assumptions shall not be made on the basis of scanty information, especially scanty radar information.
(d) In determining if risk of collision exists the following considerations shall be among those taken into account:
(i) such risk shall be deemed to exist if the compass bearing of an approaching vessel does not appreciably change;
(ii) such risk may sometimes exist even when an appreciable bearing change is evident, particularly when approaching a very large vessel or a tow or when approaching a vessel at close range.

Rule 7 Comment:
Risk of collision is normally determined by carefully watching the true bearing of the approaching vessel. If the bearing of an approaching vessel does not change, we are on a "collision course" with it. Watching the true bearing of other ships in the vicinity is the normal means used to detect a potentially dangerous situation. If the bearing is steady, action must be taken.

The converse of this rule, however, is not always true. At short ranges the bearing of another vessel may be changing and risk of collision can still exist. Figure 21–1 illustrates just such a situation. Here, though the true bearing was changing "appreciably," a collision would have occurred. Obviously the amount of bearing change required to insure safety is a function of range and the dimensions of the two vessels in question. Bearings are taken from point to point (from the starboard wing pelorus on our ship to the masthead light of the other ship, for example). Though change in point-to-point bearings insures that those two points will not collide, such change does not absolutely insure that other points on the two vessels will not collide.

Figure 21–2 shows the relative plot of the approach of a vessel which will clear us by 1,000 yards. The dimensions of vessels found at sea today are such that if a point on one passes 1,000 yards from any point on the other at its closest point of approach, a collision cannot occur. A 1,000-yard separation at the moment of passing in the open sea might thus be considered as an acceptable minimum and Figure 21-2 lists the bearing change for each successive thousand yards decrease of range required to insure the 1,000-yard minimum separation upon passing. It will be noted between 10,000 and 9,000 yards only ½° of bearing change is required to insure the 1,000-yard passing separation, but between 6,000 and 5,000 yards this has grown to 2°, and between 4,000 and 3,000 yards the change must be 5° to insure this separation.

RULE 8
Action to avoid collision
(a) Any action taken to avoid collision shall, if the circumstances of the case admit, be

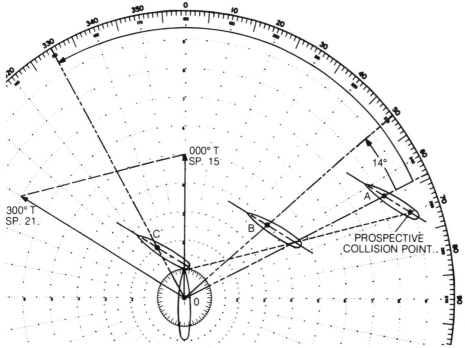

FIGURE 21–1. Collision *can* occur with true bearing changing. This figure shows last 800 yards of relative plot of collision situation. Own ship "O" taking bearings from C/L pelorus on masthead light of approaching ship. Between positions A and B bearing changed 14°. Between A and C it change 94°, but collision occurred anyhow! Own ship on course 000°T, speed 15 knots, approaching ship on 300°T at 21 knots. Both ships of cruiser dimensions. Figure 21–2. Bearing change for each 1,000 yards decrease in range. Ships are on reciprocal courses, and will pass 1,000 yards abeam. Same rate of bearing change per 1,000 yards of closing range holds good for ships approaching from any direction on such a course and speed that a 1,000-yard closest point of approach (CPA) will result.

positive, made in ample time and with due regard to the observance of good seamanship.

(b) Any alteration of course and/or speed to avoid collision shall, if the circumstances of the case admit, be large enough to be readily apparent to another vessel observing visually or by radar; a succession of small alterations of course and/or speed should be avoided.

(c) If there is sufficient sea room, alteration of course alone may be the most effective action to avoid a close-quarters situation provided that it is made in good time, is substantial and does not result in another close-quarters situation.

(d) Action taken to avoid collision with another vessel shall be such as to result in passing at a safe distance. The effectiveness of the action shall be carefully checked until the other vessel is finally past and clear.

(e) If necessary to avoid collision or allow more time to assess the situation, a vessel shall slacken her speed or take all way off by stopping or reversing her means of propulsion.

Rule 8 Comment:
This rule clearly states the key to avoiding a collision, which is the *requirement* to take positive action and in ample time. The prudent mariner takes whatever action the situation requires of him at the earliest practical moment, and his action is not only sufficient to meet the needs of the case, but also sufficient so that the conning officer of the other ship will perceive that adequate action has been taken. If in avoiding another ship a course change is called for, we

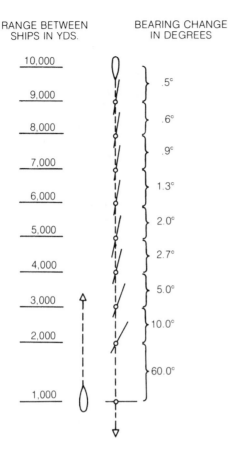

RANGE BETWEEN SHIPS IN YDS.	BEARING CHANGE IN DEGREES
10,000	
	.5°
9,000	
	.6°
8,000	
	.9°
7,000	
	1.3°
6,000	
	2.0°
5,000	
	2.7°
4,000	
	5.0°
3,000	
	10.0°
2,000	
	60.0°
1,000	

Figure 21–2. Bearing change for each 1,000 yards decrease in range. Ships are on reciprocal courses, and will pass 1,000 yards abeam. Same rate of bearing change per 1,000 yards of closing range holds good for ships approaching from any direction on such a course and speed that a 1,000-yard closest point of approach (CPA) will result.

should change course 20° or more so that it is clearly evident that we have changed course. If the situation calls for an appreciable reduction of speed, we should back our engines and give the appropriate whistle signal so that the other ship will know what we are doing.

RULE 9

Narrow channels

(a) A vessel proceeding along the course of a narrow channel or fairway shall keep as near to the outer limit of the channel or fairway which lies on her starboard side as is safe and practicable.

(b) A vessel of less than 20 meters in length or a sailing vessel shall not impede the passage of a vessel which can safely navigate only within a narrow channel or fairway.

(c) A vessel engaged in fishing shall not impede the passage of any other vessel navigating within a narrow channel or fairway.

(d) A vessel shall not cross a narrow channel or fairway if such crossing impedes the passage of a vessel which can safely navigate only within such channel or fairway. The latter vessel may use the sound signal prescribed in Rule 34(d) if in doubt as to the intention of the crossing vessel.

(e) (i) In a narrow channel or fairway when overtaking can take place only if the vessel to be overtaken has to take action to permit safe passing, the vessel intending to overtake shall indicate her intention by sounding the appropriate signal prescribed in Rule 34(c)(i). The vessel to be overtaken shall, if in agreement, sound the appropriate signal prescribed in Rule 34(c)(ii) and take steps to permit safe passing. If in doubt she may sound the signals prescribed in Rule 34(d).

FIGURE 21–3. "A collision at sea can ruin your entire day!" Two views of the destroyer *Frank E. Evans* (DD 754), damaged during a collision with the Australian aircraft carrier *Melbourne*. The ships had been participating in a southeast Asia Treaty Organization training exercise.

(ii) This Rule does not relieve the overtaking vessel of her obligation under Rule 13.
(f) A vessel nearing a bend or an area of a narrow channel or fairway where other vessels may be obscured by an intervening obstruction shall navigate with particular alertness and caution and shall sound the appropriate signal prescribed in Rule 34(e).
(g) Any vessel shall, if the circumstances of the case admit, avoid anchoring in a narrow channel.

Rule 9 Comment:
This rule contains a major departure from previous rules; i.e., small vessels (less than 20 meters in length) and sailing vessels must not impede the passage of a vessel which can navigate only within the channel. Nor are fishermen permitted to impede the channels, and crossing at inopportune times and anchoring in the channel are also prohibited. Thus, for the first time, and rightly so in the interest of practical safety, certain otherwise privileged vessels lose their privileges if they are impeding the channel.

RULE 10
Traffic separation schemes
(a) This Rule applies to traffic separation schemes adopted by the Organization.
(b) A vessel using a traffic separation scheme shall:
    (i) proceed in the appropriate traffic lane in the general direction of traffic flow for that lane;
    (ii) so far as practicable keep clear of a traffic separation line or separation zone;
    (iii) normally join or leave a traffic lane at the termination of the lane, but when joining or leaving from the side shall do so at as small an angle to the general direction of traffic flow as practicable.
(c) A vessel shall so far as practicable avoid crossing traffic lanes, but if obliged to do so shall cross as nearly as practicable at right angles to the general direction of traffic flow.
(d) Inshore traffic zones shall not normally be used by through traffic which can safely use the appropriate traffic lane within the adjacent traffic separation scheme.
(e) A vessel, other than a crossing vessel, shall not normally enter a separation zone or cross a separation line except:
    (i) in cases of emergency to avoid immediate danger;
    (ii) to engage in fishing within a separation zone.
(f) A vessel navigating in areas near the terminations of traffic separation schemes shall do so with particular caution.
(g) A vessel shall so far as practicable avoid anchoring in a traffic separation scheme or in areas near its terminations.
(h) A vessel not using a traffic separation scheme shall avoid it by as wide a margin as is practicable.
(i) A vessel engaged in fishing shall not impede the passage of any vessel following a traffic lane.
(j) A vessel of less than 20 meters in length or a sailing vessel shall not impede the safe passage of a power-driven vessel following a traffic lane.

Rule 10 Comment:
One-way channels are the coming thing and other vessels not using them must keep clear. In time, the entrance to most major ports will become "dual highways" with a separation strip in the middle. This should greatly increase the safety and increase the traffic capacity of such channels. Occasionally, traffic separation schemes will require greater distance to be travelled, but this will be compensated by increased transit speeds.

SECTION II—CONDUCT OF VESSELS IN SIGHT OF ONE ANOTHER

RULE 11
Application
Rules in this Section apply to vessels in sight of one another.

Rule 11 Comment:
The rules in this section apply only when vessels are in sight of one another. If they cannot see each other, even if they are quite close to one another, these rules do not apply and the provision of Rules 5 through 8 apply.

RULE 12
Sailing vessels
(a) When two sailing vessels are approaching one another, so as to involve risk of collision, one of them shall keep out of the way of the other as follows:
   (i) when each has the wind on a different side, the vessel which has the wind on the port side shall keep out of the way of the other;
   (ii) when both have the wind on the same side, the vessel which is to windward shall keep out of the way of the vessel which is to leeward;
   (iii) if a vessel with the wind on the port side sees a vessel to windward and cannot determine with certainty whether the other vessel has the wind on the port or on the starboard side, she shall keep out of the way of the other.
(b) For the purposes of this Rule the windward side shall be deemed to be the side opposite to that on which the mainsail is carried or, in the case of a square-rigged vessel, the side opposite to that on which the largest fore-and-aft sail is carried.

Rule 12 Comment:
This simple and excellent system was adopted in the 1960 revision from the time-tested international yacht racing rules. The vessel with the wind on its port hand or the vessel to windward shall keep clear. The reader might note that this produces an exception to the "Look right" rule in the case of two sailing vessels meeting on opposite tacks, each with the wind abaft the beam.

RULE 13
Overtaking
(a) Notwithstanding anything contained in the Rules of this Section any vessel overtaking any other shall keep out of the way of the vessel being overtaken.
(b) A vessel shall be deemed to be overtaking when coming up with another vessel from a direction more than 22.5 degrees abaft her beam, that is, in such a position with reference to the vessel she is overtaking, that at night she would be able to see only the sternlight of that vessel but neither of her sidelights.
(c) When a vessel is in any doubt as to whether she is overtaking another, she shall assume that this is the case and act accordingly.
(d) Any subsequent alteration of the bearing between the two vessels shall not make the overtaking vessel a crossing vessel within the meaning of these Rules or relieve her of the duty of keeping clear of the overtaken vessel until she is finally past and clear.

Rule 13 Comment:
The overtaking vessel is at all times responsible for the safety of the passing.

RULE 14
Head-on situation
(a) When two power-driven vessels are meeting on reciprocal or nearly reciprocal courses so as to involve risk of collision each shall alter her course to starboard so that each shall pass on the port side of the other.
(b) Such a situation shall be deemed to exist when a vessel sees the other ahead or nearly ahead and by night she could see the masthead lights of the other in a line or nearly in a line and/or both sidelights and by day she observes the corresponding aspect of the other vessel.
(c) When a vessel is in any doubt as to whether such a situation exists she shall assume that it does exist and act accordingly.

Rule 14 Comment:
This simple, clearly stated rule says that when a head-on meeting occurs, turn right and pass port-to-port. In seaman's parlance, it says "show him a red light." It also states, contrary to the

wording of previous rules, if in doubt, assume that a head-on situation exists and maneuver accordingly.

RULE 15
Crossing Situation
When two power-driven vessels are crossing so as to involve risk of collision, the vessel which has the other on her own starboard side shall keep out of the way and shall, if the circumstances of the case admit, avoid crossing ahead of the other vessel.

Rule 15 Comment:
Look right and avoid any vessel seen crossing from your right.

RULE 16
Action by give-way vessel
Every vessel which is directed by these Rules to keep out of the way of another vessel shall, so far as possible, take early and substantial action to keep well clear.

Rule 16 Comment:
Timely, positive action is the key to safety and calm nerves.

RULE 17
Action by stand-on vessel
(a) (i) Where by any of these Rules one of two vessels is to keep out of the way the other shall keep her course and speed.
     (ii) The latter vessel may however take action to avoid collision by her maneuver alone, as soon as it becomes apparent to her that the vessel required to keep out of the way is not taking appropriate action in compliance with these Rules.
(b) When, from any cause, the vessel required to keep her course and speed finds herself so close that collision cannot be avoided by the action of the give-way vessel alone, she shall take such action as will best aid to avoid collision.
(c) A power-drive vessel which takes action in a crossing situation in accordance with sub-paragraph (a)(ii) of this Rule to avoid collision with another power-driven vessel shall, if the circumstances of the case admit, not alter course to port for a vessel on her own port side.
(d) This Rule does not relieve the give-way vessel of her obligation to keep out of the way.

Rule 17 Comment:
The stand-on vessel (no longer called privileged) shall "keep her course and speed," but not into the jaws of catastrophe. She may maneuver when it appears that the other vessel is not taking appropriate action, but she should not turn to port if the other vessel is to port. Regardless of the action of the stand-on vessel, the give-way vessel has a continuing obligation to keep out of the way (Figure 21–4.)

RULE 18
Responsibilities between vessels
Except where Rules 9, 10 and 13 otherwise require:
(a) A power-driven vessel underway shall keep out of the way of:
     (i) a vessel not under command;
     (ii) a vessel restricted in her ability to maneuver;
     (iii) a vessel engaged in fishing;
     (iv) a sailing vessel.
(b) A sailing vessel underway shall keep out of the way of:
     (i) a vessel not under command;
     (ii) a vessel restricted in her ability to maneuver;
     (iii) a vessel engaged in fishing.
(c) A vessel engaged in fishing when underway shall, so far as possible, keep out of the way of:

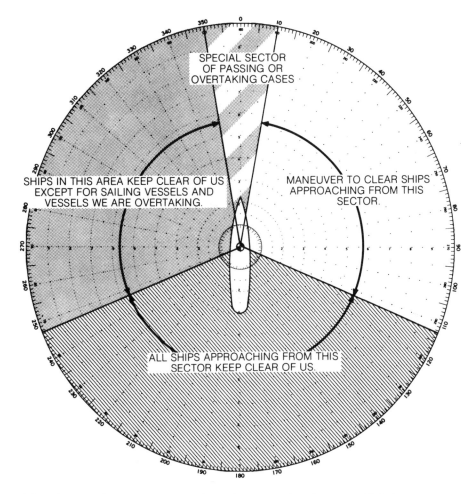

SPECIAL SECTOR
OF PASSING OR
OVERTAKING CASES

SHIPS IN THIS AREA KEEP CLEAR OF US
EXCEPT FOR SAILING VESSELS AND
VESSELS WE ARE OVERTAKING.

MANEUVER TO CLEAR SHIPS
APPROACHING FROM THIS
SECTOR.

ALL SHIPS APPROACHING FROM THIS
SECTOR KEEP CLEAR OF US.

FIGURE 21–4. Sectors of relative right of way as related to own ship's bow.

     (i) a vessel not under command;
     (ii) a vessel restricted in her ability to maneuver.
(d)   (i) Any vessel other than a vessel not under command or a vessel restricted in her ability to maneuver shall, if the circumstances of the case admit, avoid impeding the safe passage of a vessel constrained by her draught, exhibiting the signals in Rule 28.
     (ii) A vessel constrained by her draught shall navigate with particular caution having full regard to her special condition.
(e) A seaplane on the water shall, in general, keep well clear of all vessels and avoid impeding their navigation. In circumstances, however, where risk of collision exists, she shall comply with the Rules of this Part.

Rule 18 Comment:
This catch-all rule is intended to tidy up the loose ends of encounters between different classes of vessels. The principle that the more maneuverable vessel keep clear of the less maneuverable is always maintained, though the wording seems complex. The impression of irrevocable privilege of certain classes of vessels, such as sailing vessels, provided for in previous rules, has now been carefully deleted.

SECTION III—CONDUCT OF VESSELS IN RESTRICTED VISIBILITY

RULE 19
Conduct of vessels in restricted visibility
(a) This Rule applies to vessels not in sight of one another when navigating in or near an area of restricted visibility.
(b) Every vessel shall proceed at a safe speed adapted to the prevailing circumstances and conditions of restricted visibility. A poeer-driven vessel shall have her engines ready for immediate maneuver.
(c) Every vessel shall have due regard to the prevailing circumstances and conditions of restricted visibility when complying with the Rules of Section I of this Part.
(d) A vessel which detects by radar alone the presence of another vessel shall determine if a close-quarters situation is developing and/or risk of collision exists. If so, she shall take avoiding action in ample time, provided that when such action consists of an alteration of course, so far as possible the following shall be avoided:
    (i) an alteration of course to port for a vessel forward of the beam, other than for a vessel being overtaken;
    (ii) an alteration of course towards a vessel abeam or abaft the beam.
(e) Except where it has been determined that a risk of collision does not exist, every vessel which hears apparently forward of her beam the fog signal of another vessel, or which cannot avoid a close-quarters situation with another vessel forward of her beam, shall reduce her speed to the minimum at which she can be kept on her course. She shall if necessary take all her way off and in any event navigate with extreme caution until danger of collision is over.

Rule 19 Comment:
These rules outline precautions and actions required in *addition* to the rules of Section I of this Part. The guidance is clear and concise and it deals with radar as a practical aid to navigation which will permit evaluation of whether "a close-quarters situation is developing and/or risk of collision exists." If it has been determined that "risk of collision does not exist," the mandatory slowing and stopping when hearing a fog signal apparently forward of the beam is not required. Thus, a radar-equipped vessel, using her radar effectively, may proceed at a safe speed maneuvering as required to avoid other vessels and close-quarters or collision situations.

PART C—LIGHTS AND SHAPES

RULE 20
Application
(a) Rules in this Part shall be complied with in all weathers.
(b) The Rules concerning lights shall be complied with from sunset to sunrise, and during such times no other lights shall be exhibited, except such lights as cannot be mistaken for the lights specified in these Rules or do not impair their visibility or distinctive character, or interfere with the keeping of a proper lookout.
(c) The lights prescribed by these Rules shall, if carried, also be exhibited from sunrise to sunset in restricted visibility and may be exhibited in all other circumstances when it is deemed necessary.
(d) The Rules concerning shapes shall be complied with by day.
(e) The lights and shapes specified in these Rules shall comply with the provisions of Annex I to these Regulations.

Rule 20 Comment:
Annex I (see Appendix), outlines Positioning and Technical Details of Lights and Shapes.

Rule 21
Definitions
(a) "Masthead light" means a white light placed over the fore and aft centerline of the vessel showing an unbroken light over an arc of the horizon of 225 degrees and so fixed as to

show the light from right ahead to 22.5 degrees abaft the beam on either side of the vessel.

(b) "Sidelights" means a green light on the starboard side and a red light on the port side each showing an unbroken light over an arc of the horizon of 112.5 degrees and so fixed as to show the light from right ahead to 22.5 degrees abaft the beam on its respective side. In a vessel of less than 20 meters in length the sidelights may be combined in one lantern carried on the fore and aft centerline of the vessel.

(c) "Sternlight" means a white light placed as nearly as practicable at the stern showing an unbroken light over an arc of the horizon of 135 degrees and so fixed as to show the light 67.5 degrees from right aft on each side of the vessel.

(d) "Towing light" means a yellow light having the same characteristics as the "sternlight" defined in paragraph (c) of this Rule.

(e) "All round light" means a light showing an unbroken light over an arc of the horizon of 360 degrees.

(f) "Flashing light" means a light flashing at regular intervals at a frequency of 120 flashes or more per minute.

Rule 21 Comment:
No comment.

RULE 22
Visibility of lights
The lights prescribed in these Rules shall have an intensity as specified in Section 8 of Annex I to these Regulations so as to be visible at the following minimum ranges:

(a) In vessels of 50 meters or more in length:
a masthead light, 6 miles;
a sidelight, 3 miles;
a sternlight, 3 miles;
a towing light, 3 miles;
a white, red, green or yellow all-round light, 3 miles.

(b) In vessels of 12 meters or more in length but less than 50 meters in length:
a masthead light, 5 miles; except that where the length of the vessel is less than 20 meters, 3 miles;
a sidelight, 2 miles;
a sternlight, 2 miles;
a towing light, 2 miles;
a white, red, green or yellow all-round light, 2 miles.

(c) In vessels of less than 12 meters in length:
a masthead light, 2 miles;
a sidelight, 1 mile;
a sternlight, 2 miles;
a towing light, 2 miles;
a white, red, green or yellow all-round light, 2 miles.

Rule 22 Comment:
No comment.

RULE 23
Power-driven vessels underway
(a) A power-driven vessel underway shall exhibit:
  (i) a masthead light forward;
  (ii) a second masthead light abaft of and higher than the forward one; except that a vessel of less than 50 meters in length shall not be obliged to exhibit such light but may do so;
  (iii) sidelights;
  (iv) a sternlight.

(b) An air-cushion vessel when operating in the non-displacement mode shall, in addition to the lights prescribed in paragraph (a) of this Rule, exhibit an all-round flashing yellow light.

(c) A power-driven vessel of less than 7 meters in length and whose maximum speed does not exceed 7 knots may, in lieu of the lights prescribed in paragraph (a) of this Rule, exhibit an all-round white light. Such vessel shall, if practicable, also exhibit sidelights.

Rule 23 Comment:
This simple rule outlines the requirements for all different classes and sizes of power-driven vessels underway. The placement and technical details, over which the conning officer has no practical control as he steams at sea, are contained in Annex I.

RULE 24
Towing and pushing
(a) A power-driven vessel when towing shall exhibit:
  (i) instead of the light prescribed in Rule 23(a)(i), two masthead lights forward in a vertical line. When the length of the tow, measuring from the stern of the towing vessel to the after end of the tow exceeds 200 meters, three such lights in a vertical line;
  (ii) sidelights;
  (iii) a sternlight;
  (iv) a towing light in a vertical line above the sternlight;
  (v) When the length of the tow exceeds 200 meters, a diamond shape where it can best be seen.
(b) When a pushing vessel and a vessel being pushed ahead are rigidly connected in a composite unit they shall be regarded as a power-driven vessel and exhibit the lights prescribed in Rule 23.
(c) A power-driven vessel when pushing ahead or towing alongside, except in the case of a composite unit, shall exhibit:
  (i) instead of the light prescribed in Rule 23(a)(i), two masthead lights forward in a vertical line;
  (ii) sidelights;
  (iii) a sternlight.
(d) A power-driven vessel to which paragraphs (a) and (c) of this Rule apply shall also comply with Rule 23(a)(ii).
(e) A vessel or object being towed shall exhibit:
  (i) sidelights;
  (ii) a sternlight;
  (iii) when the length of the tow exceeds 200 meters, a diamond shape where it can best be seen.
(f) Provided that any number of vessels being towed or pushed in a group shall be lighted as one vessel,
  (i) a vessel being pushed ahead, not being part of a composite unit, shall exhibit at the forward end, sidelights;
  (ii) a vessel being towed alongside shall exhibit a sternlight and at the forward end, sidelights.
(g) Where from any sufficient cause it is impracticable for a vessel or object being towed to exhibit the lights prescribed in paragraph (e) of this Rule, all possible measures shall be taken to light the vessel or object towed or at least to indicate the presence of the unlighted vessel or object.

Rule 24 Comment:
These rules are a bit complex because of the different methods of towing and the different types of tows. Additionally, the optional use of the second masthead light by vessels less than 50 meters in length (and most tugs are less than 50 meters long) complicates the matter.

   For the conning officer, however, it is not complex. In the rare instance when his ship is to do the towing, he has time to review the rules and provide the required lights and shapes. In the normal case where his unencumbered ship is encountering another vessel towing, he will see a number of lights relatively close together, among them two or three lights in a vertical line. If all are white, he is abeam or ahead of the towing vessel; if one is yellow, he is in the after sector.

RULE 25
Sailing vessels underway and vessels under oars
(a) A sailing vessel underway shall exhibit:
    (i) sidelights;
    (ii) a sternlight.
(b) In a sailing vessel of less than 12 meters in length the lights prescribed in paragraph (a) of this Rule may be combined in one lantern carried at or near the top of the mast where it can best be seen.
(c) A sailing vessel underway may, in addition to the lights prescribed in paragraph (a) of this Rule, exhibit at or near the top of the mast, where they can best be seen, two all-round lights in a vertical line, the upper being red and the lower green, but these lights shall not be exhibited in conjunction with the combined lantern permitted by paragraph (b) of this Rule.
(d) (i) A sailing vessel of less than 7 meters in length shall, if practicable, exhibit the lights prescribed in paragraph (a) or (b) of this Rule, but if she does not, she shall have ready at hand an electric torch or lighted lantern showing a white light which shall be exhibited in sufficient time to prevent collision.
    (ii) A vessel under oars may exhibit the lights prescribed in this Rule for sailing vessels, but if she does not, she shall have ready at hand an electric torch or lighted lantern showing a white light which shall be exhibited in sufficient time to prevent collision.
(e) A vessel proceeding under sail when also being propelled by machinery shall exhibit forward where it can best be seen a conical shape, apex downwards.

Rule 25 Comment:
A sailing vessel does not carry a white masthead light. She may show a red and a green in a vertical line near the masthead, but not a white light. Small boats, sailing or rowing, may not be carrying any lights at all but may flash a flashlight or show a white lantern as you approach.

RULE 26
Fishing vessels
(a) A vessel engaged in fishing, whether underway or at anchor, shall exhibit only the lights and shapes prescribed in this Rule.
(b) A vessel when engaged in trawling, by which is meant the dragging through the water of a dredge net or other apparatus used as a fishing appliance, shall exhibit:
    (i) two all-round lights in a vertical line, the upper being green and the lower white, or a shape consisting of two cones with their apexes together in a vertical line one above the other; a vessel of less than 20 meters in length may instead of this shape exhibit a basket;
    (ii) a masthead light abaft of and higher than the all-round green light; a vessel of less than 50 meters in length shall not be obliged to exhibit such a light but may do so;
    (iii) when making way through the water, in addition to the lights prescribed in this paragraph, sidelights and a sternlight.
(c) A vessel engaged in fishing, other than trawling, shall exhibit:
    (i) two all-round lights in a vertical line, the upper being red and the lower white, or a shape consisting of two cones with apexes together in a vertical line one above the other; a vessel of less than 20 meters in length may instead of this shape exhibit a basket;
    (ii) when there is outlying gear extending more than 150 meters horizontally from the vessel, an all-round white light or a cone apex upwards in the direction of the gear;
    (iii) when making way through the water, in addition to the lights prescribed in this paragraph, sidelights and a sternlight.
(d) A vessel engaged in fishing in close proximity to other vessels may exhibit the additional signals described in Annex II to these Regulations.
(e) A vessel when not engaged in fishing shall not exhibit the lights or shapes prescribed in this Rule, but only those prescribed for a vessel of her length.

Rule 26 Comment:
"Red over White means fishing at night,
But a trawler shows Green, with her trawl in the stream."
        Beyond this it gets complicated, so when the conning officer sees complex lights and perhaps several vessels showing red-over-white or green-over-white among other lights, he knows he is encountering vessels fishing and should maneuver to pass well clear of both the vessels and their gear.

RULE 27
Vessels not under command or restricted in their ability to maneuver
(a) A vessel not under command shall exhibit:
    (i) two all-round red lights in a vertical line where they can best be seen;
    (ii) two balls or similar shapes in a vertical line where they can best be seen;
    (iii) when making way through the water, in addition to the lights prescribed in this paragraph, sidelights and a sternlight.
(b) A vessel restricted in her ability to maneuver, except a vessel engaged in minesweeping operations, shall exhibit:
    (i) three all-round lights in a vertical line where they can best be seen. The highest and lowest of these lights shall be red and the middle light shall be white;
    (ii) three shapes in a vertical line where they can best be seen. The highest and lowest of these shapes shall be balls and the middle one a diamond;
    (iii) when making way through the water, masthead lights, sidelights and a sternlight, in addition to the lights prescribed in sub-paragraph (1);
    (iv) when at anchor, in addition to the lights or shapes prescribed in sub-paragraphs (1) and (ii), the light, lights or shape prescribed in Rule 30.
(c) A vessel engaged in a towing operation such as renders her unable to deviate from her course shall, in addition to the lights or shapes prescribed in sub-paragraph (b)(i) and (ii) of this Rule, exhibit the lights or shape prescribed in Rule 24(a).
(d) A vessel engaged in dredging or underwater operations, when restricted in her ability to maneuver, shall exhibit the lights and shapes prescribed in paragraph (b) of this rule and shall in addition, when an obstruction exists, exhibit:
    (i) two all-round red lights or two balls in a vertical line to indicate the side on which the obstruction exists;
    (ii) two all-round green lights or two diamonds in a vertical line to indicate the side on which another vessel may pass;
    (iii) when making way through the water, in addition to the lights prescribed in this paragraph, masthead lights, sidelights and a sternlight;
    (iv) a vessel to which this paragraph applies when at anchor shall exhibit the lights or shapes prescribed in subparagraphs (i) and (ii) instead of the lights or shape prescribed in Rule 30.
(e) Whenever the size of a vessel engaged in diving operations makes it impracticable to exhibit the shapes prescribed in paragraph (d) of this rule, a rigid replica of the International Code flag "A" not less than 1 meter in height shall be exhibited. Measures shall be taken to ensure all-round visibility.
(f) A vessel engaged in minesweeping operations shall, in addition to the lights prescribed for a power-driven vessel in Rule 23, exhibit three all-round green lights or three balls. One of these lights or shapes shall be exhibited at or near the foremast head and one at each end of the fore yard. These lights or shapes indicate that it is dangerous for another vessel to approach closer than 1,000 metres astern or 500 metres on either side of the minesweeper.
(g) Vessels of less than 7 meters in length shall not be required to exhibit the lights prescribed in this rule.
(h) The signals prescribed in this Rule are not signals of vessels in distress and requiring assistance. Such signals are contained in Annex IV to these Regulations.

Rule 27 Comment:
Vessels covered by this rule are for the several reasons stated unable to maneuver freely and they are required to indicate such inability by a display of lights and shapes; the more complex the display, the more restrictive the operation. Figure A–1 (see Appendix)

summarizes the requirements will help the conning officer visualize the various signals. His response to the sighting of a vessel showing more than normal running lights or exhibiting special shapes should be extra caution—if unable to give her a wide berth, stop if necessary and refer to the rules to ascertain the nature of her operations.

RULE 28
Vessels constrained by their draught
A vessel constrained by her draught may, in addition to the lights prescribed for power-driven vessels in Rule 23, exhibit where they can best be seen three all-round red lights in a vertical line, or a cylinder.

Rule 28 Comment:
This is a new concept and should be very useful.

RULE 29
Pilot vessels
(a) A vessel engaged on pilotage duty shall exhibit:
  (i) at or near the masthead, two all-round lights in a vertical line, the upper being white and the lower red;
  (ii) when underway, in addition, sidelights and a sternlight;
  (iii) when at anchor, in addition to the lights prescribed in sub-paragraph (i), the anchor light, lights or shape.
(b) A pilot vessel when not engaged on pilotage duty shall exhibit the lights or shapes prescribed for a similar vessel of her length.

Rule 29 Comment:
"White over Red, pilot ahead."

RULE 30
Anchored vessels and vessels aground
(a) A vessel at anchor shall exhibit where it can best be seen:
  (i) in the fore part, an all-round white light or one ball;
  (ii) at or near the stern and at a lower level than the light prescribed in sub-paragraph (i), an all-round white light.
(b) A vessel of less than 50 meters in length may exhibit an all-round white light where it can best be seen instead of the lights prescribed in paragraph (a) of this Rule.
(c) A vessel at anchor may, and a vessel of 100 meters and more in length shall, also use the available working or equivalent lights to illuminate her decks.
(d) A vessel aground shall exhibit the lights prescribed in paragraph (a) or (b) of this Rule and in addition, where they can best be seen:
  (i) two all-round red lights in a vertical line;
  (ii) three balls in a vertical line.
(e) A vessel of less than 7 meters in length, when at anchor or aground, not in or near a narrow channel, fairway or anchorage, or where other vessels normally navigate, shall not be required to exhibit the lights or shapes prescribed in paragraphs (a), (b) or (d) of this Rule.

Rule 30 Comment:
The requirement to use working or equivalent lights to illuminate the deck of a vessel at anchor is a new and useful requirement.

RULE 31
Seaplanes
Where it is impracticable for a seaplane to exhibit lights and shapes of the characteristics or in the positions prescribed in the Rules of this Part she shall exhibit lights and shapes as closely similar in characteristics and position as is possible.

Rule 31 Comment:
Seaplanes are very scarce these days.

PART D—SOUND AND LIGHT SIGNALS

RULE 32
Definitions
(a) The word "whistle" means any sound signalling appliance capable of producing the prescribed blasts and which complies with the specifications in Annex III to these Regulations.
(b) The term "short blast" means a blast of about one second's duration.
(c) The term "prolonged blast" means a blast of from four to six seconds' duration.

Rule 32 Comment:
No comment.

RULE 33
Equipment for sound signals
(a) A vessel of 12 meters or more in length shall be provided with a whistle and a bell and a vessel of 100 meters or more in length shall, in addition, be provided with a gong, the tone and sound of which cannot be confused with that of the bell. The whistle, bell and gong shall comply with the specifications in Annex III to these Regulations. The bell or gong or both may be replaced by other equipment having the same respective sound characteristics, provided that manual sounding of the required signals shall always be possible.
(b) A vessel of less than 12 meters in length shall not be obliged to carry the sound signalling appliances prescribed in paragraph (a) of this Rule but if she does not, she shall be provided with some other means of making an efficient sound signal.

Rule 33 Comment:
No comment.

RULE 34
Maneuvering and warning signals
(a) When vessels are in sight of one another, a power-driven vessel underway, when maneuvering as authorized or required by these Rules, shall indicate the maneuver by the following signals on her whistle:
  –one short blast to mean "I am altering my course to starboard";
  –two short blasts to mean "I am altering my course to port";
  –three short blasts to mean "I am operating astern propulsion."
(b) Any vessel may supplement the whistle signals prescribed in paragraph (a) of this Rule by light signals, repeated as appropriate, while the maneuver is being carried out:
  (i) these light signals shall have the following significance:
    –one flash to mean "I am altering my course to starboard";
    –two flashes to mean "I am altering my course to port";
    –three flashes to mean "I am operating astern propulsion";
  (ii) the duration of each flash shall be about one second, the interval between flashes shall be about one second, and the interval between successive signals shall be not less than ten seconds;
  (iii) the light used for this signal shall, if fitted, be an all-round white light, visible at a minimum range of 5 miles, and shall comply with the provisions of Annex I.
(c) When in sight of one another in a narrow channel or fairway:
  (i) a vessel intending to overtake another shall in compliance with Rule 9(e)(i) indicate her intention by the following signals on her whistle:
    –two prolonged blasts followed by one short blast to mean "I intend to overtake you on your starboard side";
    –two prolonged blasts followed by two short blasts to mean "I intend to overtake you on your port side."
  (ii) the vessel about to be overtaken when acting in accordance with Rule 9(e)(i) shall indicate her agreement by the following signal on her whistle:
    –one prolonged, one short, one prolonged and one short blast, in that order.

(d) When vessels in sight of one another are approaching each other and from any cause either vessel fails to understand the intentions or actions of the other, or is in doubt whether sufficient action is being taken by the other to avoid collision, the vessel in doubt shall immediately indicate such doubt by giving at least five short and rapid blasts on the whistle. Such signal may be supplemented by a light signal of at least five short and rapid flashes.

(e) A vessel nearing a bend or an area of a channel or fairway where other vessels may be obscured by an intervening obstruction shall sound one prolonged blast. Such signal shall be answered with a prolonged blast by any approaching vessel that may be within hearing around the bend or behind the intervening obstruction.

(f) If whistles are fitted on a vessel at a distance apart of more than 100 meters, one whistle only shall be used for giving maneuvering and warning signals.

Rule 34 Comment:
The system of maneuvering and warning signals in international waters is very simple and very effective. When in sight of another vessel, the conning officer simply sounds one blast every time he changes course to starboard and two blasts every time he changes course to port. He can expect all other vessels to do the same and perhaps augment it with corresponding light signals. If he hears no signals or sees no lights, he may assume that the other ships are holding their courses. If he backs his engines, he sounds three blasts and he can expect others to do likewise when they back. There is no direct connection between a vessel's responsibilities in meeting and passing and its whistle signals. Its responsibilities to keep clear or hold a course in a given situation are fundamental and stand alone. The whistle signals are used only if maneuvering is required by the passing situation, or for any other reason. In case of doubt on the part of any vessel regarding the intentions or actions of any other vessel approaching, such doubt can be readily signaled by using the five-blast danger signal.

For passing, the new International Rules prescribe a system very similar to the old system in U. S. Inland Rules but not exactly so. By Rule 9 (e)(i), if in a narrow channel or fairway, and the passing can take place only if the vessel overtaken takes some action to permit the safe passing, the ship intending to pass is required to sound a signal proposing a passage to starboard or to port. If the overtaken vessel agrees, it sounds an answering signal indicating agreement, and then is required to take the necessary steps to permit the safe passage. If in doubt as to the safety of the passage (or unwilling to take the required action), the overtaken vessel may sound the danger signal. In any case, whether agreement has been signaled or not, the overtaking vessel must at all times keep clear of the overtaken vessel.

RULE 35
Sound signals in restricted visibility
In or near an area of restricted visibility, whether by day or night, the signals prescribed in this Rule shall be used as follows:

(a) A power-driven vessel making way through the water shall sound at intervals of not more than 2 minutes one prolonged blast.

(b) A power-driven vessel underway but stopped and making no way through the water shall sound at intervals of not more than 2 minutes two prolonged blasts in succession with an interval of about 2 seconds between them.

(c) A vessel not under command, a vessel restricted in her ability to maneuver, a vessel constrained by her draught, a sailing vessel, a vessel engaged in fishing and a vessel engaged in towing or pushing another vessel shall, instead of the signals prescribed in paragraphs (a) or (b) of this Rule, sound at intervals of not more than 2 minutes three blasts in succession, namely one prolonged followed by two short blasts.

(d) A vessel towed or if more than one vessel is towed the last vessel of the tow, if manned, shall at intervals of not more than 2 minutes sound four blasts in succession, namely one prolonged followed by three short blasts. When practicable, this signal shall be made immediately after the signal made by the towing vessel.

(e) When a pushing vessel and a vessel being pushed ahead are rigidly connected in a composite unit they shall be regarded as a power-driven vessel and shall give the signals prescribed in paragraphs (a) or (b) of this Rule.

(f) A vessel at anchor shall at intervals of not more than one minute ring the bell rapidly for

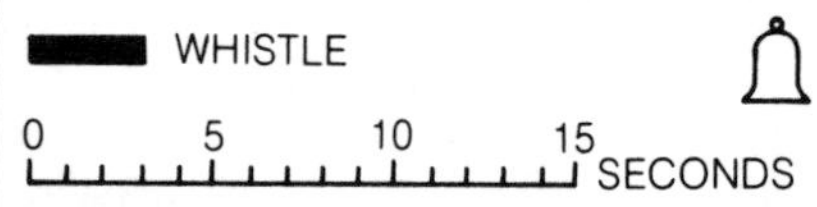

▬▬ WHISTLE	⌂ BELL	⊙ GONG
0 5 10 15 SECONDS		

SIGNAL VISIBILITY	INTERNATIONAL RULES INTERVAL	INLAND RULES INTERVAL
▄ CLEAR	CHANGING MY COURSE TO STARBOARD	a. INTEND TO LEAVE YOU TO MY PORT b. AGREE TO YOUR PROPOSAL
▄ ▄ CLEAR	CHANGING MY COURSE TO PORT	a. INTEND TO LEAVE YOU TO MY STARBOARD b. AGREE TO YOUR PROPOSAL
▄ ▄ ▄ CLEAR	MY ENGINES ARE BACKING	SAME
▄ ▄ ▄ ▄ ▄ CLEAR	DANGER, DOUBT OR DISAGREEMENT	SAME
▬▬ ANY	APPROACHING BLIND BEND OR ANSWERING	SAME, PLUS BACKING FROM DOCK OR BERTH
▬▬ ▬▬ ▄ OVERTAKING, CLEAR	INTEND TO PASS YOU ON YOUR STARBOARD SIDE	SAME
▬▬ ▬▬ ▄ ▄ OVERTAKING, CLEAR	INTEND TO PASS YOU ON YOUR PORT SIDE	SAME
▬▬ ▄ ▬▬ ▄ OVERTAKEN, CLEAR	AGREE TO YOUR PASSING AND WILL TAKE STEPS TO PERMIT IT	SAME
▬▬ FOG	UNDERWAY, WAY ON 2 MIN	SAME
▬▬ ▬▬ FOG	UNDERWAY, STOPPED 2 MIN	SAME

FIGURE 21–5. Summary of sound signals.

▬▬ ▬ ▬ FOG	a. NOT UNDER COMMAND b. RESTR. MANEUVERABILITY c. CONSTRAINED BY DRAFT d. SAILING VESSEL e. FISHING f. TOWING 2 MIN	SAME
▬▬ ▬ ▬ ▬ FOG	VESSEL TOWED 2 MIN	SAME
▬ ▬▬ ▬ FOG	AT ANCHOR OR AGROUND WARNING SIGNAL WHEN REQ	SAME
🔔 5 SEC. RAPID FOG	ANCHORED UNDER 100 M. 1 MIN	SAME
🔔 ⊙ 5 SEC. 5 SEC. RAPID RAPID FOG	ANCHORED OVER 100 M. 1 MIN	SAME
🔔 🔔 🔔 ⊙ 3 5 SEC. 5 SEC. 3 STKS. RAPID RAPID STKS. FOG	AGROUND 1 MIN	SAME
NOTES: 1. "CLEAR" MEANS VESSELS ARE IN SIGHT OF ONE ANOTHER. 2. "FOG" MEANS FOG OR REDUCED VISIBILITY.		

about 5 seconds. In a vessel of 100 meters or more in length the bell shall be sounded in the forepart of the vessel and immediately after the ringing of the bell the gong shall be sounded rapidly for about 5 seconds in the after part of the vessel. A vessel at anchor may in addition sound three blasts in succession, namely one short, one prolonged and one short blast, to give warning of her position and of the possibility of collision to an approaching vessel.

(g) A vessel aground shall give the bell signal and if required the gong signal prescribed in paragraph (f) of this Rule and shall, in addition, give three separate and distinct strokes on the bell immediately before and after the rapid ringing of the bell. A vessel aground may in addition sound an appropriate whistle signal.

(h) A vessel of less than 12 meters in length shall not be obliged to give the above-mentioned signals but, if she does not, shall make some other efficient sound signal at intervals of not more than 2 minutes.

(i) A pilot vessel when engaged on pilotage duty may in addition to the signals prescribed in paragraphs (a), (b) or (f) of this Rule sound an identity signal consisting of four short blasts.

Rule 35 Comment:
The sound signals used in restricted visibility are for a different purpose than the signals for maneuvering. They are first to alert approaching vessels of the presence of the signalling vessel and then to the extent practical inform it of the character and motion of the signalling vessel. A summary of the sound signals prescribed by Rule 34 and 35 is presented graphically in Figure 21–5.

RULE 36
Signals to attract attention
If necessary to attract the attention of another vessel any vessel may make light or sound signals that cannot be mistaken for any signal authorized elsewhere in these Rules, or may direct the beam of her searchlight in the direction of the danger, in such a way as not to embarrass any vessel.

Rule 36 Comment:
No comment.

RULE 37
Distress signals
When a vessel is in distress and requires assistance she shall use or exhibit the signals prescribed in Annex IV to these Regulations.

Rule 37 Comment:
No comment.

PART E—EXEMPTIONS

RULE 38
Exemptions
Any vessel (or class of vessels) provided that she complies with the requirements of the International Regulations for Preventing Collisions at Sea, 1960, the keel of which is laid or which is at a corresponding stage of construction before the entry into force of these Regulations may be exempted from compliance therewith as follows:
(a) The installation of lights with ranges prescribed in Rule 22, until four years after the date of entry into force of these Regulations.
(b) The installation of lights with colour specifications as prescribed in Section 7 of Annex I to these Regulations, until four years after the date of entry into force of these Regulations.
(c) The repositioning of lights as a result of conversion from Imperial to metric units and rounding off measurement figures, permanent exemption.
(d)   (i) The repositioning of masthead lights on vessels of less than 150 meters in length, resulting from the prescriptions of Section 3(a) of Annex I, permanent exemption.
     (ii) The repositioning of masthead lights on vessels of 150 meters or more in length, resulting from the prescriptions of Section 3(a) of Annex I to these Regulations, until nine years after the date of entry into force of these Regulations.
(e) The repositioning of masthead lights resulting from the prescriptions of Section 2(b) of Annex I, until nine years after the date of entry into force of these Regulations.
(f) The repositioning of sidelights resulting from the prescriptions of Section 3(b) of Annex I, until nine years after the date of entry into force of these Regulations.
(g) The requirements for sound signal appliances prescribed in Annex III, until nine years after the date of entry into force of these Regulations.

Rule 38 Comment:
No comment.

The four Annexes to the International Rules which contain details of the lights and signals are contained in Appendix. They cover the following:

Annex I–Positioning and technical details of lights and shapes
Annex II–Additional signals for fishing vessels fishing in close proximity
Annex III–Technical details of sound signal apparatus
Annex IV–Distress signals

INLAND RULES

As this edition of *Naval Shiphandling* goes to press, the Commandant of the Coast Guard is in the process of refining the text of the proposed new Inland Rules. Though the final wording has not yet been settled, the Commandant has proposed to adopt the new International Rules "without change or modification" except for the few points outlined below. It is the intent of the Commandant that these new Inland Rules shall apply to all of the navigable waters of the United States so that the differences in regulation found by the mariner as he passes from the high seas to the various waterways of the United States will be minimized.

The only really significant difference between the proposed new Inland Rules and the International Rules is in the matter of the whistle signals, Rule 34, to be used between two vessels when they meet and pass close aboard. The Commandant has proposed to retain the old U. S. Inland practice of exchanging passing signals and thus establishing a "contract" before the passing is attempted. As the reader will recall, the International system requires whistle signals only as the ship's course is changed. Thus, on the high seas, ships may pass one another close aboard with no whistle signals at all if neither ship finds it necessary to change course. On the contrary, under Inland Rules, an exchange of whistle signals is required before the passing is attempted whether or not any change of course is required by either ship.

It is the author's opinion that it will be regrettable if this difference is maintained in the Inland Rules. It is not intended by the framers of the new Inland Rules that there be any difference in responsibility or method of maneuver; the difference has only to do with the sounding and meaning of the whistle signals. Under International Rules, each individual ship simply warns all others when she changes her course. Under Inland Rules, a ship sounding her whistle is endeavoring to reach an agreement with another, and in a busy channel, it is not always clear with which ship she intends to communicate. Thousands of ships ply the busy harbors and channels of Rotterdam, Antwerp, London and Tokyo every day under the International system of whistle signals and those American mariners who have entered such harbors have generally felt completely comfortable with the International system of signals. It is hoped that eventually the International Rules will be adopted in its entirety for all United States waters.

Specifically, the Commandant of the Coast Guard has proposed the following additions to the International Rules in applying them to Inland waters:

Rule 9 Narrow Channels

When power-driven vessels meet in a river or narrow channel, the descending vessel shall have the right-of-way.

FIGURE 21-6. An aerial view from a Coast Guard plane shows the bow of a U.S. containership embedded in the port side of a Colombian freighter after the two vessels collided east of Cape Hatteras, North Carolina.

Rule 15 Crossing Situation

An exception to the Right Hand Rule in a crossing situation will provide that a vessel towing down stream in a river or narrow channel will be given the right-of-way over a vessel crossing that river or channel.

Rule 24 Towing and Pushing

When a power-driven vessel is pushing ahead or towing alongside, in addition to the two masthead lights in a vertical line required by the International Rules, it shall display two yellow towing lights in a vertical line above its stern light.

For the vessel being pushed or towed alongside, in addition to sidelights and sternlight (when required), it shall exhibit as far forward as practical a flashing yellow light covering the same arc as a masthead light. This light will flash about once each second and must be visible for 2 miles.

Rule 25 Sailing Vessels, etc.

The International Rule 25(d)(ii) for vessels under oars will be extended to cover rafts and other craft propelled by hand, horse or the river current.

Rule 27 Vessels Not Under Command

A group of vessels moored together in "stringouts" or nested together and restricted in their ability to maneuver shall be lighted as one vessel as appropriate to their restrictive operations.

Rule 30 Anchored Vessels

Additional regulations will be established to cover special lights required for barges moored singly or in groups.

Rule 34 Maneuvering and Warning Signals

Already discussed. In lieu of using the International Rule 34, the Inland Rule will provide for the following whistle signals and meaning:

One short blast—"I intend to meet and pass you on your port side."
Two short blasts—"I intend to meet and pass you on your starboard side."

The three-blast signal for backing and the optional use of light signals to augment the whistle signals will also be included as in the International Rules.

Conclusion

From the above, it will be apparent that the Coast Guard hopes to adopt the International Rules of the Road for all U. S. waters with only one significant exception—whistle signals for passing. This is a tremendous step forward and will certainly eliminate a great deal of complication and confusion. The mariner will find it easier to learn, to understand and to apply this much simpler and much improved body of law. It is also certain that the mariner's ability to prevent collisions will be enhanced.

appendix: technical annexes to the international rules of the road, 1972

ANNEX I

POSITIONING AND TECHNICAL DETAILS OF LIGHTS AND SHAPES

1. *Definition*
   The term "height above the hull" means height above the uppermost continuous deck.

2. *Vertical positioning and spacing of lights*
   (a) On a power-driven vessel of 20 meters or more in length the masthead lights shall be placed as follows:
      (i) the forward masthead light, or if only one masthead light is carried, then that light, at a height above the hull of not less than 6 meters, and, if the breadth of the vessel exceeds 6 meters, then at a height above the hull not less than such breadth, so however that the light need not be placed at a greater height above the hull than 12 meters;
      (ii) when two masthead lights are carried the after one shall be at least 4.5 meters vertically higher than the forward one.
   (b) The vertical separation of masthead lights of power-driven vessels shall be such that in all normal conditions of trim the after light will be seen over and separate from the forward light at a distance of 1000 meters from the stem when viewed from sea level.
   (c) The masthead light of a power-driven vessel of 12 meters but less than 20 meters in length shall be placed at a height above the gunwale of not less than 2.5 meters.
   (d) A power-driven vessel of less than 12 meters in length may carry the uppermost light at a height of less than 2.5 meters above the gunwale. When, however, a masthead light is carried in addition to sidelights and a sternlight, then such masthead light shall be carried at least 1 meter higher than the sidelights.
   (e) One of the two or three masthead lights prescribed for a power-driven vessel when engaged in towing or pushing another vessel shall be placed in the same position as the forward masthead light of a power-driven vessel.
   (f) In all circumstances the masthead light or lights shall be so placed as to be above and clear of all other lights and obstructions.
   (g) The sidelights of a power-driven vessel shall be placed at a height above the hull not greater than three quarters of that of the forward masthead light. They shall not be so low as to be interfered with by deck lights.
   (h) The sidelights, if in a combined lantern and carried on a power-driven vessel of less

LIGHTS FOR NIGHT OR REDUCED VISIBILITY
SHAPES FOR USE IN DAYLIGHT

LIGHTS:

SYMBOLS FOR ARCS
ALL-ROUND—360°
FWD TO 22½° ABAFT BEAM
22½° ABAFT BEAM TO STERN

SHAPES:

AS INDICATED

COLORS AS INDICATED

RULE ACTIVITY	EXAMPLE	NOTES

23
UNDERWAY

    a. SHIP

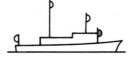

    b. LESS THAN 50 M

    c. LESS THAN 7 M & 7 KN.

FLASHING

    d. AIRCUSHION

24 TOWING OR PUSHING

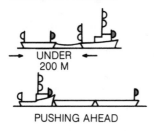

UNDER 200 M

PUSHING AHEAD

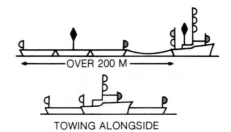

OVER 200 M

TOWING ALONGSIDE

NOTE 1

25 SAILING

NORMAL   OPTIONAL   UNDER POWER

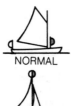

UNDER 12 M

UNDER 7 M

UNDER OARS

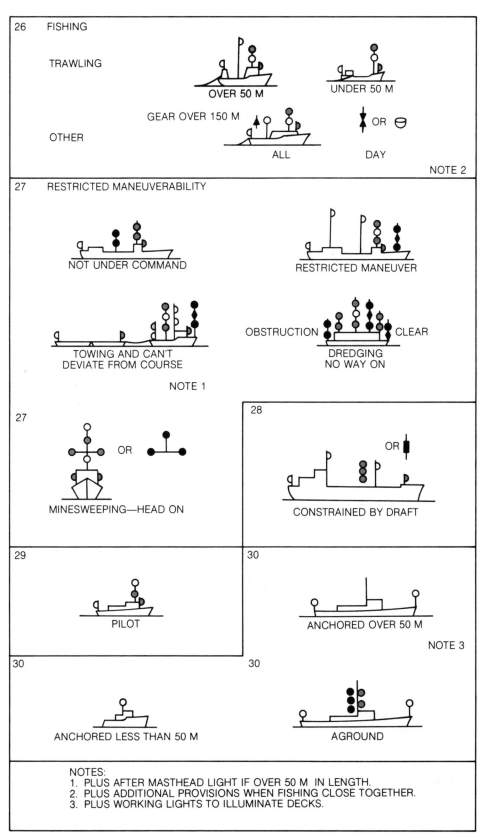

FIGURE A–1. Summary of lights and shapes specified under International Rules, 1972.

than 20 meters in length, shall be placed not less than 1 meter below the masthead light.

(i) When the Rules prescribe two or three lights to be carried in a vertical line, they shall be spaced as follows:

    (i) on a vessel of 20 meters in length or more such lights shall be spaced not less than 2 meters apart, and the lowest of these lights shall, except where a towing light is required, not be less than 4 meters above the hull;

    (ii) on a vessel of less than 20 meters in length such lights shall be spaced not less than 1 meter apart and the lowest of these lights shall, except where a towing light is required, not be less than 2 meters above the gunwale;

    (iii) when three lights are carried they shall be equally spaced.

(j) The lower of the two all-round lights prescribed for a fishing vessel when engaged in fishing shall be at a height above the sidelights not less than twice the distance between the two vertical lights.

(k) The forward anchor light, when two are carried, shall not be less than 4.5 meters above the after one. On a vessel of 50 meters or more in length this forward anchor light shall not be less than 6 meters above the hull.

3. *Horizontal positioning and spacing of lights*

(a) When two masthead lights are prescribed for a power-driven vessel, the horizontal distance between them shall not be less than one half of the length of the vessel but need not be more than 100 meters. The forward light shall be placed not more than one quarter of the length of the vessel from the stem.

(b) On a vessel of 20 meters or more in length the sidelights shall not be placed in front of the forward masthead lights. They shall be placed at or near the side of the vessel.

4. *Details of location of direction-indicating lights for fishing vessels, dredgers and vessels engaged in underwater operations*

(a) The light indicating the direction of the outlying gear from a vessel engaged in fishing as prescribed in Rule 26(c)(ii) shall be placed at a horizontal distance of not less than 2 meters and not more than 6 meters away from the two all-round red and white lights. This light shall be placed not higher than the all-round white light prescribed in Rule 26(c)(i) and not lower than the sidelights.

(b) The lights and shapes on a vessel engaged in dredging or underwater operations to indicate the obstructed side and/or the side on which it is safe to pass, as prescribed in Rule 27(d)(i) and (ii), shall be placed at the maximum practical horizontal distance, but in no case less than 2 meters, from the lights or shapes prescribed in Rule 27(b)(i) and (ii). In no case shall the upper of these lights or shapes be at a greater height than the lower of the three lights or shapes prescribed in Rule 27(b)(i) and (ii).

5. *Screens for sidelights*

The sidelights shall be fitted with inboard screens painted matt black, and meeting the requirements of Section 9 of this Annex. With a combined lantern, using a single vertical filament and a very narrow division between the green and red sections, external screens need not be fitted.

6. *Shapes*

(a) Shapes shall be black and of the following sizes:

    (i) a ball shall have a diameter of not less than 0.6 meter;

    (ii) a cone shall have a base diameter of not less than 0.6 meter and a height equal to its diameter;

    (iii) a cylinder shall have a diameter of at least 0.6 meter and a height of twice its diameter;

    (iv) a diamond shape shall consist of two cones as defined in (ii) above having a common base.

(b) The vertical distance between shapes shall be at least 1.5 meter.

(c) In a vessel of less than 20 meters in length shapes of lesser dimensions but commensurate with the size of the vessel may be used and the distance apart may be correspondingly reduced.

7. *Colour specification of lights*

The chromaticity of all navigation lights shall conform to the following standards, which lie within the boundaries of the area of the diagram specified for each colour by the International Commission on Illumination (CIE).

The boundaries of the area for each colour are given by indicating the corner coordinates, which are as follows:

    (i) *White*

x	0.525	0.525	0.452	0.310	0.310	0.443
y	0.382	0.440	0.440	0.348	0.283	0.382

    (ii) *Green*

x	0.028	0.009	0.300	0.203
y	0.385	0.723	0.511	0.356

    (iii) *Red*

x	0.680	0.660	0.735	0.721
y	0.320	0.320	0.265	0.259

    (iv) *Yellow*

x	0.612	0.618	0.575	0.575
y	0.382	0.382	0.425	0.406

8. *Intensity of lights*

    (a) The minimum luminous intensity of lights shall be calculated by using the formula:

$$I = 3.43 \times 10^6 \times T \times D^2 \times K^{-D}$$

    where I is luminous intensity in candelas under service conditions,

           T is threshold factor 2×10^{-7} lux,

           D is range of visibility (luminous range) of the light in nautical miles,

           K is atmospheric transmissivity.

              For prescribed lights the value of K shall be 0.8, corresponding to a meteorological visibility of approximately 13 nautical miles.

    (b) A selection of figures derived from the formula is given in the following table:

Range of visibility (luminous range) of light in nautical miles D	Luminous intensity of light in candelas for K = 0.8 I
1	0.9
2	4.3
3	12
4	27
5	52
6	94

NOTE: The maximum luminous intensity of navigation lights should be limited to avoid undue glare.

9. *Horizontal Sectors*

    (a) (i) In the forward direction, sidelights as fitted on the vessel must show the minimum required intensities. The intensities must decrease to reach practical cut-off between 1 degree and 3 degrees outside the prescribed sectors.

         (ii) For sternlights and masthead lights and at 22.5 degrees abaft the beam for sidelights, the minimum required intensities shall be maintained over the arc of the horizon up to 5 degrees within the limits of the sectors prescribed in Rule 21. From 5 degrees within the prescribed sectors the intensity may decrease by 50 per cent up to the prescribed limits; it shall decrease steadily to reach practical cut-off at not more than 5 degrees outside the prescribed limits.

(b) All-round lights shall be so located as not to be obscured by masts, topmasts or structures within angular sectors of more than 6 degrees, except anchor lights, which need not be placed at an impracticable height above the hull.

10. *Vertical Sectors*
    (a) The vertical sectors of electric lights, with the exception of lights on sailing vessels shall ensure that:
       (i) at least the required minimum intensity is maintained at all angles from 5 degrees above to 5 degrees below the horizontal;
       (ii) at least 60 per cent of the required minimum intensity is maintained from 7.5 degrees above to 7.5 degrees below the horizontal.
    (b) In the case of sailing vessels the vertical sectors of electric lights shall ensure that:
       (i) at least the required minimum intensity is maintained at all angles from 5 .degrees above to 5 degrees below the horizontal;
       (ii) at least 50 per cent of the required minimum intensity is maintained from 25 degrees above to 25 degrees below the horizontal.
    (c) In the case of lights other than electric these specifications shall be met as closely as possible.

11. *Intensity of nonelectric lights*
    Nonelectric lights shall so far as practicable comply with the minimum intensities, as specified in the Table given in Section 8 of this Annex.

12. *Maneuvering light*
    Notwithstanding the provisions of paragraph 2(f) of this Annex the maneuvering light described in Rule 34(b) shall be placed in the same fore and aft vertical plane as the masthead light or lights and, where practicable, at a minimum height of 2 meters vertically above the forward masthead light, provided that it shall be carried not less than 2 meters vertically above or below the after masthead light. On a vessel where only one masthead light is carried the maneuvering light, if fitted, shall be carried where it can best be seen, not less than 2 meters vertically apart from the masthead light.

13. *Approval*
    The construction of lanterns and shapes and the installation of lanterns on board the vessel shall be to the satisfaction of the appropriate authority of the State where the vessel is registered.

ANNEX II

ADDITIONAL SIGNALS FOR FISHING VESSELS FISHING IN CLOSE PROXIMITY

1. *General*
   The lights mentioned herein shall, if exhibited in pursuance of Rule 26(d), be placed where they can best be seen. They shall be at least 0.9 meter apart but at a lower level than lights prescribed in Rule 26(b)(i) and (c)(i). The lights shall be visible all round the horizon at a distance of at least 1 mile but at a lesser distance than the lights prescribed by these Rules for fishing vessels.

2. *Signals for Trawlers*
   (a) Vessels when engaged in trawling, whether using demersal or pelagic gear, may exhibit:
      (i) when shooting their nets:
          two white lights in a vertical line;
      (ii) when hauling their nets:
           one white light over one red light in a vertical line;
      (iii) when the net has come fast upon an obstruction:
            two red lights in a vertical line.
   (b) Each vessel engaged in pair trawling may exhibit:

(i) by night, a searchlight directed forward and in the direction of the other vessel of the pair;

(ii) when shooting or hauling their nets or when their nets have come fast upon an obstruction, the lights prescribed in 2(a) above.

3. *Signals for purse seiners*

Vessels engaged in fishing with purse seine gear may exhibit two yellow lights in a vertical line. These lights shall flash alternately every second and with equal light and occultation duration. These lights may be exhibited only when the vessel is hampered by its fishing gear.

ANNEX III

TECHNICAL DETAILS OF SOUND SIGNAL APPLIANCES

1. *Whistles*

(a) *Frequencies and range of audibility*

The fundamental frequency of the signal shall lie within the range 70–700 Hz.

The range of audibility of the signal from a whistle shall be determined by those frequencies, which may include the fundamental and/or one or more higher frequencies, which lie within the range 180–700 Hz (± 1 per cent) and which provide the sound pressure levels specified in paragraph 1(c) below.

(b) *Limits of fundamental frequencies*

To ensure a wide variety of whistle characteristics, the fundamental frequency of a whistle shall be between the following limits:

(i) 70–200 Hz, for a vessel 200 meters or more in length;

(ii) 130–350 Hz, for a vessel 75 meters but less than 200 meters in length;

(iii) 250–700 Hz, for a vessel less than 75 meters in length.

(c) *Sound signal intensity and range of audibility*

A whistle fitted in a vessel shall provide, in the direction of maximum intensity of the whistle and at a distance of 1 meter from it, a sound pressure level in at least one ⅓-octave band within the range of frequencies 180–700 Hz (± 1 per cent) of not less than the appropriate figure given in the table below.

Length of vessel in meters	⅓-octave band level at 1 meter in dB referred to 2×10^{-5} N/m²	Audibility range in nautical miles
200 or more	143	2
75 but less than 200	138	1.5
20 but less than 75	130	1
Less than 20	120	0.5

The range of audibility in the table above is for information and is approximately the range at which a whistle may be heard on its forward axis with 90 per cent probability in conditions of still air on board a vessel having average background noise level at the listening posts (taken to be 68 dB in the octave band centered on 250 Hz and 63 dB in the octave band centered on 500 Hz).

In practice the range at which a whistle may be heard is extremely variable and depends critically on weather conditions; the values given can be regarded as typical but under conditions of strong wind or high ambient noise level at the listening post the range may be much reduced.

(d) *Directional properties*

The sound pressure level of a directional whistle shall be not more than 4 dB below

the sound pressure level on the axis at any direction in the horizontal plane within ±
45 degrees of the axis. The sound pressure level at any other direction in the
horizontal plane shall be not more than 10 dB below the sound pressure level on the
axis, so that the range in any direction will be at least half the range on the forward
axis. The sound pressure level shall be measured in that ⅓-octave band which
determines the audibility range.

(e) *Positioning of whistles*
When a directional whistle is to be used as the only whistle on a vessel, it shall be
installed with its maximum intensity directed straight ahead.
A whistle shall be placed as high as practicable on a vessel, in order to reduce
interception of the emitted sound by obstructions and also to minimize hearing
damage risk to personnel. The sound pressure level of the vessel's own signal at
listening posts shall not exceed 110 dB (A) and so far as practicable should not
exceed 100 dB (A).

(f) *Fitting of more than one whistle*
If whistles are fitted at a distance apart of more than 100 meters, it shall be so
arranged that they are not sounded simultaneously.

(g) *Combined whistle systems*
If due to the presence of obstructions the sound field of a single whistle or of one of the
whistles referred to in paragraph 1(f) above is likely to have a zone of greatly reduced
signal level, it is recommended that a combined whistle system be fitted so as to
overcome this reduction. For the purpose of the Rules a combined whistle system is
to be regarded as a single whistle. The whistles of a combined system shall be
located at a distance apart of not more than 100 meters and arranged to be sounded
simultaneously. The frequency of any one whistle shall differ from those of the others
by at least 10 Hz.

2. *Bell or gong*
(a) *Intensity of signal*
A bell or gong, or other device having similar sound characteristics shall produce a
sound pressure level of not less than 110 dB at 1 meter.

(b) *Construction*
Bells and gongs shall be made of corrosion-resistant material and designed to give a
clear tone. The diameter of the mouth of the bell shall be not less than 300 mm for
vessels of more than 20 meters in length, and shall be not less than 200 mm for
vessels of 12 to 20 meters in length. Where practicable, a power-driven bell striker is
recommended to ensure constant force but manual operation shall be possible. The
mass of the striker shall be not less than 3 per cent of the mass of the bell.

3. *Approval*
The construction of sound signal appliances, their performance and their installation on
board the vessel shall be to the satisfaction of the appropriate authority of the State where
the vessel is registered.

ANNEX IV

DISTRESS SIGNALS

1. The following signals, used or exhibited either together or separately, indicate distress
and need of assistance:
   (a) a gun or other explosive signal fired at intervals of about a minute;
   (b) a continuous sounding with any fog-signalling apparatus;
   (c) rockets or shells, throwing red stars fired one at a time at short intervals;
   (d) a signal made by radiotelegraphy or by any other signalling method consisting of the
       group . . . – – – . . . (SOS) in the Morse Code;
   (e) a signal sent by radiotelephony consisting of the spoken word "Mayday";
   (f) the International Code Signal of distress indicated by N.C.;

(g) a signal consisting of a square flag having above or below it a ball or anything resembling a ball;

(h) flames on the vessel (as from a burning tar barrel, oil barrel, etc.)

(i) a rocket parachute flare or a hand flare showing a red light;

(j) a smoke signal giving off orange-colored smoke;

(k) slowly and repeatedly raising and lowering arms outstretched to each side;

(l) the radiotelegraph alarm signal;

(m) the radiotelephone alarm signal;

(n) signals transmitted by emergency position-indicating radio beacons.

2. The use or exhibition of any of the foregoing signals except for the purpose of indicating distress and need of assistance and the use of other signals which may be confused with any of the above signals is prohibited.

3. Attention is drawn to the relevant sections of the International Code of Signals, the Merchant Ship Search and Rescue Manual and the following signals:

(a) a piece of orange-colored canvas with either a black square and circle or other appropriate symbol (for identification from the air);

(b) a dye marker.

index

The **Naval Institute Press** is the book-publishing arm of the U.S. Naval Institute, a private, nonprofit professional society for members of the sea services and civilians who share an interest in naval and maritime affairs. Established in 1873 at the U.S. Naval Academy in Annapolis, Maryland, where its offices remain today, the Naval Institute has more than 100,000 members worldwide.

Members of the Naval Institute receive the influential monthly magazine *Proceedings* and discounts on fine nautical prints, ship and aircraft photos, and subscriptions to the quarterly *Naval History* magazine. They also have access to the transcripts of the Institute's Oral History Program and get discounted admission to any of the Institute-sponsored seminars regularly offered around the country.

The Naval Institute's book-publishing program, begun in 1898 with basic guides to naval practices, has broadened its scope in recent years to include books of more general interest. Now the Naval Institute Press publishes more than forty new titles each year, ranging from how-to books on boating and navigation to battle histories, biographies, ship and aircraft guides, and novels. Institute members receive discounts on the Press's more than 375 books.

Full-time students are eligible for special half-price membership rates. Life memberships are also available.

For a free catalog describing the Naval Institute Press books currently available, and for further information about U.S. Naval Institute membership, please write to:

Membership & Communications Department
U.S. Naval Institute
Annapolis, Maryland 21402

Or call, toll-free, (800) 233-USNI. In Maryland, call (301) 224-3378.